THE WEST END HORROR

The West End Horror

A POSTHUMOUS MEMOIR OF
John H. Watson, M.D.

AS EDITED BY
Nicholas Meyer

E. P. DUTTON & CO., INC. / NEW YORK

For Elly and Leonore

CONTENTS

CONTENTS

FOREWORD

One of the interesting consequences of publishing *The Seven-Per-Cent Solution* has been the great number of letters I have received—in my capacity as editor—from all over the world. As I predicted at the time of publication, the manuscript has become the centre of a heated controversy, and people have written to me on all sorts of paper, with varying grammar, spelling, and punctuation, to tell me what they think about the book's authenticity. (I even number among my correspondents an eleventh grader in Juneau, Alaska, who called me on the phone quite early one morning—apparently supposing Los Angeles time to be an hour *later* instead of otherwise—to tell me that he thought I was a fraud.)

A more bizarre result of the book's appearance has been the surfacing of a number of other "missing" Watsonian manuscripts, to wit: no less than five, all submitted for my consideration as editor. They arrived from sources as diverse as their astonishing contents, from an airline pilot in Texarkana, Texas; a diplomat in the Argentine; a widow in Racine, Wisconsin; a rabbi in Switzerland (this one written in Italian!); and a retired gentleman of undefined occupation in San Clemente, California.

The manuscripts were all interesting, and all contained pedigrees, explaining their belated appearance and the circumstances under which they were composed. At least two of them—while perfectly charming—were obvious forgeries (one a pornographic put-on), a third a thinly disguised political tract, another the ravings of a disordered mind, the fourth attempt to prove Holmes's Jewish ancestry (this was *not* from the Swiss rabbi), and one . . .

The case you are about to read is taken from a manuscript that belongs to Mrs. C. K. Verner of Racine, Wisconsin. Before it was given to me, I received the following letter from Mrs. Verner, mailed to me, care of my publishers in New York:

December 14, 1974

Dear Mr. Meyer:

I was really interested to read the manuscript you edited, called *The Seven-Per-Cent Solution*. My late husband, Carl, was descended from the Vernet* family, which as you probably know, Sherlock Holmes was descended from, too.

I wonder if you would be interested in looking at another "long lost manuscript" of Dr. Watson's, only this one was never exactly lost. Carl, my husband, got it from his father, who was willed it (he used to tell us) from Mr. Holmes personally.

It is hand-written and a bit difficult to read in spots, mainly

* Emile Jean Horace Vernet (1789–1863), called Horace Vernet, famous French painter and portraitist, was the great-uncle of Sherlock Holmes.

because of some water damage suffered to it by Carl's father back in the 30s when he couldn't afford to fix the roof of his attic.

Carl's father (Grandpa Verner—he died in '46) never let any publisher see the manuscript because it's quite clear from the beginning of it that Mr. Holmes didn't want people to read it. But there's a lot of water under the bridge since then, and those people are all dead, anyway.

I read in the paper last week all about what they just found about Gladstone's personal life, and I guess this can't be any more hurtful than that.

Carl is gone since last February, and as you know, the economy is not doing too well. I'm probably going to have to sell the farm and could surely use some cash. If you want to see the papers and you are interested in them, we could come to some understanding about money. (I think I'll take your uncle Henry's advice, though, and try to sell the original copy! I think I read in *Time* magazine where he got a bundle on it from some jasper in New Mexico who collects stuff like that.)

Very truly yours,

Marjorie Verner (Mrs.)

This letter was the first of a great many which passed between Mrs. Verner and myself. On my advice, she consulted her family lawyer, and that individual proved (to my cost) to know his business. Eventually, however, matters were satisfactorily settled and I flew to Racine to pick up the manuscript after several Xeroxes had been made.

It was extremely difficult to read in places and presented very different problems from its predecessor's.

The water damage was severe. In places words and even

phrases were obliterated and impossible to decipher. I was obliged to consult specialists in this sort of thing (and I give special thanks here to Jim Forrest and the laboratories at U.C.L.A.), who worked technical wonders at bringing up missing pieces.

There were many occasions, however, when the results were unsuccessful. Here I have been forced to put in the word or phrase that seemed to fit the rest of the paragraph or page. I have done my best, but I am not Watson, and thus the reader may find a jarring note here and there. For this he must blame not the good doctor but my humble self. I thought of indicating these passages in the book but then decided such bracketing would be too intrusive. I'm sure the worst offenses will be quite obvious, anyway, and my clumsy hand will be instantly perceived.

Aside from the water damage, the most nettlesome problem was dating the manuscript. Internal evidence makes it quite clear that *The West End Horror* begins March 1, 1895. Ascertaining the date of its composition, however, is another matter. It was evident (to me, anyhow) that it was composed a lot later than 1895. Not only does Watson refer to intervals of years between efforts on his part to get Holmes's permission for the project, he also points out that among considerations *pro* permission were the deaths of many of the principals concerned with the case. Inasmuch as these names are not changed (impossible to disguise really, as Holmes points out), the dates are fairly easily determined. They hint at a relatively late date of composition, certainly after 1905. The fact, however, that the manuscript is in Watson's own hand, indicates with equal clarity that he was not yet crippled by arthritis. Beyond that, it is difficult to say. My own hunch—and it is only a hunch—is that *The West End Horror* was set down sometime after the First World War and before Holmes's death, in 1929. One of the things that makes me pick so late a period is that Watson—as in *The Seven-Per-Cent Solution* (but not so much)—continues to describe things that obviously aren't there any more. That Watson never sought to recover the manuscript after Holmes's death suggests to me that his own ailments had begun to overtake him (possibly the onslaught of crippling arthritis, which plagued his last decade)—another argument for the latish dating.

It may be noted that Watson's use of "Americanisms" persists, and this, I feel, deserves comment. Readers skeptical of the authenticity of *The Seven-Per-Cent Solution* base part of their argument for forgery on the fact that the book contains these Americanisms, which they deem "telltale." But they disregard two very crucial points. In the first place, Americanisms crop up all through Watson's case histories; in the second, there is a very simple reason for this. Between 1883 and 1886, Watson was working as a physician in San Francisco, California, to pay off some of his brother's debts. He married his first wife, Constance Adams, there, as any student of W. S. Baring-Gould's excellent biography of Holmes and Watson* knows. As Holmes (after living in America for two years) remarked to Watson, in *His Last Bow,* "My well of English seems to be permanently defiled." So much for Americanisms.

As for footnotes, I have again attempted to keep them to a minimum, though there are so many facts which check out (an argument in favor of the manuscript's authenticity) that I felt obliged to include many of them.

* *Sherlock Holmes of Baker Street: A Life of the World's First Consulting Detective,* by William S. Baring-Gould, published by Bramhall House, 1962.

Finally, a brief comment regarding the authenticity question. We have no way of proving such things. Indeed, healthy skepticism demands that we doubt. To have discovered one missing Watsonian account might seem like a miracle; to have unearthed another smacks suspiciously of coincidence. In self-defense I point out that I cannot claim to have actually discovered either of these documents, and in the case of the second, as Mrs. Verner points out, it wasn't exactly missing.

As regards authenticity, the reader must decide for himself, and I am aware of the controversy (am I ever!) that will surround this narrative. I conclude by referring you all to that charming poem of Vincent Starrett, which includes the wonderful words, "Only those things the heart believes are true."

Nicholas Meyer
Los Angeles
August 1975

THE WEST END HORROR

INTRODUCTORY

"No, Watson, I'm afraid my answer must remain the same," said Sherlock Holmes. "You're setting down 'the West End Horror,'" he went on, chuckling at my expression. "Don't look so astonished, my dear fellow. Your thought process was simplicity itself. I saw you at your writing table, arranging your notes. Then you came upon something you had forgotten about; it stopped you cold; you held it, read it, shaking your head with an air of familiar disbelief. Then you turned your gaze to our collection of theatrical programmes and then to my little monograph on ancient English charters. Finally, you stole a surreptitious glance in my direction as I sat absorbed in tuning my fiddle. *Voilà.*" He sighed and drew his bow across the strings in a tentative fashion, resting the end of the instrument on his knee. "I'm afraid it must still be 'No.'"

"But why?" I retorted with energy, not pausing to acknowledge his mental legerdemain. "Do you think I would fail to do justice to the case—or to yourself?" This last protest was tinged with irony, for his early criticisms of my efforts to keep some record of his professional activities had been harsh, indeed. They had mellowed to something less than full approval when, with the passage of time, he saw that my accounts brought him more than a modicum of agreeable notoriety. His vanity, which was not inconsiderable, was usually flattered at the prospect.

"On the contrary. What I fear is that you *would* do justice to it."

"I shall change the names," I offered, beginning to see where the problem lay.

"That is precisely what you cannot do."

"I have done so before."

"But cannot possibly do so now. Think, Watson, think! Never have our clients been so well known! The public may argue about the true identity of the King of Bohemia*; they may guess at the real title of the Duke of Holderness. But here there could be no room for doubt—there are no fictitious characters you could substitute for those of the principals in this affair and hope to deceive your readers. To disguise them sufficiently, you would find yourself in phantasy up to the neck."

I confessed this difficulty had not occurred to me.

"Besides," Holmes went on, "you would be obliged to recount our part in the business, as well. While scarcely unethical, it could hardly be termed legal. Destruction of a corpse without notifying the authorities is a clear violation of

---

* Long assumed by scholars to be King Edward VII. However, Michael Harrison has recently demonstrated beyond a shadow of a doubt that the King of Bohemia was in reality His Serene Highness Prince Alexander ("Sandro") of Battenberg, once king of Bulgaria.

law and could be construed in this case as suppression of evidence."

There the conversation ended—as it usually did—and I tucked away my notes on the entire incredible story till I should chance upon them again after another year or two and broach the subject once more.

Getting Holmes to change his mind once he had got hold of an idea was like trying to reverse the direction of the global orbit. Once it had begun spinning on its course, it was virtually impossible to stem the momentum, let alone alter the axis. An idea would fix itself in his brain, take root there, and flourish like a tree. It could not be uprooted, only felled—and this only when struck by a better idea. It was Holmes's unshakable conviction in the present instance that "the West End Horror" (as he liked to call it) was a story for which the world was not yet prepared and that it could not be revealed save with consequences he wished to avoid.

Several things finally combined to change his views on the topic. The passage of years and the deaths of many of the principals involved, as well as the changing mores of society, wrought a subtle alteration in his obstinacy. Then I advanced a clever argument myself, which was designed to allay his fears of publication.

I told him in so many words that my chief concern was setting down the case as a matter of historical record (there he conceded its usefulness) and not as sensational literature for the scandalmongering Press. So far from looking for a publisher, I offered Holmes sole and exclusive proprietorship of the manuscript, to do with as he saw fit, *when* he saw fit. My only stipulation was that it not be destroyed.

He procrastinated for several days following my offer, during which he appeared to have forgot entirely our latest discussion (I think perhaps he was trying to) and busied himself with his criminal index, which demanded constant revision if it was to be of any use. I did not press him, knowing that his mind was turning over this new possibility without my having to say anything further.

"How could you possibly organise it?" he asked me once, while we were at the Turkish baths. "The cast of characters and events is large and diffuse. It will provide you with none of the compact symmetry of my more typical cases, the kind of material with which you work so well."

I answered that I should simply set down what happened in the order in which it happened.

"Oho," he laughed. "Resorting to the tricks of cheap fiction, are you? No one will believe you, you know."

I added that remark to my arsenal of incentives and aimed it back at him. He brooded over it amidst the rising steam and said nothing.

Another week went by, and then, quite abruptly, he looked up from his chaotic filing arrangements and said in an offhand tone, "Oh, well, you might as well do it. But see that you give it to me, as you promised, when you have done."

I did not dare say anything to provoke second thoughts on his part but replied with equal offhandedness that I would. And so I shall, making only one disclaimer before beginning. Since the case which follows involves a great many of the greatest names on the British stage, there is a great temptation to write the story today* with the benefit of that comforting hindsight, which allows us to claim with a certain smugness that we knew all along who was destined for greatness and other like matters. It may also strike the contemporary reader —should Holmes ever let this manuscript out of his hands!—

---

* Another bit of evidence for the latish dating.

that some of my suspicions at the time were nothing short of preposterous. I will resist the temptation to modify or dilute those suspicions. I did not at the time, nor do I now, believe that positions of power or influence render a subject immune from investigation. My suspicions* may seem absurd today, but I will let them stand, for all that, and tell my story as it fell out at the time.

*Another bit of evidence for the latish dating.

ONE

SHERLOCK HOLMES IN RESIDENCE

All theatrical London gossiped and speculated about the murder of Jonathan McCarthy when news of it first appeared in the papers. Theories were rife concerning the acerbic writer and the many enemies his pen had made. But curiosity, unsatisfied, eventually dies a death of boredom. McCarthy's assassin was never caught, much less discovered, and as no new facts were forthcoming, the police were finally forced to join the public and own themselves baffled. The case was never closed, but their interest was inevitably arrested by more current events. The mysterious death of the actress at the Savoy had the same tongues wagging for weeks, and Scotland Yard was hard put to explain the peculiar disappearance of its police surgeon—who vanished, taking two corpses along with him from the mortuary, and was never heard of again. In McCarthy's case the police ignored, as well (or forgot, because they could not understand it), the bizarre clue the dead man had left behind.

How the populace would have trembled had they deciphered it! Instead of being idly (or in the case of the police, professionally) interested in an affair which, however sensational, held no personal concern for them, they would have found themselves—all of them!—very real participants in a crime so monstrous that it threatened to blot the nineteenth century and alter the course of history.

The winter of '94-'95 had been a fearful one. Not in recent memory had London been pelted so with snow; not in recent memory had the wind howled in the streets and icicles formed on drainpipes and in the eaves as they did in January of 1895. The inclement weather continued unabated through February, keeping the street sweepers perpetually occupied and exhausted.

Holmes and I stayed comfortably indoors at Baker Street. No cases appeared out of the snowdrifts, for which we were unashamedly grateful. I spent much of the time organising my own notes after first extracting a promise from Holmes to desist from chemical experiments. I pointed out that in fair weather it was possible to dispel the stench he created with his test tubes and retorts by opening the windows and going out for a walk, but that should he become carried away now by his hobby we would inevitably freeze to death.

He grumbled a deal at this but saw the logic of it and settled down for a time to indoor target practise, one of his favourite recreations. For an hour at a time—as I sat at my desk and endeavoured to work—he reclined on the horsehair divan, his pistol propped between his knees, and squeezed off round after round at the wall above the deal table which contained his chemical apparatus.

He had managed to spell Disraeli with bullet pocks when this diversion, too, was denied him. Mrs. Hudson knocked at our door and told him in no uncertain terms that he was menacing the neighbourhood. There had been complaints from the house next door, she said, by an elderly invalid who claimed that Holmes's artillery was having a deleterious effect on her already unstable constitution. In addition, the reports had caused several large icicles to fall before they had melted sufficiently to be rendered harmless. One of these stalactites, it appeared, had nearly driven itself through the head of the dustman, who had threatened to bring an action against our landlady as a result.

"Really, Mr. Holmes, you'd think a grown man like yourself would be able to occupy his time in a more sensible fashion!" she exclaimed, her bosom heaving with emotion. "Look at all them fine books you have, just sittin' there, waiting to be read. And *there—*" she pointed to several bundles on the floor, tied with string—"some you haven't even opened as yet."

"Very well, Mrs. Hudson. You have carried the day. I will immerse myself." Holmes escorted her wearily to the door and returned with a disgruntled sigh. I was grateful that we no longer kept cocaine lying about, for in earlier times such frustrations and boredom would have provoked instant recourse to its dubious comforts.

Instead, Holmes took the landlady's advice and began cutting the strings on his parcels of books with a small penknife and inspecting their contents. He was a compulsive bibliophile, always buying volumes, having them sent 'round to our rooms, and never finding time to read them. Now he squatted down in their midst and began glancing at the titles of works he had forgot he owned.

"I say, Watson, look at this," he began, but subsided on to the floor with the tome in one hand whilst with the other absently felt into the pocket of his dressing gown for a pipe.

He devoured the book, along with several bowlsful of shag

(almost as malodorous as some of his chemicals), and then went on to another volume. He had become interested in ancient English charters and now prepared to devote himself to serious research on the subject. His preoccupation did not greatly astonish me, as I knew his range of interests to be wide, varied, and occasionally odd. He had mastered a number of arcane topics—matters quite unrelated to the art of criminal detection—and could speak brilliantly (when he chose) on such diverse matters as warships of the future, artificial irrigation, the motets of Lassus, and the mating habits of the South American jaguar.

Now English charters occupied his mind with a passion which totally conformed to his other pursuits in its single-minded application of his powerful intellect. He had apparently been interested in them at some earlier date, for most of the books he had purchased (and neglected to open) dealt with this peculiar subject, and at the end of the week the floor of our sitting room was virtually paved with them. Eventually such volumes as were at his immediate disposal were deemed insufficient for his purposes and he was obliged to sally forth into the snow and make his way to the British Museum for sustenance. These forays lasted for several afternoons during the last week of February, the nights which followed being spent in the laborious transcription of his notes.

It was a sunny, cold morning, March 1, when he flung his pen across the room in disgust.

"No use, Watson," said he. "I shall have to go to Cambridge if I am to approach this seriously. The material simply isn't here."

I remarked that his interest threatened to develop into a mania, but he appeared not to have heard me. He hunted up his pen on the floor whither he had hurled it and prepared to address himself again to his notes, observing the while, with a didactic formality which contrasted oddly with his posture upon hands and knees, "The mind is like a large field, Watson. It is available for cultivation only if the land is used sensibly and portions of it are permitted to lie fallow periodically. Part of my mind—my professional mind—is on holiday at the moment. During its leave of absence I am exercising another quarter of it."

"It's a pity your professional mind is out of town," I remarked, looking out of the window and into the street.

He followed my gaze from his position on the floor. "Why? What are you looking at?"

"I believe we are about to have a visitor, someone interested in that portion of your intellect that is currently lying fallow."

Outside, I could see stepping—or rather hopping nimbly—between the shovels of the snow cleaners and the brooms of the housemaids, one of the queerest creatures I had ever beheld.

"He certainly appears a likely candidate for admittance to 221b," I went on, hoping to distract my companion from the volumes which had failed him.

"I am not in the mood for visitors," Holmes returned moodily, thrusting his fists into the pockets of his dressing gown. "What does he look like?" The question was automatic and escaped his lips involuntarily.

"He isn't wearing a coat, for one thing. On a morning like this he must be mad."

"Clothes?"

"Norfolk jacket and knickerbockers—in this weather! They

look well worn, even at this distance. He keeps adjusting his shirt cuffs."

"Probably false. Age?"

"Roughly forty, with an enormous beard, slightly reddish, like his hair, which is blowing over his shoulder as he walks."

"Height?" Behind me I could hear a vesta being struck.

"Rather tall, I should say, under medium height."

"Gait?"

I pondered this, wondering how to describe the newcomer's hopping, skipping pace.

"The man walks like a gigantic leprechaun."

"What? Why, this sounds like Shaw." Holmes came up behind me, quite animated now, as we gazed together at the advancing figure. "Hello, it *is* Shaw. I'm blest if it isn't!" he exclaimed, smiling, his pipe clenched between his teeth. "Whatever brings *him* out on a morning like this? And what has made him change his mind and decide to pay me a visit?"

"Who is he?"

"A friend."

"Indeed?" No one as familiar as I with the personal life and habits of Sherlock Holmes could have received this statement with anything less than wonder. Aside from myself, his brother, and various professional acquaintances, I was not aware that Holmes cultivated any friends. The peculiar fellow advancing below us was now examining house numbers with some care before hopping on and stopping before our door. The bell rang with a truculent jingle several times.

"I met him at a concert of Sarasate's* some years ago," Holmes explained, turning to make some hasty order of our shambles. He kicked a few books out of the way, forging a path of sorts from the door to a chair by the hearth. I seldom accompanied him any more to concerts and the opera, preferring more convivial amusements of the sort he found trivial.

"We got into a rather heated disagreement about Sarasate's abilities, as I recall, but finally buried the hatchet. He is a very brilliant Irishman." Holmes removed his pistol from the chair he proposed to offer our guest and put it on the mantel. "A brilliant Irishman who has not yet found his métier. But he will. He will. You will find him amusing, if naught else. He has got hold of some of the oddest notions."

"How do you know he is brilliant?"

We could hear a muffled conversation taking place at the foot of the stairs, doubtless between our visitor and Mrs. Hudson.

"How do I know? Why, he told me so himself. He has no qualms about hiding his light under a bushel. Furthermore," he looked up at me, the coal scuttle in his hands, "he understands Wagner. He understands him perfectly. This alone qualifies him for some magnificent destiny. At the moment, miserable man, he's as poor as a church mouse."

We could now hear feet rapidly ascending our stair.

"What does he do?"

There was a knock on our door of the same energetic variety which had manifested itself towards our bell some moments earlier.

"Oh, you want to be careful of him, Watson. You want to

* Sarasate was a well-known violin virtuoso of the day. For a full (though not entirely accurate) account of the meeting, see Baring-Gould's biography of Holmes.

watch him and give him a wide berth." He added some coal to the fire and passed me with a conspiratorial finger on his lips as he went to the door. "He is a critic."

With this, he flung wide the door and admitted his friend. "Shaw, my dear fellow, welcome! Welcome! You have heard me speak of Dr. Watson, who shares these lodgings with me? Ah, good. Watson, allow me to present 'Cornetti di Basso,' known to his intimates as Mr. Bernard Shaw."*

* Shaw wrote music criticism under the name Cornetti di Basso.

TWO

AN INVITATION TO INVESTIGATE

Mr. Bernard Shaw's resemblance to an outsized leprechaun increased on closer inspection. His eyes were the bluest I had ever beheld, the colour of the Côte d'Azur. They twinkled with merriment when he spoke lightly and flashed when he became animated, which was not infrequently, for he was an emotional individual and a lively talker. His complexion was almost as ruddy as his hair, and he boasted a disputatious nose, broad and blunt at the tip, where the nostrils twitched and flared. His speech added to the leprechaunish impression he conveyed, for it was tinged with the faintest and most pleasant of Irish brogues.

"By God, I believe your rooms are more untidy than my own," he began, stepping across our threshold and nodding to us both. "However, they are somewhat larger than my hovel, which allows you to be creative with your sloppiness."

I was annoyed by these remarks, which struck me as an unseemly preamble for a guest, but he flashed me an impish grin which managed, somehow, to take away the sting of his words. Holmes, apparently used to his brusque and forthright manner, appeared not to have heard.

"You've no idea what a pleasant surprise this is," he informed the critic. "I'd quite given up hope of ever persuading you to set foot in these digs."

"I made a bargain with you," Shaw reminded him with some asperity. "I said that I would call upon you at your convenience if you in turn would attend a meeting of the Fabian Society." He accepted the chair indicated by Holmes and sat down, stretching forth his small hands and surprisingly skinny legs toward the comfort of our blaze.

"I'm afraid I must continue to decline your gracious invitation." The detective drew up a chair opposite. "I am not a joiner by nature, I fear, and while I would cheerfully dole out coin of the realm to hear you discourse on Wagner, you must permit me to go about the reformation of the race in my own way."

"You call it reformation?" the Irishman snorted. "Ha, you right wrongs, one by one, imagining yourself to be some sort of mediaeval knight errant." Holmes inclined his head slightly, but the other snorted again. "You are only addressing yourself to the effects of society's ills, not the causes, whereas the Fabians, with our motto, 'Educate, Agitate, Organise,' are trying to—"

Holmes laughed and held up a deprecating hand. "My dear Shaw, spare me your polemics at this hour of the morning. I trust, in any event, that you have not come to Mohammed on this frosty day to visit him with the philosophy of socialism."

"It wouldn't hurt you if I had," Shaw returned equably. "My eloquence on the subject has been declared alarming by those in a position to know."

"Even so. I can't offer you any breakfast—that's long since been cleared away—but in any case, I perceive by your right sleeve that you have already dined on eggs and—"

Shaw chuckled and inspected his sleeve. "That's yesterday's breakfast. I see you are fallible. How comforting."

"Would you like some brandy? It will take the chill off your bones."

"And shorten my life by ten years," the elf replied with a merry smile. "Thank you, I'll remain as I am."

"You aren't prolonging your life by going about in this weather without a coat," I observed. He smiled thinly.

"I was obliged to pawn it yesterday, a temporary expedient until my next week's wages. A ludicrous state of affairs for a middle-aged man, don't you find? Critics are not revered as they should be."

"Shaw writes for the *Saturday Review*," Holmes informed me, "and apparently they pay no more for reviewing drama than the *Star* did for writing about music."

"Not by half," the Irishman agreed. "Could you manage on two guineas a week, Doctor? Your writing brings you a deal more, I daresay."

"Why don't you attempt something in a more lucrative vein?" I suggested. "You might try your hand at a novel."

"I've tried my hand at five and collected eight hundred rejections among them. No, I shall continue as critic and pamphleteer, occasionally turning out a play of my own on the side. Did either of you gentlemen happen to attend a performance of *Widowers' Houses* a year or two back?"

We shook our heads, I, for my part, never having heard of the play.

The Irishman did not appear surprised or put out. "It would have astonished me if you'd said yes," he remarked with mordant humour, "though it would have lent you a kind of distinction in the years to come. No matter, I shall keep at it. After all"—he held up his fingers—"all the great English playwrights are Irish. Look at Sheridan! Goldsmith! Look in our own time at Yeats, and look at Oscar Wilde! All Irish! One day Shaw will be included in that glorious pantheon."

The man's bumptiousness was past bearing.

"Shakespeare was English," I pointed out, mildly. Instantly I perceived I had struck an exposed nerve. Shaw paled, his beard quivered, and he leapt to his feet.

"Shakespeare?" He rolled the word around his mouth with scornful relish. "Shakespeare? A mountebank who had not the wit to invent his own plots, much less embellish them! Tolstoy was right—a conspiracy of nineteenth-century academia, that's what Shakespeare is. I ask you, do people really 'kiss away kingdoms,' or don't they rather hold on to power just as long and as tenaciously as they can? *Antony and Cleopatra*—what ineffable romantic twaddle! Claptrap! Humbug! They were as cynical a pair of politicians as you could conjure, both of 'em!"

"But the poetry," I protested.

"Poetry—rubbish!" His colour was changing again to a scarlet hue as he danced about the room, occasionally stumbling over the books on the floor. "People don't talk poetry, Doctor! Only in books—and bad plays! The man had a brilliant mind," he allowed, calming somewhat, "but he should never have wasted his intellect on plays. He should have been an essayist. He had not the gifts of a playwright."

This last statement was so completely astounding that I fancy Holmes and I must both have simply gaped at him for some moments—which he affected not to notice as he resumed his seat—before Holmes recovered himself with a little laugh.

"Surely you didn't come here this morning to take on Shakespeare any more than the evils of capitalism," said he, filling a pipe from the Persian slipper on the mantel, "though I am tempted to dwell on the contrast between your views on the redistribution of wealth and your own desire for an increase in salary."

"You've swayed me from the point," Shaw acknowledged with a sour look, "with all this talk of Shakespeare. As for my salary, that you must take up with Mr. Harris, if you think you can face him. I have come to you this morning on quite a different errand." He paused, whether for dramatic effect or merely to collect himself, I could not tell. "There has been a murder done."

Silence filled the room. Holmes and I instinctively exchanged glances as Shaw surveyed us with evident satisfaction.

"Who has been murdered?" Holmes enquired calmly, crossing his legs, all attention now.

"A critic. You don't read the drama notices? Ah, well, then, you've missed him. Jonathan McCarthy writes for the *Morning Courant*—or wrote, I should say, since he will no more."

Holmes picked up a pile of papers by his chair. "I confine my attentions as a rule to the agony columns," he confessed, "but I can't have missed a story such as—"

"You won't find it in the papers—yet," Shaw interrupted. "Word of the deed was just circulating at the *Review* offices this morning. Instead of writing my piece due tomorrow, I came here straightway to tell you of it."

Throughout this recital, he attempted to maintain a jocular demeanour, as one who is not affected personally by such grisly tidings. Yet beneath his gallows-humour delivery, I sensed a very real anxiety. Perhaps the murder of a colleague threatened him in a way he could hardly have acknowledged.

"You came here straightway," Holmes echoed, filling his pipe with dextrous fingers. "With what end in view?"

The Irishman blinked in surprise.

"Surely that is obvious. I wish you to investigate the matter."

"Is it so very complicated? Will not the police suffice?"

"Come, come. We both know the police. I want neither their inefficiency nor a whitewash by the authorities. I want an honest, unbiased, and complete examination of the matter. I continue to read Dr. Watson's accounts of your doings in the *Strand* and long to see you in action for myself. Are you not up to the challenge? The man was stabbed," he added as incentive.

Holmes cast a longing look in the direction of his literary researches, but it was clear he was interested, despite himself.

"Had he any enemies?"

Bernard Shaw laughed long and heartily.

"You ask that question about a critic? In any case, it must surely be obvious that he possessed at least one. For McCarthy I should postulate a score." He winked roguishly in my direction. "He was even less agreeable than I."

Sherlock Holmes considered this for some moments, then rose abruptly and threw off his dressing gown.

"Come, let us have a look. Have you the unfortunate man's address?"

"Number Twenty-four South Crescent, near Tavistock Square. One moment."

Holmes turned and regarded him.

"You are forgetting the matter of a fee."

"I haven't yet said that I will take the case."

"Nevertheless. I must tell you I am not capable of paying a brass farthing for your services."

"I have worked for less on occasion, if the matter interested me." He smiled. "Are you still writing your treatise on Wagner?"

"*The Perfect Wagnerite*, yes."

"Then perhaps I shall trouble you for a signed first edition." Holmes slipped into his jacket and ulster. "*If* I take the case." He moved to the door, then stopped. "What is your real reason for wishing me to look into this business?"

The leprechaun threw out his hands. "The satisfaction of my own curiosity, I give you my word. If Dr. Watson pays his share of the rent with prose accounts of your work, perhaps I can do the same by putting you on the stage."

"Pray do not," Holmes responded, holding open the door for us. "I have little enough privacy as it is."

THREE

THE BUSINESS AT SOUTH CRESCENT

"Well, Watson, what do you make of him?" my companion demanded. We were sharing a hansom on our way to 24 South Crescent, where Shaw had promised to meet us. He had some business matters of his own to attend to in the mean time. I huddled into the recesses of my coat and pulled up my scarf against the biting wind before replying.

"Think of him? I must say I find him insufferable. Holmes, how can you tolerate the conversation of that know-all?"

"He reminds me of Alceste, I fancy. At any rate, he amuses me as much as Alceste. Don't you find him stimulating?"

"Stimulating?" I protested. "Come now, do you really suppose Shakespeare would have been better occupied writing essays?"

Holmes chuckled. "Well, admit I warned you that he held some queer ideas. With Shakespeare, unfortunately, you tumbled on to his *bête noire*. There, I confess, his views appear radically unsound, but then, his prejudices can be explained. He reads plays not as thou dost, Watson, but rather to take the measure of himself against the minds of other men. 'Such men as he be never at heart's ease whilst they behold a greater than themselves.'"

"'And therefore are they very dangerous,'" I concluded the passage for him. I looked out of the window at snowbound London and found myself wondering if the big leprechaun could be dangerous. Certainly, he was handy enough with words to turn them into lethal weapons, but there was something so impishly ingratiating about the man that I found it hard to reconcile my opinions of him.

"Here we are," my companion cried, interrupting my reverie. We found ourselves in Bloomsbury, in a pleasant, well-kept semicircle of houses which faced private gardens maintained with equal devotion. The area was at present covered with snow, but the outlines of a formal garden peeped through and affected the contours of the drifts. The houses themselves were four-storeyed and painted white. They were all boarding establishments, but I noticed no signs proclaiming vacancies and decided the location was too desirable and the charges probably too high for that. Number 24 occupied a space in the middle of the semicircle. It looked no different from its neighbours to the left and right, save for the crowd gathered before it and the uniformed constables who barred the curious from access to the open front door.

"I have a premonition we are about to meet an old friend," Holmes murmured as we descended from the cab. There was no great difficulty in our being admitted to number 24, as Holmes was well known to the members of the force. They assumed he had been summoned to view the situation in his capacity as consulting detective, and he did nothing to discourage this belief as they passed us in.

The murdered man's flat occupied a first-floor suite of

rooms facing the gardens and was easily reached at the top of the stairs. We hadn't opened the door (which stood slightly ajar) before a familiar voice assailed our ears:

"Well, if it's not my old friends Mr. Holmes and Dr. Watson! What brings you gentlemen to South Crescent, as if I didn't know. Come in, come in!"

"Good morning to you, Inspector Lestrade. May we survey the damage?"

"How did you come to know there was any?" The lean, ferret-like little man shifted his gaze from one to the other of us. "It wasn't Gregson* sent you 'round, was it? I'll have to have a word with that cheeky—"

"I give you my word it was not," Holmes assured him smoothly. "I have my own sources, and they appear sufficient. May we have a look?"

"I don't mind if you do," was the lofty reply, "but you'd best be quick. Brownlow and his boys'll be here any minute now for the body."

"We shall try to stay out of your way," the detective rejoined and began a cursory examination of the flat from where he stood.

"The fact is, I was thinking of coming by your lodgings a bit later in the day," the Scotland Yarder confessed, watching him narrowly. "For a cup of tea," he added firmly, apparently for the benefit of a young, sandy-haired sergeant, who was the room's only other living occupant.

"Can't make head or tail of it, eh?" Holmes stepped into the room, shaking his head over the mess Lestrade and his

---

* Inspector Tobias Gregson, also of Scotland Yard. A perennial rivalry existed for many years between Gregson and Lestrade. On the whole, Holmes had a higher opinion of the former.

men had made of the carpet. "Will they never learn?" I heard him mutter as he looked around.

The place combined the features of a library and sitting room. Lavishly equipped with books, it boasted a small tea table, which at the moment supported two glasses containing what looked like brandy. One glass had been knocked on its side but not broken, and the amber liquid remained within it. Next to the same glass, a long, oddly-shaped cigar sat unmolested in a brass ashtray, where it had been allowed to go out of its own volition.

Behind the table was set a day bed and beyond that, facing the window, the writing table of the dead man. It was covered with papers, all related—so far as I was able to discern from a casual glance—to his calling. There were programmes, theatre tickets, notices of substitutions in casts, as well as cuttings from his own reviews, neatly arranged for easy reference. Beside these papers was an engraved invitation to the première of something called *The Grand Duke,* at the Savoy two days hence.

Those walls devoid of bookshelves were literally papered with portraits of various members of the theatrical profession. Some were photographs, others were executed in pen and ink, but all bore the signatures of the notables who had sat for them. One was assailed by the testimonials of affection from all quarters and awed by the likenesses of Forbes-Robertson, Marion and Ellen Terry, Beerbohm-Tree, and Henry Irving, who stared or scowled dramatically down at the visitor.

All these, however—the books, the desk, the pictures, and the table—were but as set decorations for the *pièce de théâtre.* The corpse of Jonathan McCarthy lay on its back at the base of a set of bookshelves, the eyes open and staring, the black-bearded jaw dropped, and the mouth wide in a terrible, silent scream. McCarthy's swarthy looks were not pleasant in and of themselves, but coupled with his expression in death, they combined to produce a truly horrible impression. I had seldom beheld a more unnerving sight. The man had been stabbed in the left side, somewhat below the heart, and had bled profusely. The instrument of his death was nowhere apparent. I knelt and examined the corpse, determining that the blood had dried on the silken waistcoat and on the oriental carpet beside it. The body was cold, and parts of it were already quite hard.

"The other rooms are undisturbed, I take it?" Holmes enquired behind me. "No handwriting on the walls?"

"Gad, sir, but you've a long memory,"* Lestrade laughed. "No, the only writing on the walls is on those pictures. This room's where the business took place, all right."

"What are the facts?"

"He was found like this some two and a half hours ago. The girl came up with his breakfast, knocked on the door, and receiving no answer, made so bold as to enter. He'd overslept before, it seems, on more than one occasion. As to what happened, that's clear enough, up to a point. He was entertaining here last night—though he came home late and let himself in with his latchkey, so nobody got a look at his company. They sat down to a brandy and cigars here at the table when an altercation began. Whoever it was reached behind him to the writing desk and grabbed this." He paused and held out his hand. The young sergeant, taking his cue, passed

---

* In 1881, the word *Rache* was found written in blood on the wall of an empty house in Lauriston Gardens. The only other feature of interest was the corpse of a man, recently murdered. Watson's account, titled "A Study in Scarlet," was the first of Holmes's cases to be written up. It was published in the Beeton's Christmas annual of 1887 under the pen name of Watson's literary agent, Dr. A. Conan Doyle.

over something wrapped in a handkerchief. Lestrade set it gently on the table and threw back the folds of material to reveal an ivory letter opener, its yellowish blade tinged a tawny red, some of which had run onto and splattered the finely worked silver hilt.

"Javanese," Holmes murmured, examining it with his magnifying glass. "It came from the desk, you say? Ah, yes, here is the sheath which matches it. Go on, pray."

"Whoever it was," Lestrade resumed with a self-important air, "seized the letter opener and stabbed his host, knocking over his brandy glass as he thrust home. McCarthy crumpled in a heap at the foot of the table while the other departed, leaving his cigar burning where he had left it. McCarthy stayed beneath the table for some time—you can see quite a pool of blood—and then with his last reserves of strength, he crawled to those bookshelves—"

"So much, as you say, is obvious," Holmes observed, drily, pointing to a ghastly scarlet trail which led directly to the body. He stepped forward and carefully picked up the cigar, holding it gently in the middle. "This cigar is less so. I cannot recall having ever seen one like it. Can you, Lestrade?"

"You're going to tell me about all those tobacco ashes you can recognise," the inspector scoffed.

"On the contrary, I am trying to tell you about one I cannot. May I have a portion of this?" He held up the cigar.

"As you wish."

Holmes inclined his head in a little bow of thanks. He withdrew his penknife, leaned on the edge of the table, and carefully sawed off two inches of the cigar, putting the stub back where he had found it and pocketing the sample where it would not be crushed. He straightened up ready with another question, when a noise was heard below, followed by a thunderous rush upon the stairs. Shaw arrived, breathless but triumphant.

"Why, man," he cried, "your name's a regular passe-partout! Well, where's the carrion?"

"And who might this gentleman be?" Lestrade growled, looking fearlessly up into Shaw's beard.

"It's all right, Inspector Lestrade. He's a colleague of the deceased, Mr. Bernard Shaw of the *Saturday Review*." The two men bowed slightly.

"There's a police wagon arrived downstairs with a stretcher in it," Shaw informed Lestrade.

"Very good. Well, gentlemen, as you can see—"

"You haven't yet told him about the book, Inspector," interposed the young sergeant shyly. He had been following Holmes's every move with eager interest, almost as though trying to memorise his actions.

"I was going to, I was going to!" Lestrade shot back, growing more annoyed by the minute. "You just stay in the background, young man. Pay attention and you'll learn something."

"Yes, sir. Sorry, sir."

His chief grunted. "Now where was I?"

"You were about to show us the book poor McCarthy had used his last ounce of energy to retrieve," Holmes prompted quietly.

"Oh, yes." The little man made to fetch the volume, then turned. "Stop a bit. Here, how did you come to know he was after a book before he died?"

"What other reason for him to have struggled so valiantly towards the bookshelves," Holmes replied mildly. "A volume of Shakespeare, is it not? I perceive one is missing."

Instinctively I stole a glance at Shaw, who heard this information with a snort and began his own examination of the room.

"Kindly refrain from trampling the clues," Holmes ordered sharply and signed for him to join us by the table. "May we see the book?"

Lestrade nodded to the sergeant, who brought forth another object, wrapped in a second handkerchief, which he placed on the table. Before us lay a volume of *Romeo and Juliet* published by Oxford and obviously part of the complete edition which rested on the shelf above the corpse. Holmes brought forth his glass again and conducted a careful examination of the volume, pursing his lips in concentration.

"With your permission, sir." It was the sergeant, again.

"Yes?"

"When we found it, it was opened."

"Indeed?" Holmes shot a keen glance at Lestrade, who shifted his weight uncomfortably. "And where was that?"

"The book wasn't in his hands," the little man replied defensively. "He'd let go of it when he died."

"But it was open."

"Ay."

"To what page?"

"Somewheres in the middle," Lestrade grumbled. "It's a perfectly ordinary book," he added testily. "No secret messages stuck in the binding, if you're thinking along those lines."

"I am not thinking at all," Holmes replied coldly. "I am observing, as you, evidently, have failed to do."

"It was page forty-two," the sergeant volunteered. Holmes favored him with an interested look, then began carefully turning the bloodstained pages.

"You're very keen," he commented, studying the leaves. "How long have you been down from Leeds? Five years?"

"Six, sir. After my father—" The sergeant stopped short in confusion and regarded the detective with amazement.

"Here, Holmes," his superior broke in, "if you know the lad, why not say so?"

"It is no great matter to infer his birthplace, Lestrade. Surely you can't have failed to remark on his distinctive *a*'s and his peculiar manner of handling diphthongs? I would hazard Leeds or possibly Hull, but then, he has been in London these last six years, as he says, and acquired a local overlay, which makes it difficult to be precise. You live in Stepney now, don't you, Sergeant?"

"Ay, sir." The sergeant's eyes were wide with awe. For his part, Shaw had listened to the entire exchange with the strictest attention stamped on his features.

"But this is wonderful!" he shouted. "Do you mean you can actually place a man by his speech?"

"If it's in English, within twenty miles.* I'd know your Dublin origins despite your attempts to conceal them," Holmes answered. "Ah, here we are, page forty-two. It concludes Act three, Scene one—"

"The duel between Tybalt and Mercutio," Shaw informed Lestrade, who was still pondering, I could see, the detective's linguistic feat. Holmes looked at him sharply over the volume, whereat the Irishman coloured slightly.

"Well, of course I've read it," he snarled. "Romantic twaddle," he added, to no-one in particular.

---

* In 1912 Shaw wrote *Pygmalion,* a play very obviously inspired by Holmes, about an eccentric bachelor with the same gift for placing people by their speech. Dr. Watson finds his counterpart in Colonel Pickering, who like Watson, has met his roommate on his return from Indian climes.

"Yes, the death of Mercutio—and also Tybalt. Hmm, a curious reference."

"If he made it," Lestrade persisted. "The book wasn't in his hand, as I've said, and the pages might have fallen over in the interim."

"They might," Holmes agreed. "But since there is no message in the book, we must infer that he meant to tell us something with the volume. It could hardly have been the man's whim to pass the time with a little Shakespeare while he bled to death."

"Hardly," Shaw agreed. "Even McCarthy would not have been capable of such a gesture."

"You don't seem very disturbed by what's happened to the deceased," Lestrade observed suspiciously.

"I'm not disturbed in the slightest. Except by his browsing Shakespeare at the last. The man was a charlatan and a viper and probably merited his end."

"Shakespeare?" Lestrade was now totally perplexed.

"McCarthy." Shaw pointed at the photographs and sketches. "You see those signatures on the walls? Lies, every one of 'em, I'll swear to it. Proffered in fear."

"Fear of what?"

"Bad notices, malicious gossip, scandal in print or out of it. McCarthy kept his ear to the ground. He was notorious for it. Do you remember the suicide some three years ago of Alice Mackenzie? She played the lead in that thing by Herbert Parker at the Allegro*? Well, that was almost certainly provoked by an item with this blackguard's name on it."

Sherlock Holmes was not listening. As we watched, he pro-

---

* This is fiction on Watson's part or Shaw's. I can find no mention of a scandal involving such a theater, author, or actress. There may have been such a tragedy, of course, but if there was, the names have been changed.

ceeded to give the room a thorough inspection of the kind only he could manage. He crawled about on all fours, peering through his glass; he examined the walls, the shelves, the desk, the table, the day bed, and finally made the most minute inspection of the corpse itself. Throughout this tour, which lasted some ten minutes or more, he kept up a running commentary of whistles, exclamations, and mutterings. Part of this time was spent in examination of the other rooms in the flat, though it was clear from his expression when he returned that Lestrade had been accurate in saying that the drama had not overflowed the confines of the library.

At length he straightened up with a sigh. "You really must learn not to disturb the evidence," he informed Lestrade. He turned to the young sergeant. "What is your name?"

"Stanley Hopkins, sir."

"Well, Hopkins, in my opinion, you'll go far,* but you oughtn't to have touched the book. It might have made all the difference in the world had I been able to see the relation between the man's fingertips and the volume. Do you understand?"

"Yes, sir. I shall see that such a thing never happens again. We neither of us touched the body," he added in a gallant attempt to redeem himself in the detective's eyes.

"Good lad. Well, gentlemen, I think that is about all."

"And what have you uncovered with all your creeping and crawling about that I haven't?" Lestrade demanded with a sour grin.

"Nothing very much, I grant you. The murderer is a man. He is right-handed, has a working knowledge of anatomy,

---

* Holmes's prediction proved correct. Hopkins became chief inspector in 1904 and had a forensic laboratory named for him upon his retirement in 1925.

and is very powerful, though somewhat under six feet—as calculated by the length of his stride. He wore new boots, expensive and probably purchased in the Strand, and he smoked what is definitely a foreign-made cigar, purchased abroad. And before he left, he tore out the page in McCarthy's engagement diary with his name on it. Good day, Inspector Lestrade."

FOUR

CONCERNING BUNTHORNE

On our way downstairs, we passed the police surgeon, Mr. Brownlow, and his men with the stretcher. Holmes exchanged a few words with that grey-bearded individual, with whom he had a nodding acquaintance. We then passed through the police barriers outside, and Holmes withdrew his watch.

"I'm in the mood for lunch," he declared, sucking in the cold fresh air and looking about. "Watson, this used to be your stamping ground; where shall we dine?"

"There's the Holborn; it's not far from here."

"Excellent. Let us repair to it for sustenance. Are you coming, Shaw?" He began to walk through the dirty snow at a smart pace, obliging the critic to skip briskly.

"How can you even think of food after what you have just witnessed?" Shaw cried in dismay.

"It is because of what I have witnessed that I find it crossing my mind," the detective returned. "Food is one of the principal means by which death is avoided."

"I really ought to be at work," Shaw growled as he sat

down with us at the Holborn and eyed askance the Masonic tiling with which the establishment was decorated. "I've two pieces due by noon tomorrow, and I haven't begun either of 'em yet." In spite of which statement he showed no disposition to leave.

"Watson," Holmes turned to me, his face hidden by the menu, "what do you say to some Windsor soup, beefsteak pie, roly-poly pudding, and a respectable Bordeaux?"

"That would suit me down to the ground."

"Good. Shaw, my dear fellow?"

"Certainly not. I am no carnivore, preying upon my fellow creatures. You may order me a small salad."

Holmes shrugged and gave our order to the waiter. It nettled me, I confess, to have my eating and drinking habits constantly challenged and rebuked by this waggish fellow. Furthermore, I perceived that far from paying Holmes for his services, the Irishman was now prepared to accept his luncheon as part of the detective's largesse.

We sat in silence for some moments, awaiting our meal and listening to the hubbub around us: the chat of the many customers crowding the restaurant at midday, the clatter of cutlery, and the incessant swinging of the doors that led to the kitchen. Holmes paid no attention to the chaos, but sat lost in thought, his eyes closed and his chin sunk upon his breast. With his great hawk's bill of a nose, he resembled nothing so much as some sleeping bird of prey.

"Well?" Shaw demanded, tiring of watching him. "Will you take the case?"

Holmes did not move or open his eyes. "Yes."

"Excellent!" The Irishman beamed, his countenance wreathed in smiles. "What must we do first?"

"We must eat." Holmes opened his eyes in search of our

waiter, who arrived at that moment, carrying a large tray. Suiting action to the word, the detective refused to utter so much as a syllable for the next thirty minutes. He cheerfully ignored all Shaw's insistent enquiries but favoured that peppery individual with a smile every now and then by way of encouragement.

More familiar with his humours than was the critic, I did my best to contain my speculations and addressed myself to my own victuals, until at length Holmes took a final sip of wine, patted his mouth delicately with his napkin and proceeded to fill his pipe.

"You're not going to smoke!" Shaw protested. "Great heavens, man, are you intent on killing yourself?"

"The case is not without its features of interest," my companion began as though the other had not spoken. "Young Hopkins has a career unless I am very much mistaken. Are there any points which occur to you, Watson?"

"Aside from the business of the book, I must confess I was perplexed by the manner in which rigor mortis had set in," I replied. "One does not expect to find it so pronounced in the neck and abdomen and so conspicuously absent in the fingers and joints."

"Hmm."

"But what about the book?" Shaw interposed, excitedly. "Surely its importance cannot be overestimated. It must have been a ghastly ordeal for him to reach it."

"I do not underestimate its importance, I assure you. I merely question its value at the moment. Oh, I have encountered such evidence before." He waved a languid hand. "In a man's dying extremity, he tries to communicate the name of his murderer or else that murderer's motive. Unfortunately, without knowing more of Jonathan McCarthy than any of us do at present, it is highly unlikely that his *outré* clue can be forced into yielding much of value. What are we supposed to infer from it? That he saw himself as Mercutio? As Tybalt? That he was involved in a familial vendetta? Is it a word, a phrase, a passage, or a character that we are looking for? You see?" he threw out both hands in an expressive gesture. "It tells us nothing."

"But he must have thought otherwise," I protested.

"He must indeed. Or possibly he could not think of anything else in the crisis. I doubt he could have managed pen and paper, even had he reached them—and they were farther away, still. Then again, the clue may be perfectly obvious to a specific individual for whom he intended it." He shrugged.

"Then where do we begin?" Shaw demanded, puzzled. He was brushing his beard forward with his fingers into rather a fierce attitude.

Holmes smiled.

"Dunhill's would seem as likely a point of departure as any."

"Dunhill's?"

"They may be able to assist me in identifying the origins of the murderer's cigar. I shall go there after luncheon. In the meantime, I suppose we might begin with Bunthorne. Any idea who that might be?"

"Bunthorne?" We stared at him, I, for one, never having heard the name. He smiled yet more broadly, then drew forth his pocket book and produced a torn piece of paper from it.

"This is from McCarthy's engagement diary."

"I thought you said his murderer had pinched his engagements for February the twenty-eighth."

"So he did. This, as you can see, is for February the twenty-seventh, and I pinched it."

"It contains but one entry," I observed, "for six-thirty at the Café Royal."

"Precisely. With someone named Bunthorne."

Shaw silently reached forward and took up the paper, a scowl on his face, rendering his features more comical than usual. Abruptly he broke into an amused chuckle of appreciation.

"I can tell you who Bunthorne is—and so could anyone else in the West End, I fancy, but as you don't frequent anything but Covent Garden and the Albert Hall, I doubt very much if you'd know."

"Is he famous, then, this Bunthorne?" I asked.

The critic laughed again. "Quite famous. One might even say infamous—but not under that name. My late colleague appears to have noted his engagements in a sort of code."

"How do you know for whom Bunthorne stands? Is it a nickname?" Holmes enquired.

"Not precisely. Still I daresay he would answer to it." Shaw spread the paper out and jabbed at it with a thin forefinger. "It's the restaurant that makes it certain. He is usually to be found there, holding court."

"Holding court?" I ejaculated. "Who the devil is he, the Prince of Wales?"

"He is Oscar Wilde."

"The playwright?"

"The genius."

"What links him with this 'Bunthorne'?" Holmes wondered.

Shaw laughed once more. "For that you must be familiar—as I suspect you are not—with the comic operas of Messrs. Gilbert and Sullivan. Do you never go to the Savoy?"

"*The Mikado* and so forth?" Holmes shook his head and relit his pipe.

"Then you are missing the greatest combination of words and music since Aristophanes, Wagner excepted. Bunthorne is to be found in *Patience.*"

"I have heard the tunes, I expect, on the barrel organ."

"Of course you have. Every hurdy-gurdy in London grinds all Sullivan's music interchangeably." He regarded Holmes with a trace of scorn. "On what planet do you spend your time?" he wondered. "You are at least familiar with 'Onward Christian Soldiers' and 'The Lost Chord'?" He was amazed, I could see, by the detective's ignorance, which nonetheless did not seem strange to me. Sherlock Holmes was the man who once said it was a matter of utmost indifference to him whether the earth circled the sun or the sun the earth, provided the fact did not affect his work. Aside from his own particular musical interests (which leaned towards violin concerts and the grand opera), nothing was less likely than his knowing anything of London's fads and rages. He ignored Shaw's gibes and persisted with his own line of enquiry.

"Tell me about *Patience,*" he demanded.

"Just a moment," I cried, rubbing my forehead. "It comes to me now. Holmes, when I returned from Afghanistan in eighty-one, I saw this play! At the Savoy, was it?" I turned to Shaw.

"I believe it opened the theatre," the critic assented.

"I'm almost certain of it, though I can't remember what it was about, for the life of me. I always forget the plots and so forth within a week or two. I remember this one because I couldn't understand what it was about at the time I was watching it—soldiers and someone with very long hair who was liked by all the chorus."

"Can you be more precise?" Holmes asked Shaw.

"The opera parodies the whole Oscar Wilde cult of aesthet-
icism in rather a smart fashion. It was lost on you, Doctor,
because you were out of the country when Wilde and his
cronies burst upon the scene. Wilde himself appears in the
piece in the person of Reginald Bunthorne—'A Fleshly
Poet.'" Shaw grinned, coughed, and broke into song, his
voice proving to be surprisingly musical, a pleasant, not quite
robust baritone that caused a nearby head or two to turn in
our direction:

> If you're anxious for to shine in the high aesthetic
> line as a man of culture rare,
> You must get up all the germs of the transcendental
> terms, and plant them everywhere.
>
> You must lie upon the daisies and discourse in
> novel phrases of your complicated state of mind,
> The meaning doesn't matter if it's only idle chatter
> of a transcendental kind.
>
> And every one will say,
> As you walk your mystic way,
>
> "If this young man expresses himself in terms too
> deep for *me*,
>
> Why what a very singularly deep young man this
> deep young man must be!"

Seeing that we made no move to interrupt, he went on:

> Then a sentimental passion of a vegetable fashion
> must excite your languid spleen,
> An attachment *à la* Plato for a bashful young potato,
> or a not too French French-bean!

Though the Philistines may jostle you will rank
as an apostle in the high aesthetic band,
If you walk down Piccadilly with a poppy or a lily
in your mediaeval hand.

And every one will say—

Here he broke off, coughing again and looking embarrassed.

"It goes something like that for another verse or so. Anyhow, that's Bunthorne—and depend upon it, that's Oscar." He looked at his watch. "Heavens, I must be off. I've had my fun, and now I must pay for it. Where shall we meet? I want you to catch me up on what progress you make."

"Willis's for supper?" I hazarded.

"That's a trifle rich for my blood."

"What about Simpson's?"

"Very well." He started to rise. "A little before eight?"

"One moment." Holmes laid a hand on his arm. "You know Mr. Wilde personally?"

"I know him, though not well. We are too awed by one another's gifts, with the result that we intimidate ourselves."

Holmes maintained his loose hold on the critic's arm. "Is he really a genius?"

"Oscar? Some of the cleverest people in London suppose so —Harris, Max Beerbohm, Whistler—"

"Do you?"

"What does it matter whether he is or is not a genius and if I think so or not?"

"I am trying to understand the dramatis personae in this business. You didn't think much of Jonathan McCarthy; I should like your estimate of Oscar Wilde."

"Very well," he frowned, gnawing a bit of his beard. "Yes.

I would say definitely yes, he is a genius. His plays will be remembered as among the most scintillating in the language—and they are the least of his creations. *Patience*, on the other hand, will become passé within his lifetime.* A genius," he repeated, unwillingly, "but he is courting ruin."

"Why?"

Shaw sighed and considered how best to answer the question. It was more difficult than I would have imagined for him to frame a response.

"I am not at liberty to be specific," he temporized after a pause.

"Then be general," Holmes advised.

Shaw thought again, his Mephistophelian brows arching in concentration. "Oscar has antagonised the world," he began, choosing his words with care. "He delights in antagonising the world. He doesn't take it seriously." He put his hands on the table and interlaced the fingers. "But the world does. The world takes it very seriously and is not inclined to forgive him for it. The world is waiting to take vengeance. There are sacred rites and conventions which will not be flouted."

"Mr. Gilbert has flouted them for years, hasn't he?" I asked. "Are they howling for his blood, as well? I don't believe it."

Shaw looked at me. "Mr. Gilbert's private life is beyond reproach. Or if it isn't, Mr. Gilbert is discreet. The same cannot be said of Oscar Wilde." He rose abruptly, as though annoyed with himself for having spoken too much. "Good day, gentlemen."

---

* Shaw's ability to predict the future popularity of plays and operettas is questionable. He postulated an early demise for Sardou's play, *Tosca*, which in operatic form enjoys the same robust health as *Patience*.

"Shaw," Holmes looked up languidly. "Where can we find Wilde?"

"These days I believe he puts up at the Avondale, in Piccadilly. Good day," he said again and bobbed his head in elfish acknowledgement before leaving with that curious dancing gait.

Sherlock Holmes turned to me. "Coffee, Watson?"

We proceeded after lunch to Dunhill's, in Regent Street, where Mr. Fitzgerald, who knew the detective well, examined the bit of cigar we exhibited.

"Dinna tell me you're at a loss," the Scot laughed, his blue eyes twinkling as he took the cigar.

Holmes was not amused. "I can identify twenty-three kinds of tobacco from the ash alone," he responded somewhat testily, it seemed to me. "When you have told me what this is, I shall have incorporated a twenty-fourth into my repertoire."

"Ay, ay," the honest fellow went on chuckling as he bent over the thing. "Well, it's foreign but not imported by anyone I know," he began.

"So much I had already deduced."

"Did you, indeed? Ay, well that narrows the field." He held it up and smelled it. "From the scent and the wrapping, I'd say it was Indian." He turned it back and forth between his thumb and forefinger, holding it to his ear and listening to the crackle, then sighted along its length like a rifle. "A cheroot. Notice the square-cut end and the heavy proportion of Latakia? They're a great favorite with the boys in the Indian army, but then those laddies'll smoke anything. I doubt I'd have the stomach for it, but I've heard you can acquire a taste for them."

"You can't buy them in England?"

"No, Mr. Holmes, I don't believe you can. They're too tough for civilians, as I've said, though some of the lads come home with boxes because they know there're none to be found here."

"Mr. Fitzgerald, I thank you."

"Not at all, Mr. Holmes. Does it figure in a case?"

"It may, Mr. Fitzgerald. It may."

FIVE

THE LORD OF LIFE

Holmes and I had of course seen caricatures of Oscar Wilde. Over the years his strange haircut, corpulent physique, and outlandish mode of dress had become familiar to us—as to all —through countless pen-and-ink sketches in various papers. And though we had not seen either play, we were aware that the brilliant Irishman was the author of two comedies playing simultaneously to packed houses. His latest, *The Importance of Being Earnest,* had opened only a fortnight or so before and been highly endorsed by the critics and public alike.

Yet neither the cartoons nor the articles by or about the man nor yet his plays themselves (had we seen them) could have prepared us in the slightest for the living embodiment of Oscar Wilde.

After our stop at Dunhill's we trudged 'round to Piccadilly and presented ourselves at the Avondale, enquiring after the playwright.

"You'll find him in the lounge," the clerk informed us with a dour expression.

"I take it that is from whence all this noise emanates?"

asked Holmes politely. The man grunted by way of reply and busied himself behind the counter.

There was certainly a great deal of noise coming from the direction of the lounge, and Holmes and I followed it to its source, frankly curious. The clinking of glasses and the babble of animated, overlapping voices were discerned, the latter punctuated by sudden, shrill bursts and hoots of laughter.

My first impression, upon entering the room, was that I had journeyed backwards in Mr. Wells's time machine and stumbled upon a Roman Saturnalia of some sort, peopled by satyrs, Pan-like cherubs, and elves. A second glance assured me that the dozen or so young men gathered there, singing, reciting poetry, and drinking each other's health, were all dressed in the garb of the present century, albeit some of it rather askew. It took but a moment to realise who was chiefly responsible for this Attic impression. Standing in the centre of the room and towering over his guests both in size and stature was the leviathan Oscar Wilde himself. His odd long hair was wreathed with laurel or something very like it, and his deep, rich, and sonorous voice dominated the place as much as did his person.

Oblivious of the pandemonium, he was declaiming a poem having to do with Daphnis and Chloe (I was able to catch only a snatch here and there through the confusion of sound), with his arm draped over the shoulders of a slender young man whose blond curls framed the face of an angel.

After a moment or two our presence on the threshold made itself felt, and one by one all the revellers subsided, their songs and jests dying on their lips—save only Wilde himself. With his back to the door, he continued unaware of the intrusion, until the gradual halt in merriment caused him to turn and face us. One disagreeably flabby hand reached up and tugged the vine leaves from his tangled dark hair. His face was astonishingly comely and youthful, though I knew he must be forty. Too much food and too much drink had taken their toll and bloated his features. Nevertheless, his eyes were grey and clear and alert, his expression pleasing. Only his thick, sensual lips and his girth told of the dissipations in which he indulged.

As he focussed his gaze upon us, subdued whispers circulated, speculating about our business. More than once I caught the word *policemen.*

"Policemen?" Wilde echoed. His voice was soft as a caress and deep as a monastery bell. "Policemen?" He came forward slowly, carrying his coronet, and inspected us attentively. "No, no," he concluded with a ravishing smile. "I think not. By no means. There is nothing so unaesthetic on the planet as a policeman."

This provoked a few titters in the background. I noticed that when he spoke he had the odd trick of covering his mouth with a crooked finger. He looked at Holmes with interest, and the detective returned his gaze with a steadfast regard of his own. Their grey eyes locked.

"We may be less aesthetic than you think," Holmes told him without blinking, and reaching into his breast pocket, he presented his card. The urban Dionysus took in its contents with a careless glance.

"Dear me, dear me," he murmured without surprise. "*More* detectives. Not a very aesthetic lot, you force me to agree. I shall not dissemble, however, and pretend I haven't heard of Mr. Sherlock Holmes." The subdued revellers passed the name around behind him in reverential tones, a lone giggle marring the seriousness of the response. "And this must be Dr. Watson," Wilde went on, swivelling his luminous eyes in my direction and taking inventory. "Yes, it must; it positively must. Well," he sighed and collected himself with his charming smile, "what is it you gentlemen wish? Can I offer you some refreshment?"

"A minute or two of your time in private, sir, no more."

"Is it about the Marquess?" he demanded, his voice rising and beginning to tremble. "If so, I must tell you the whole affair is now in the hands of my solicitor, Mr. Humphreys, and you must take the matter up with him."

"It is about Jonathan McCarthy."

The playwright's dreamy eyes bulged briefly. "McCarthy? Then he has dared, after all—" his thick lips compressed with a show of annoyance coupled with resolve.

"He has dared nothing, Mr. Wilde. Jonathan McCarthy lies dead in his flat this day, the victim of a fatal assault by a person or persons unknown—some hours after his rendezvous with you at the Café Royal. I really think this interview might better be conducted elsewhere," Holmes concluded in a low tone.

"Murdered?" It took Bacchus a moment or two to grasp the meaning of the word. In that instant I perceived the truth of Shaw's observation. Wilde might antagonise people and defy convention, but he didn't really mean it or understand it to be harmful. Underneath his carefully nurtured decadence and his depraved, perverse ideas, the man was an utter innocent, far more shocked by the idea of murder than I was—and I fancied myself a deal more conventional than he.

"Come this way," he offered, composing himself, and on unsteady legs led us into the adjacent writing room. There was one elderly gentleman there, but his hat was over his eyes, his legs stretched before him, and it was clear that what the revelry next door had failed to accomplish, we need not even try. Holmes and I took seats, and Wilde threw himself heavily on to a sofa opposite. He made none of his public pretences to grace, but sat with his fat hands dangling between his knees, like a cabby's on the box, wearily holding a pair of non-existent reins.

"I take it I am under suspicion in the matter?" he began.

"Dr. Watson and I do not represent the police. Where their suspicions may fall, we have no way of knowing, though I may say from past experience"—Holmes smiled—"they occasionally take some quaint directions. Can you account for your whereabouts after your meeting with Jonathan McCarthy?"

"Account for them?"

"It may be helpful—for the police—should you be able to furnish them with an alibi," I pointed out.

"An alibi, I see." He leaned back with something like a smile. I caught another glimpse of him then, and I was reminded of Cassius's "aweary of the world." Despite an essentially humourous and sunny disposition, the man laboured under some terrible burden.

"Yes, that's all right," he brightened now without conviction, "I was with solicitor Humphreys. Tell me, how was it managed?"

"I beg your pardon?"

"The murder, my dear fellow, the murder!" His eyes gleamed as he warmed to the topic. "Was there incense burning? Did you find the footprints of a naked woman who had danced in his blood?"

Ignoring his macabre associations, Holmes briefly outlined the circumstances of the critic's death, omitting the business with the book and adding instead his own observation that no-one we had spoken with thus far appeared either surprised or grieved by the news.

Wilde shrugged. "I can't imagine the West End will consider him a great loss, no."

"What was the nature of your appointment with him yesterday?"

"Must I tell you?"

"We have no means to coerce testimony," Holmes answered, "but the police are another matter. At the moment they do not know of your appointment."

Wilde's eyes flashed with hope in an instant, and he sat up straight in his chair.

"Is that true?" he cried clasping his hands. "Is that really true?" Holmes assured him that it was. "Then all may yet be well!" He looked from one to the other of us, his elation subsiding as he realised we must still be dealt with. "Better you than the police, is that it?" he sighed. "How life sometimes resembles Sardou, don't you find? What a pity! For Sardou." He chuckled at his own wit and ran a chubby set of fingers through his unruly hair.

"Was your meeting connected with your visit to a solicitor this morning?" Holmes prompted.

"In a way, I suppose you might think so. You gentlemen did not know Jonathan McCarthy, did you? No, I can see you didn't. How can I explain to you what that man was?" He rubbed his lips meditatively with the crooked forefinger. "Have you heard ever of Charles Augustus Milverton?"

"The society blackmailer? Our paths have not yet crossed, but I know of him."*

---

* Holmes's path crossed Milverton's right before the latter's murder in January 1899.

"That simplifies matters. Jonathan McCarthy pursued a similar line of country."

"He was engaged in blackmail?"

"Up to the neck, my dear Holmes, up to the very neck. He did not prey upon society, as Milverton does, but rather upon us denizens of the theatre. He had his sources, his little spies, and he squeezed hard. Of course the world of the theatre overlaps the social world now and again. At all events, I've had some experience of blackmailers and know how they must be dealt with. They get hold of letters I've written from time to time and threaten me with them. But I have a cure for that."

I asked him what that might be, and he smiled behind the crooked finger.

"I publish them."

"Was McCarthy threatening you with a letter?" Holmes asked.

"With several. He'd heard about the business at the Albemarle* earlier in the day and sent me an earnest of his intentions."

"You will have to speak more plainly, I'm afraid."

Wilde sat back, pale, astonishment writ large upon his features.

"But you've heard! Surely you've heard! It must be across all of London by now!"

"Everywhere but Baker Street," Holmes assured him drily.

Wilde licked his purplish thick lips and eyed us nervously. "The Marquess of Queensberry," he began in a voice hoarse with emotion, "the father of that splendid young man back

---

* Wilde's club.

there in the lounge—but no more like him than Hyperion's like Hercules—left a card for me at the Albemarle, yesterday. I do not propose to tell you the words the barbarian wrote on that card—beside the fact that he misspelled them—only that having read the words, I was not prepared to ignore them.* I was advised by several friends to do so, but I did not. I went 'round to Mr. Humphreys after dinner (he was referred to me by my friend Mr. Ross), and this morning he accompanied me to Bow Street, where I swore out a complaint for criminal libel. By this time tomorrow, the Marquess of Queensberry will have been arrested and charged, and soon I shall be rid for ever of that monster in human clothing. Hence the little celebration next door," he concluded with a sheepish grin.

"And McCarthy, you say, heard of the incident at the Albemarle?"

Wilde nodded.

"I believe he knew of Queensberry's intentions beforehand. He notified me and arranged a meeting at the Café Royal, where he declared his willingness to furnish certain correspondence of mine to the Marquess and his solicitors. He felt these documents would certainly prejudice my case."

"And were you of that opinion?"

"It was not necessary yesterday, nor is it necessary today that I answer that question. I had cards of my own to play, and I played them."

"I think it may be as well to lay them on the table now."

"As you like. To be brief, I am the repository of a great

---

* Written on the card by Queensberry: "To Oscar Wilde posing as somdomite." Watson must have known the contents of this notorious message when he set down the case but tactfully omitted them.

many secrets myself, concerning alarums and excursions in the West End. Theatre people are so colorful, don't you find? I know, for example, that George Grossmith, who does the patter songs for Gilbert (he played me, you know!), has been taking drugs. Gilbert scares him so at rehearsals that he has had recourse to them. I know that Bram Stoker keeps a flat in Soho, the existence of which neither his wife nor Henry Irving is aware. I cannot explain to what use he puts it, but my intuition tells me it isn't to play chess. Then again, I know about Sullivan's games of chemin de fer with—"

"And what did you know of Jonathan McCarthy?" Holmes interrupted, concealing his distaste.

Wilde replied without hesitation, "He was keeping a mistress. Her name is Jessie Rutland, and she is an ingenue at the Savoy. For a man who played the part of middle-class British rectitude to hypocritical perfection, such a disclosure would mean instant ruin. He understood that at once," Wilde added as an afterthought, "and very shortly we discovered that we had nothing to say to one another. A sordid story, I fear, but mine own."

Holmes stared at him for some moments, his face devoid of expression. He rose abruptly, and I followed suit.

"Thank you for your time, Mr. Wilde," said he. "You are certainly a font of information."

The poet looked up at him. There was something so ingenuous and pleasant in his countenance that I found myself charmed despite everything he had said.

"We are all of us as God made us, Mr. Holmes—and many of us much worse."

"Is that yours?" I enquired.

"No, Doctor—" he smiled slightly—"but it will be." He

turned again and faced the detective. "You do not approve of me, I fear."

"Not altogether."

Wilde would not relinquish his eyes. "I find myself wishing that you did."

"It may be that one day I shall."

SIX

THE SECOND MURDER

It was twilight when Holmes and I left the Avondale and joined the rush-hour crowds in Piccadilly. The wind had risen, and it cut our faces, biting our throats, too, as we walked. Cabs were not to be had for love or money, but the Savoy Theatre was no great distance from the hotel. We simply trudged in that direction, elbowing our way amidst the throng and avoiding as best we could the dirty piles of snow shoveled up next to the kerbs.

I remarked as we walked that I could not remember encountering a more singular set of people than those we had met in connection with the murder of Jonathan McCarthy.

"The theatre is a singular calling," Holmes concurred. "A noble art but a dreary profession and one that reveres that which the rest of society condemns." He favoured me with a sidelong glance. "Deception. The ability to dissemble and deceive, to pass for what you are not. You will find it better expressed in Plato. These, however, are the actor's stock in trade."

"And the stock in trade of those who write their speeches for them," I noted in addition.

"You will find that in Plato, as well."

We walked for a time in silence.

"The chief difficulty with this case," he observed at length, as we entered the Strand, "besides the fact that our client cannot afford to pay for his meals, let alone our expenses—the chief difficulty, I say, is the superfluity of motives. Jonathan McCarthy was not a well-liked individual, that much seems clear, which only serves to complicate matters. If half the tales Wilde told us just now are true, there may be upwards of a dozen people whose interests would be well served by eliminating him. And they all dwell within that circumscribed world of the theatre, where passions—real and feigned —abound."

"What is more," I pointed out, "their professional gifts are likely to render their complicity in a crime rather more difficult than usual to detect."

Holmes said nothing, and we walked in silence a few paces more.

"Has it occurred to you," I went on, "that McCarthy's use of Shakespeare was meant to be taken generally?"

"I don't follow you."

"Well, your friend Shaw—our client—cannot abide Shakespeare. The *Morning Courant,* for which McCarthy wrote, is well known as a rival to the *Saturday Review.* There can be little doubt that with McCarthy out of the way, Bernard Shaw's star and literary following would rise more or less together. Could McCarthy's reference to *Romeo and Juliet* possibly mean not the Montagues and Capulets but rather the two periodicals? Doesn't Mercutio, dying, refer to 'a plague *on both your houses'?"* I continued, warming to my theme.

"At the same time, the use of Shakespeare, whom Shaw detests, might serve to point an unerring finger in his direction as the assassin."

"Watson, what a devious mind you possess!" Holmes stopped, his eyes twinkling. "That is positively brilliant. Brilliant! Of course, you have neglected all the evidence, but I cannot fault your imagination." He resumed his steps. "No, I'm afraid it won't do. Can you honestly envision our Shaw drinking brandy? Or smoking a cigar? Or running his rival through—apparently on impulse—with a letter opener?"

"He's almost the right height," I contended feebly, not wishing to abandon my theory without a struggle. "Besides, his objections to drink and smoke might merely have been lodged for our benefit."

"They might," he agreed, "though I have known of his prejudices in those directions for some time. In any event, why would he come to me at all if he wished to remain undetected?"

"Perhaps his vanity was flattered by the prospect of deceiving you."

He considered this briefly in silence.

"No, Watson, no. It is clever but rather too cumbersome, and what is more, his footwear does not match the impressions left by the assassin. Shaw's shoes are quite old—it pains me to think of his walking about with them in this weather—whereas our man wore new boots, purchased, as I think I said, in the Strand. Oscar Wilde, at least, was wearing the right shoes."

"What of Wilde, then? Did you notice that when he spoke, he continually covered his mouth with his finger? Do you accept at face value his story of having checkmated

McCarthy's blackmail scheme with knowledge of the man's illicit liaison?"

"I neither accept it nor reject it at the moment," he returned, undaunted. "That is why we are at the Savoy. As for Wilde's peculiar habit of covering his mouth, you surely observed that his teeth are ugly. It is merely improbable vanity on his part to conceal them in conversation."

"Did you see his teeth?"

"Didn't I just say he makes a considerable effort to hide them?"

"Then how do you know they are ugly?"

"Elementary, my dear fellow. He does not open his mouth when he smiles. Hmm, the house is dark, tonight. Let us go 'round by the stage door and see if there are folk within."

We walked into the alley that led to the stage door and found the door open. There was activity within the theatre, though it was clear from the bustle backstage that no play was in progress. We threaded our way amongst actors and stagehands until our presence was discovered by the manager, who politely enquired as to our business there. Holmes tendered his card and explained that we were in search of either Mr. Gilbert or Sir Arthur Sullivan.

"Sir Arthur ain't here, and Mr. Gilbert's leading the rehearsal," we were told. "Perhaps you'd best speak with Mr. D'Oyly Carte. He's in the stalls. Right through this door and very quiet, gentlemen, please."

We thanked the man and stepped into the empty auditorium. The house lights were on and I marvelled once again at the lighting in the Savoy. It was the first theatre in the world to be totally lit by electricity, and the resultant illumination differed greatly from that supplied by gas. I thought back fifteen years and tried to recall my first visit to the place. I had worried then about the danger of fire originating from an electrical failure, since I could not understand who Reginald Bunthorne was supposed to be and allowed my mind to wander from the piece. My fears were apparently without foundation, because years have gone by since and the Savoy still stands unharmed.

A lone figure was seated in the stalls towards the back, and he favoured us with a baleful stare as we walked up the aisle in his direction. He was a small man, dwarfed by his chair, wearing a dark, pointed beard that complemented his black eyes. Something in his glower, at once so regal and so forbidding, made me think of Napoleon. It was my subsequent impression that this was his intention.

"Mr. Richard D'Oyly Carte?" Holmes asked when we were close enough to be heard in a whisper.

"What do you want? The press is not permitted here before opening nights; that is a rule at the Savoy. There's a rehearsal in progress, and I must ask you to leave."

"We are not from the papers. I am Sherlock Holmes, and this is my associate, Dr. Watson."

"Sherlock Holmes!" The name had produced the desired effect, and D'Oyly Carte's countenance broke into a smile. He half-rose from his chair and proffered two seats beside him. "Sit down, gentlemen, sit down! The Savoy is honoured. Please make yourselves comfortable. They have been at it all day and are at rather low ebb just now, but you are welcome, nonetheless."

He appeared to think we had entered his theatre on a whim, having for some reason taken it into our heads to attend a rehearsal. For the present Holmes encouraged this view.

"What is the name of the piece?" he enquired in a polite undertone, slipping into his seat beside the impresario.

"*The Grand Duke.*"

We turned our attention to the stage, where a tall man in his late fifties, of military bearing, was addressing the actors. I say "addressing them," but it would be more truthful to say he was drilling them. It seemed in no wise inconsistent with his military stamp, which marked him as a compulsive man of precision. The stage was devoid of scenery, making it difficult to understand what the piece was about. Gilbert—obviously the military fellow was he—directed a tall, gangling actor to repeat his entrance and first speech. The man disappeared into the wings only to emerge seconds later with his lines, but Gilbert cut him off in mid-sentence and requested him to do it again. Next to us our host made several rapid notations in a book propped upon his knees. With some little hesitation the actor retreated once more upon his errand. Though nothing was said, it was clear that all were fatigued and that tempers were fraying. Carte looked up at the stage, pen in hand, a scowl creasing his features. He tapped the stylus nervously against his teeth.

"They're played out," he proclaimed in a mutter directed to no one in particular. From his inflection, it was impossible to determine whether he meant the players or the authors.

The actor made his entrance a third time and launched into his speech, getting somewhat further along before the author interrupted and asked him to repeat it.

"Our visit here is not entirely a social one," Holmes leaned towards the impresario. "I believe there is a young woman attached to the company by the name of Jessie Rutland? Which is she?"

The manager's demeanour underwent an instant metamorphosis. The harassed but generous impresario became the suspicious property owner.

"Why d'ye want to know?" he demanded. "Is she in any difficulty?"

"The difficulty is none of hers," Holmes assured him, "but she must respond to some questions."

"Must?"

"Either to me or the police, quite possibly to both."

Carte regarded him fixedly for a moment, then slumped into his seat, almost willing it to swallow him.

"I could ask for nothing more," he mused darkly. "A scandal. There has never been a breath of scandal at the Savoy. The conduct of the members of this company is beyond reproach. Mr. Gilbert sees to that."

"Mr. Grossmith uses drugs, does he not?"

Carte stared at him from the recesses of his chair, wonder written on his face.

"Where did you hear such a thing?"

"No matter where, the story will go no further than it has. May we speak with Miss Rutland now?" Holmes pursued.

"She's in her dressing room," the other replied gruffly. "Not feeling well—said something about a sore throat."

On stage voices were being raised. "How many times will you have it, Mr. Gilbert?" the actor exploded.

"Until I have it right will do, Mr. Passmore."

"But I've done it fifteen times!" the actor wailed. "I'm not Mr. Grossmith, you know. I am a singer, not an actor."

"Both facts are evident," Gilbert responded coldly. "However, we must do the best we can."

"I will not be spoken to in this way!" Passmore declared, and shaking with anger, he stamped into the wings. Gilbert watched him go, then turned his attention to the ground, apparently studying something there.

Carte rose to his feet. "Gilbert, my dear, let's halt for supper."

The author gave no sign of having heard.

"Ladies and gentlemen—" Carte raised his voice and adopted a cheerful timbre—"let us forbear for two hours and renew our energies over supper. We open within thirty-six hours, and we must all sustain our strength. Played out," he muttered again as the group on the stage started to disperse.

"The dressing rooms are downstairs?" Holmes asked as we got to our feet.

"Women stage left, men stage right." The impresario waved us absently towards the proscenium, absorbed by a more immediate crisis. We had started down the way we had come when the air was rent with an unearthly wail. So odd was the noise that for a moment no-one was able to identify it. In the empty theatre the hideous sound echoed and reverberated. The people on stage, preparing to leave, stood momentarily frozen with surprise and collective horror.

"That's a woman!" Holmes cried. "Come on, Watson!" He dashed across the footlights and into the wings, his coattails flying as I followed. Backstage, we plunged into a labyrinthine mass of theatrical apparatus that obstructed our path to the wrought iron spiral steps which led to the dressing rooms below. Behind us we could hear the pounding feet of the chorus, hurrying in our wake.

At the foot of the steps a passage led off to our left, and Holmes flew down it. A series of doors on either side of the corridors, some of them ajar, led to the ladies' dressing quarters. Holmes flung these open in rapid succession, stopping abruptly at the fifth door and blocking my view with his back.

"Keep them out, Watson," said he quietly and closed the door behind him.

Within seconds a group of thirty or so members of the Savoy company surrounded me, all babbling questions. I was struck with the ironic observation that they sounded like themselves—that is to say, like a chorus of Savoyards, singing, "Now what is this and what is that and why does father leave his rest, at such a time of night as this, so very incompletely dressed?" Suddenly into their midst, parting them firmly left and right as though he were breasting the Red Sea, strode Gilbert. His muttonchop whiskers bristled, his blue eyes were very bright.

"What is happening here?"

"Sherlock Holmes is endeavouring to find out," I gestured behind me to the closed door. The large blue eyes blinked in the direction of the door, then refocussed themselves on me.

"Holmes? The detective?"

"That is correct. I am Dr. Watson. I sometimes assist Mr. Holmes. The woman who screamed, I take it, was Miss Rutland," I went on. "She complained of not feeling well, and you sent her downstairs to rest."

"I dimly remember doing something of the kind." He passed a weary hand over his broad forehead. "It has been a tiring day."

"Do you know Miss Rutland well, sir?"

He answered my question automatically, too preoccupied to object to my forwardness in quizzing him. "Know her? Not really. She is in the chorus, and I do not engage the chorus." A trace of bitterness crept into his voice, undisguised.

"Sir Arthur engages the singers. Sir Arthur is not here at the moment, as you have quite possibly divined. Sir Arthur is either at cards with some of his titled friends or else at the Lyceum, where he is wasting his talents on incidental music for Irving's new *Macbeth*. It would be too much to ask him for the overture to our piece before opening night, but I daresay he will deign to have it ready by then. Perhaps Sir Arthur will even find time to coach the singers once or twice before we open, but I am not sure." Now he turned and spoke to the company. "Here, everybody!" he cried, "go and have your supper. We shall continue at eight o'clock sharp with Act One from the sausage-roll number. Go on and eat, my dears; there's nothing of consequence that need detain you here, and you must keep up your strength!"

They dispersed on cue, Gilbert patting a head occasionally or saying something encouraging in a low voice to another as they passed by, until we were alone. For all his military gruffness, a reciprocal bond of affection and trust between him and the players was evident.

"Now let me pass," he ordered in a tone that brooked no objection. Before I could answer, we were interrupted by a clatter on the spiral stairs at the end of the corridor as Carte descended hurriedly with another man, whose black bag proclaimed him a member of the same profession as myself.

Carte, rushing towards us, cried, "Dr. Watson, this is Dr. Benjamin Eccles, the doctor who is on call at the Savoy." I shook hands briefly with a man of medium height and pale complexion, with deep-set green eyes and a small, delicate-looking nose.

"I make the rounds of several theatres in the district when I am on call," Eccles explained, looking past me at the closed door, "and I'd just stepped into the stalls to see how the rehearsal was getting on when Mr. Carte saw me and summoned me downstairs, as he seemed to think I might be needed." He glanced from one to the other of us—uncertainly, confused, perhaps, by the presence of another physician.

Behind us the door opened and Holmes stood there in his shirt-sleeves. Clearly he had only been waiting for the members of the chorus to depart. I introduced Dr. Eccles, and Holmes favoured him with a curt inclination of his head.

"There has been a murder," he announced in sombre tones, "and all must remain as it is until viewed by the authorities. Watson, you and Dr. Eccles may come in. Mr. Gilbert and Mr. Carte, I must ask that you remain beyond the threshold. It isn't a pretty sight," he added under his breath, standing aside to let me in.

The sight, indeed, had little to commend it. A young woman with dark russet hair, who could not have been more than twenty-five, lay on her side upon a small sofa, which constituted the sole article of furniture in the room, save for a dressing table and chair. Her nap had been rudely interrupted by a crimson gash across her pearl white throat, and her life's blood, quite literally like a leaky tap, dripped on to the floor, where it had begun to collect in a small pool.

The sight was so horrible, the corruption of her existence so woefully and inappropriately complete, that it robbed us of articulation. Eccles coughed once and set about examining the wretched creature's remains.

"Her throat has been severed quite cleanly," he reported in a faint voice. "It is slightly hard above the cut. Can rigor have set in so quickly?" he asked himself. "It isn't present in her fingers, and her blood is still—is still—"

"She complained of a sore throat," I explained, suppressing an hysterical impulse to giggle at the thought. "Her glands are merely swollen." As I said this, it occurred to me that my own throat felt raw—a ghastly enough identification.

"Ah, that must be it." Eccles looked about the small room. "I don't see a weapon."

"It is not here," Holmes replied. "Or if it is, my search has failed to reveal it."

"But why, *why?* Why was she slain?" Carte shouted from the doorway, his small hands clawing clumsily at his collar and tearing it asunder. "Who would want to do such a thing?"

No-one was able to answer him. I looked at Gilbert. He had sunk on to a bench across from the entrance to the room and was staring glazily before him.

"I didn't know her at all well," he spoke woodenly, like one in a dream. "Yet she always seemed sweet enough and willing. A sweet young thing," he repeated, his eyes beginning to blink rapidly.

"There is nothing further for us here, Watson," Holmes declared, resuming his jacket and ulster.

Carte rushed forward and seized him by the lapels. "You can't go!" he cried. "You mustn't! You know what this is about! I insist that you tell me. What questions were you going to put to the girl?"

"My questions were for her ears alone," the detective replied solemnly. Gently he removed the other's quaking hands. "You may refer the police to Dr. Watson and myself for our depositions. They know where we are to be found. Come, Doctor." He turned to me. "We have an appointment at Simpson's which now assumes greater importance."

We bowed and shook hands with Gilbert, who responded in a trance, leaving Carte and the shaken Dr. Eccles, who would write up the relevant particulars of his examination.

Poor man, he was more used to sore throats than cut ones, I fancy.

As we walked down the corridor, I heard Carte suggest to Gilbert that the rest of the rehearsal be cancelled.

"We can't," Gilbert replied in a hoarse rejoinder, his voice cracking with emotion.

SEVEN

ASSAULTED

Simpson's Café Divan was but a few yards farther along the Strand, and it was no great matter to get there from the theatre.* Nevertheless, as we left the Savoy and stepped on to the pavement, the frigid wind hit me like a wave and I stumbled against the kiosk next to the ticket office.

"Are you all right, Watson?"

"I think so—only a bit dizzy."

Holmes nodded sympathetically. "It was quite warm inside —and appalling. I confess to feeling slightly faint myself." He took my arm, and we entered the restaurant.

At this hour Simpson's was by no means full. We were recognised at once by Mr. Crathie and experienced no difficulty in obtaining a table. It wanted fifteen minutes of eight, granting us some moments for private reflection regarding the unexpected turn events had taken. I, for one, did not feel in the least like eating. I was aware, however, of an overpowering thirst and ordered a brandy and a carafe of water.

---

* It still isn't. Simpson's and the Savoy remain happily extant, though both have been since rebuilt.

The brandy burned along my throat like fire, and I found I could not swallow enough water.

"If we persist in tramping about in this weather," Holmes noted, "we are bound to catch our death." He, too, drank a good deal of water and looked, I thought, paler than was his wont.

We sat for some moments, studying our menus without enthusiasm, each wrapped in his own thoughts. Around us the restaurant was filling with animated diners.

"The case begins to assume a familiar shape," Holmes stated, setting aside the wine list.

"Which shape is that? I am utterly at a loss, I confess."

"A triangle, if I am not mistaken. I shall be greatly astonished if it does not prove to be the old story of a jealous lover, discarded by his mistress in favour of another patron. Possibly a more powerful one," he added darkly. He reached into his jacket and withdrew his pocketbook, carefully extracting again the slip of paper from Jonathan McCarthy's engagement calendar.

"It must be a very peculiar triangle," I countered, "if it includes so odd an angle as McCarthy. Are you asking me to believe that sweet-faced young woman took up with a man of his stamp? My mind rejects the whole idea."

"I must ask your mind to remain open a little longer, Doctor, for she *did* take up with him. At least, the evidence points strongly in that direction."

"What evidence?" My head had begun to throb almost as badly as the old wound in my leg.

"Wilde's, of course. If his information about George Grossmith's recourse to drugs elicited the response it did from Carte, we may, I think, grant its accuracy—at least provisionally—in other areas, as well. What have you to offer in rebuttal of such a charge? Her innocent appearance and the testimony of Gilbert, who by his own admission scarcely knew her. The latter information rebuts itself. As for the former," he mused, staring dreamily at the paper before him, "what can a woman's appearance signify? Women are devious creatures, even the best of them, and capable of vastly more than we men would like to suppose. That she was McCarthy's mistress, I am prepared to credit on the basis of the evidence so far; what her motives were for so being, I am prepared to learn."

"From whom?"

He shrugged. "I fancy that will depend to a degree on Arthur Sullivan. He hired her; it is to him I shall turn for a better portrait. Hullo!" He sat forward suddenly, pulled forth his magnifying glass, and held it over the torn scrap, scrutinising it beneath the lens.

"What is it?"

"Last night's entry, or I am much mistaken. Have a look." He moved the paper over to where I could see and held the glass above it for my benefit. Enlarged beneath the lens I saw faint impressions, evidently formed by a pencil pressing down on another piece of paper.

"There is something there!" I exclaimed.

"I think so, too, though whether it will be of any use to us is problematical." He looked about and hailed a nearby waiter, importuning him for a pencil. When the man had delivered it and gone, Holmes threw back a corner of the white tablecloth and positioned the paper carefully upon the wood. Holding the pencil at the mildest possible angle, he began to rub the lead lightly back and forth across the surface of the sheet. Slowly, like a spirit photograph, the indentations appeared in sharp relief:

Jack Point—here

"Who can that be?" we wondered simultaneously.

"Here is our oracle in these matters," Holmes observed, looking up. "Perhaps he can help us."

Shaw stood at the entrance to the restaurant, still without a coat (it caused my teeth to chatter just to look at him). He held his nose in the air as though sniffing the place out, unwilling to put a foot forward until certain of his welcome. Holmes held up a hand and waved him over. He advanced rapidly and slid on to the banquette without ceremony as the detective replaced the tablecloth and deftly slid the paper back into his pocketbook.

"What have you learned?" the critic demanded without preamble. "I'm famished," he volunteered before either of us could answer and began a perusal of the menu.

"We wish to consult you first," Holmes said easily. "Do you know of anyone named Jack Point?"

Shaw looked up from the menu, knitting his brows.

"Jack Point?" he repeated cautiously. "No, I can't say that I do. Why?"

"Could it be someone in the theatre world? An actor perhaps?" Holmes persisted. The critic's frown of puzzlement deepened.

"Or the name of another Gilbertian creation?" I struck in.

He brightened at once, snapping his fingers.

"Of course. *Yeomen of the Guard!* Another of their operas," he explained. "A serious one, laid in the Middle Ages and having to do with the Tower of London."

"And Point? Who is he?"

"A jester—rather a foolish and pathetic figure; he loses his lady love to a highborn lord, if my memory serves."

Holmes smiled sadly. "Ah. Jack Point is our man, no doubt. You see, Watson? We are dealing with that geometrical construction I postulated some minutes ago."

"What are you talking about?" Shaw demanded brusquely. "And why are you both so pale? It's your diet, you know. With all that mutton, drink, and tobacco, you're digging yourselves early graves, the pair of you. Look at me! I haven't even a coat in this weather, and you don't see me shaking like the dickens."

"Spare us your sovereign remedies, I beg you."

"Then tell me what has happened. Did you find Wilde?"

"At the top of his form." The detective thereupon detailed for our salubrious client the encounter at the Avondale lounge and its singular aftermath in the writing room. When he mentioned the Marquess of Queensberry and spoke of Wilde's warrant, the most extraordinary change came over Shaw. He paled, leapt to his feet, and stood trembling.

"The man's taken leave of his senses!" he cried and, squeezing past, ran from the restaurant. Holmes and I stared at one another in disbelief and perplexity.

"What is going on?" I demanded, but he shrugged noncommittally.

"Our difficulties lie at Twenty-four South Crescent and the dressing room of the Savoy Theatre—not the lounge of the Avondale. At least, they don't as yet." He looked at his watch and sighed. "We are not going to run Sir Arthur to ground this evening; that much seems evident."

"He probably wouldn't enjoy it if we interrupted a game of

chemin de fer played with his titled friends,"* I agreed.

"And I can't say I feel very much like dining. Shall we go? It is quite a three-pipe problem, and my cherrywood has a larger bowl than the oily briar I am carrying. Not that I feel like smoking, either." He shook his head and started to rise. "Perhaps it's Shaw's influence."

"I think I shall remain here for a few minutes more," I said quietly.

"My dear fellow, you're not truly ill?" He pressed a hand to my brow. "You feel quite warm, but then so do I." He repeated the experiment with his own forehead. "It appears we've both caught colds."

"I'll be myself in a little," I protested, thinking the while that this was the oddest cold I'd ever contracted. "You go on and I'll catch you up."

"You're quite sure?"

He hesitated a moment or so longer, scanning my features and generally subjecting me to a close inspection before straightening up with a sigh. "Very well. Come to think of it, early to bed at Baker Street may do as well for me. Come as soon as you feel able."

I nodded heavily and he moved off. When he had gone, I sat for some time, feeling the fever take possession of my body. I drank some more water from the carafe. The waiter returned and asked if I wished to order. I told him that we had all changed our minds and started to rise. He perceived I was ill and asked if he might fetch me a cab.

"Thank you, I'll walk. The fresh air might do me good."

I got feebly to my feet and staggered out of doors, observing that it had begun to snow quite heavily again. I struck off

---

* According to biographical accounts, these games, played for high stakes, frequently included the Prince of Wales.

down the street, perspiring profusely amidst the silent, frosty deluge, aware that more sensible folk had forsaken the night air in favour of a warm fire and a toasty bed.

And then something so unexpected happened that I could scarcely credit it. I was seized from behind by a powerful pair of arms and pulled bodily out of the glare of the gas lamps into an alley that adjoined the restaurant. In my weakened condition struggle was useless. One of the gloved hands now reached 'round and held my nose, so that I could not breathe save through my mouth, whilst the other brought a vial of liquid to my lips and forced them open. It was either drink or suffocate, and I drank, perforce, my head reeling, my ears pounding, my feet slipping madly about beneath me on the icy pavement. I was unable to see either my assailant or the colour of what I was swallowing. It tasted bitter and was faintly charged with alcohol. I was obliged to drink off the entire mess and was then released. The shock of the attack and my fever combined to render me helpless. I collapsed in a darkness like oblivion, dimly conscious of the snow piling up about me.

How long I remained in that alley, I did not learn until much later. Eventually, two constables on their rounds espied me and forced some brandy down my throat. At first they supposed that I had consumed too much liquor at some earlier point in the evening, but awakening, I identified myself and related what had happened. Ascertaining that I was unable to describe my attacker, they put me in a cab and I returned to Baker Street.

There another surprise awaited me. Sherlock Holmes, in bed with pillows propping him up, informed me that upon leaving the restaurant, he too had been assaulted in the same manner.

EIGHT

MAMA, THE CRAB, AND OTHERS

Breakfast the next morning at Baker Street was a subdued repast. Aside from hearing my story and telling me his—so very similar—Holmes ate in silence. In spite of my vigil in the snow, I slept well and my fever had quite vanished. With its departure my appetite reasserted itself and I made a good breakfast as we puzzled over the affair in disjointed syllables.

"It doesn't seem to have done us any harm," Holmes allowed finally.

"Rather the reverse, I should say."

He nodded and poured some more coffee. "I have known parents who cozened reluctant children into swallowing medicine in that fashion." He set aside his napkin and reached for his clay. We could neither of us begin to describe our mysterious assailant. What motive inspired him was—like so much else regarding this bizarre business—tabled for the time being, pending the accumulation of further data.

"Is it still your intention to seek out Arthur Sullivan?"

"More than ever. I'm hoping he can add to our negligible

store of information regarding Jack Point. If he cannot, we shall be obliged to perform the real drudgery of detective work of the kind they do so well at Craig's Court.* By which I mean going to Miss Rutland's lodgings, talking with the neighbours, and so forth. It is the kind of refined spying that usually requires an effective disguise, for people become closemouthed if they think you desire such information, whereas they positively press it on you if it appears you do not. Are you coming?"

"Yes, indeed."

I had started to suit action to the word and put on my jacket when a knock on the door was followed by the entrance of our landlady.

"A boy left this for you at the front door, Mr. Holmes."

"Thank you, Mrs. Hudson." He came forward and took the small brown envelope.

"May I tell the girl to clear?"

"What? Yes, yes."

Utterly absorbed, like a child with a new toy, Holmes walked over to the bow window and held the packet up to the grey sunlight.

"Hmm. No postmark, of course. Address typewritten—on a Remington in need of a new ribbon. Paper. Hmm. Paper is Indian—yes, definite watermark—no visible fingerprints—"

"Holmes, in heaven's name open it."

"In good time, my dear fellow, in good time."

He had, however, completed his examination of the envelope and now proceeded to slit open one end, using the jackknife he kept on the mantel for such purposes. He withdrew

---

* Craig's Court, in Whitehall, was the center of the private detective business, with no fewer than six agencies housed there.

a folded sheet of the same dark stock and spread it out upon his knee.

"*Liverpool Daily Mail, Morning Courant, London Times,* and the *Saturday Review,* if I am not mistaken," he murmured, running his eye over it with a practised air.

"What are you talking about?"

"The different sources for these cuttings. Here." He passed the paper to me. Its message ran:

> aS you VALUE your liveS
> STAY out of the Strand

There was no signature. As I looked at the message, with its arbitrary configurations of letters, scissored to reorder their sense, I thought of our adventure outside Simpson's the night before and experienced a very real tingle of fear. I have not known the sensation often, but I venture to say I am no stranger to it. I shuddered and could feel my blood running cold, as though my fever had returned. I looked up from the paper and beheld Holmes's grey eyes searching mine.

"Still game, Watson?" cried he. It was plain to see that he regarded the paper as a challenge.

"Still. Tell me, are you certain of the papers from which these words were taken?"

"You know that I am perfectly capable of identifying no fewer than twelve periodicals by their typeface," he responded with an injured look.

"Then does the printing itself suggest nothing to you?"

"Beyond the fact that the writer wishes to remain anonymous, very little." His eyes twinkled. "What does it suggest to you?"

"Why look at the sources he has used!" I cried with some

excitement. "The *Morning Courant* and the *Saturday Review*. Does that not bring us back to my theory of a deadly rivalry between those two papers?"

"Say, does it not rather steer us away from your theory? Only a fool, in the position in which you place our man, would compose his message with either of the typefaces at issue. And then, how does your theory explain the murder of poor Miss Rutland?"

"It fails to," I admitted ruefully. "At the moment. But what do you make of Shaw's bolting out of the restaurant like that? Where does that fit in your precious triangle?"

"Do you imply that it was Shaw who waited outside and initiated the curious attacks?"

"He hasn't the strength for it, obviously. Besides, we have no way of determining if the attacks were even related to this business."

Holmes threw on his coat. "I should be surprised to learn that they were not, and so should you; come, confess it. No, my dear doctor, I fancy our correspondent merely chose the words he required where he chanced upon them. "The *Courant* and the *Review*, after all, are both prominent sheets. Come along."

On our way to the Lyceum, we read the morning papers in the cab. There was a brief piece on the warrant sworn out by Wilde against the Marquess of Queensberry, as well as quite a detailed account (on another page) of the murder at 24 South Crescent. Heavy emphasis was placed on the pronouncements of Inspector G. Lestrade, who promised to "lay the culprit by the heels" in "very short order" and who described the critic's murderer for the benefit of the press in a neat paraphrase of Sherlock Holmes's own summation.

Holmes chuckled as he ran over the account. "There are

some comforting consistencies in this reeling world of ours, Watson," said he, "and Lestrade must be accounted one of them. The man hasn't changed a hair in the last dozen years."

"The paper nowhere makes mention of Miss Rutland," I noted.

"Quite possibly not. I believe the *Times* goes to bed too early in the evening, but we shall find it, no doubt, in this afternoon's edition. The murderer will have the dubious satisfaction of seeing himself in print twice in one day."

"You're convinced it is the same man, then?"

"I think it would be stretching coincidence if it were not. Besides, he has the same style—and shoes."

"I was not aware of any great similarity between the crimes. Quite the contrary, the first appears to have been committed on impulse, whereas the second obviously involved a deal of premeditation."

"That is true. It is also true, however, that in both cases a knife-like weapon was employed—how fittingly McCarthy referred to him in his diary as Jack Point!—and in both cases the man displayed a more than rudimentary knowledge of anatomy. Indeed, his throat-slitting was accomplished with surgical precision and must have dispatched his second victim with humane immediacy."

"Humane!"

"Well, relatively."

"How do you reconcile the crime of impulse with the crime of premeditation?"

"I do not reconcile them as yet, but I will advance a provisional theory: Jack Point, our discarded lover, in talking with Jonathan McCarthy for whatever reason, learns of the latter's infatuation. In a rage of impulse he slays the man, and in one of forethought, he revenges himself upon his faithless mistress. Ah, here is the Lyceum!"

We stepped out of the cab before the imposing columns of that reverend structure. Like a man in a trance, I advanced to the third pillar from the left.

"Are you all right, Watson? I had forgotten."

"I think so." I hesitated for some moments, leaning against the pillar, my eyes filling with tears. It was to this column, some seven years before, that Holmes and I accompanied young Mary Morstan, my future wife, on the errand of intrigue which first brought her to our door.* It was now almost three years since her untimely death, and I had never, in all that time, found myself so near the starting point of our great adventure together. With an effort I regained my composure and indicated that I was ready to proceed.

The front doors of the Lyceum were open, and we stepped into the elegant foyer.

"Can I help you?" The deep voice which spoke these words startled us, the more so as we could not determine whence it came. The mystery was quickly solved when the shuttered windows of the box office were banged open and we were confronted by a dark, bearded man with a pinched aquiline nose and expressionless black eyes. He sat behind a set of bars like a teller's window, and my first thought was that he should stay behind them.

"Can I help you?" he repeated with the same wooden inflection.

"We are looking for Sir Arthur Sullivan," Holmes explained. "Is he here this morning? We were told he would be."

* Details of the case may be found in Watson's second opus, *The Sign of the Four.*

"Who wants to know?"

"Mr. Sherlock Holmes."

The bearded apparition remained stock-still at these words, then rose with startling decision and slammed the shutters. In another moment the door to the box office opened and he strode out, a man just under six feet, wearing a dark, impeccably tailored suit, which failed to conceal a powerful, not to say athletic physique.

"Sherlock Holmes?" His bottomless black eyes travelled from one to the other of us. Holmes inclined his head slightly.

"You wish to see Sir Arthur? He is occupied with Sir Henry. Can I help you with something?" There was no warmth behind the offer.

"You can help me to Sir Arthur," Holmes answered, undismayed by the man's threatening visage. "And you may pay my compliments to John Henry Brodribb."

He blinked as though a riding crop had been swung before his face. It was his only human response thus far. Without further comment he spun on his heel and entered the theatre.

"What a singular personage. I declare, Holmes, there doesn't seem to be a sane individual connected with this profession."

"There was a time when decent hotels wouldn't put them up," he agreed, "and it used to be a commonplace to observe that an actor shot President Lincoln." He pursed his lips, trying to recall something. "Did that man say 'Sir Henry'? Surely not."

I was about to reply to this with some speculation of my own when the clatter of horses' hooves upon the cobblestones outside the theatre attracted our attention.

A brougham had driven up, and out of it there stepped the prettiest woman I can remember ever having seen. Her figure was trim and girlish, though I saw when she drew close, that she must be nearing fifty. Nevertheless, her hair was blonde beneath a rakishly tilted hat and her eyes a radiant blue. Her nose was diminutive but not without nobility and was set above an expressive, humourous mouth. When she smiled—which was often—I caught a glimpse of perfect white teeth that shone like ropes of pearls. It was not her features individually, however, that provoked admiration, but rather the *tout ensemble* created by the engaging intellect that yoked them together. An air of healthy common sense and warmth pervaded, in distinct contrast to the last person we had seen in this lobby. What a place of extremes!

The woman descending from the brougham blew a kiss to the coachman (of all things!) and danced into the foyer.

"Good morning!" she called cheerily, noticing us. "Tickets do not go on sale before noon, you know—though you are quite right to be here early; they've been going like hot cakes all week!"

"Have I the honour of addressing Miss Ellen Terry?" Holmes smiled.

The ravishing creature returned his smile and responded to his bow with a lithesome curtsey.

"You look familiar, too, if you don't mind my saying so," she replied. "Have you been an actor?"

"Not for many years—on the stage, that is. But once, long ago, I trod the boards with John Henry Brodribb." Her eyes went wide with astonishment, and she burst into a peal of girlish laughter.

"No! You acted with the Crab before he *was* the Crab?

You don't look old enough to have done any such thing," she challenged playfully.

"I assure you, I wasn't. I was eight at the time and played a page during a performance of *Hamlet* at York. My parents discovered me from the audience and were thoroughly appalled."*

"But this is wonderful! Does he know you are here to see him? He will be so amused! Oh, but I'm afraid he may be dreadfully busy just now. Revivals are so trying. We're attempting to recall what we did with *Macbeth* when we got it right the first time."†

"There was a dark-haired, bearded gentleman here a moment ago. I believe he has gone upon my errand."

"Oh, you've met Mama."

"I beg your pardon?"

"You must forgive my penchant"—she pronounced it as though it were a French word—"for nicknames. Irving says I'm quite incorrigible."

"Irving, I take it, is the Crab?"

"But of course!" she giggled mischievously. "Oh, but you mustn't say I said so. He's terribly sensitive about the way he walks."

"And Mama?"

"That is Mr. Stoker, our business manager and general secretary. He is so very protective of us all that I call him Mama."

"Bram Stoker?"

"Why, yes. Do you know him, as well? I don't know either

---

* This placing of Holmes in the vicinity of York when he was eight years old seems to corroborate Baring-Gould's biography, in which the detective's childhood in Donninthorpe is described.

† Irving first produced *Macbeth* in 1888.

of your names," she realised suddenly, with another laugh, "and here I've been gossiping as though we were all old friends."

"Forgive me. My name is Sherlock Holmes, and this is my friend, Dr. Watson."

"*Now* I know why you looked familiar!" She clapped her gloved hands together delightedly. "I've seen your likenesses in the *Strand* magazine, haven't I?" She laughed at having placed us, then stopped short. "Are you here on business?"

"In a way, though my business is with Sir Arthur Sullivan, not with Sir Henry."

"Oh, you mustn't call him that yet, you know; it's two months off.* Mama does it, of course—he's so fond of titles—but it drives Irving quite wild. With Sullivan, is it?" She frowned, tapping her foot, then smiled with resolution. "Well, come with me, and I'll see if we can't beard the pair of 'em." She turned to enter the theatre when the door opened suddenly and Stoker reappeared. Miss Terry gave a little shriek of fright, then laughed again, placing a hand on her bosom.

"How you startled me, Bram!"

"I beg your pardon," said he stiffly. From the suddenness with which he opened the door, I suspected him of having eavesdropped on a considerable portion of the conversation. "Sir Arthur will see you now," he informed us coldly.

"I'll take them, thank you, Bram."

"They're in the Club Room, Ellen." He stood to one side, holding the door to let us pass, bowing low to the lady with what I thought exaggerated formality. We entered the theatre and started down the aisle in her wake.

---

* Henry Irving was knighted two months later by Queen Victoria, the first of his profession to be so honored.

"Dear Mama," she commented.

The Lyceum, which I had not seen for some time, was a theatre lavish beyond belief and famed for the unstinting artistic effort and money that went into its productions. Confronting us on the stage as we walked towards it was a stunning rendition of what I took to be the blasted heath which opens *Macbeth*. Real trees were in evidence, as well as shrubbery and a three-dimensional rocky terrain. The effect was so startling that we stopped for a moment in wonder.

"Isn't it remarkable?" Miss Terry remarked. "Sir Edward Burne-Jones does a great many of our productions. Sometimes I think the public comes here just to look at the sets."

"What is the Club Room?" I asked as we went through a side door and entered the complicated backstage portion of the theatre. All around us carpenters were hammering, sawing, and yelling instructions to one another, obliging us to shout over the din.

"Ah, that is Irving's pride and joy. Samuel Arnold,* the composer, who built the first Lyceum—predecessor of this theatre—added it years ago for his Sublime Society of Beefsteaks. Sheridan was a member, you know! And Irving has restored it. There's a kitchen, and he so loves to entertain and relax after a performance. Here we are." She stopped before a door that gave out from the back of the building.

"It seems to me I have met Mr. Stoker before," Holmes remarked offhandedly. "Doesn't he live in Soho?" Ellen Terry spun around, her finger to her lips.

"Hush! Oh, please, *please*, you mustn't mention anything of the kind in there. It was such a sore point when it hap-

* The great-grandfather of Edgar Allan Poe.

pened the first time! I don't know that Irving's ever forgiven him for it, and that was years ago."

"What do you mean? Is he—?"

"Hush, I *beg* you, Mr. Holmes!" She put her head to the door and listened intently, then with a little smirk, signed for us to do the same. Despite her advancing years, she had the disposition and energy of a very young girl. Following her instructions, we put our heads to the door.

"No, no, no, my dear chap!" came an odd-sounding deep voice, very nasal. "As music, it may be all very well, but it's not right for our purpose at all. Listen! I *see* the daggers, and I want them *heard* by the audience."

"But, Henry, what do daggers sound like?" a high-pitched voice protested in a slight whine.

"What do they sound like? They sound like—" And then we heard the queerest succession of grunts and growls, alternately sounding like squeaks and a beehive.

"Oh, yes, yes! I see what you mean! That's much better!" the high, piping voice exclaimed. "Yes, I think I can do that."

"Good."

Miss Terry, having amused herself sufficiently, knocked peremptorily on the door and opened it without waiting for a response.

"I'm sorry to disturb you, my dears," she adopted a business-like, matter-of-fact tone, "but here are the two gentlemen who wished to see Sir Arthur." What a little actress she was!

The spacious quarters into which we were shown indeed suggested an ideal retreat after a strenuous night's work in the theatre. Dominating the place was a long oak table at which thirty guests might easily put in a pleasant hour or two over several cold birds and bottles.

At the far end of the table, beneath portraits of David Garrick and Edmund Kean, two figures sat cloistered together, looking like conspirators interrupted in the midst of an anarchist plot.

The taller of the two was a melancholy man in his late fifties, with cavernously hollow cheeks, long grey hair, piercing eyes of an indeterminate colour, and a studiously grave demeanour. He rose courteously and bowed as we entered. Over his shoulders was carelessly draped a massive maroon cloak, which lent to his distinguished appearance an appropriately theatrical touch.

Sir Arthur Sullivan rose, as well. He was not nearly so tall as Henry Irving, nor as dramatic in his costume. He wore his expensive clothes unaffectedly, as one who is used to fine things, and though a trifle stout, was possessed of dark, slightly Semitic good looks. His sad eyes were a lustrous brown and reminded me forcibly of a cow's as they peered myopically through the pince-nez that rested familiarly on the bridge of his nose. Like Gilbert, he affected large sidewhiskers, and their effect, I judged, was to make him seem older than he really was. He held his right hand at an unnatural angle throughout our conversation, pressing it against his stomach. Altogether there was in his face and in his bearing that which did not suggest a healthy man.

"Gentlemen," said Irving in his odd nasal voice, "we are sorry to have kept you waiting."

"And we are equally sorry to interrupt your business."

"I've been with the police most of the morning," Sullivan informed us sadly as we shook hands. "I don't know what I can say to you that I haven't told them. May I ask at whose behest you come to see me?"

Suddenly he gasped and clutched spasmodically at his side, turning quite pale. Irving caught him tenderly as he stumbled, breaking the fall, and gently lowered him into a chair. He whispered his thanks to the actor, then turned, catching his breath, and repeated his question.

"We are here at the behest of justice," Holmes informed him, ignoring, for the moment, his seizure. "More prosaically, we were asked to look into the matter by Mr. Bernard Shaw."

The reaction of the two men to this piece of intelligence was startling. Sullivan knit his brows, perplexed, while Irving straightened up abruptly, his face clouding over, rendering his appearance more sombre than it was already.

"Shaw?" he cried, his courtly attitude slipping a little as he darted a glance at Ellen Terry. "Nellie, is this any of your doing?"

"Henry, dearest, I give you my word I know nothing about it," Miss Terry replied, obviously taken aback. "I met these gentlemen only moments ago in the lobby."

Irving started ominously down the length of the table. As he walked—or rather, shuffled—I was struck by his manner of thrusting his right shoulder forward, and I had to smile at Miss Terry's pet name for him.

"I give you warning, Nellie—" he spoke at the door—"I give you fair warning. I will not have that degenerate in this theatre—"

"He's not a degenerate, Henry. What are you talking about?" she spoke up with spirit. Irving went on as though he hadn't heard.

"I will not have him in this theatre, and I will not produce his revolting plays. And if he publishes any more drivel about the way we do things here, I will thrash him personally."

"Henry," she protested, looking anxiously around him at us and smiling nervously, "this is not the time or the place—"

"Let him stay at the Court with Granville Barker, where he belongs," Irving grumbled, calming somewhat. "Where they *all* belong. I don't want him or his plays here. Is that understood?"*

"Yes, Henry," said she meekly. "Come along and let's leave these gentlemen to their business."

This recalled the actor to himself and he turned to us with another bow.

"I apologise for my outburst, gentlemen. I know I am sometimes carried away. The theatre in this country will go in one of two directions shortly, and I feel quite strongly about which it's to be."

He spoke simply and with such evident feeling that, strangers to his ideas, we lowered our heads, embarrassed and, I think, moved by the display of raw emotion.

"Come, Henry." He allowed her to lead him from the room, a wearying Titan, I thought, following a Dresden shepherdess, herself no longer young.

Alone now with the composer, we turned and faced him.

---

* This reference to the Court Theatre is mystifying as it anticipates events by many years. Perhaps Watson's memory plays him false here. Then again, it may be this editor's mistake as the water damage suffered by the manuscript is particularly severe at this point. Nonetheless, it *does* look like "the Court with Granville Barker," etcetera.

NINE

SULLIVAN

"Were you really sent 'round by Bernard Shaw?" Sullivan began testily when the door was closed. "Why is he meddling in this? The man's an infernal busybody, and aside from his knowledge of music, I find him utterly depraved."

"He did not engage us specifically in the matter of Miss Rutland," Holmes acknowledged, moving forward and pulling up one of the large chairs, "but rather in connection with the murder of Jonathan McCarthy."

Wincing at another spasm, the composer screwed himself 'round in his seat and faced the detective.

"That makes still less sense, if I may say so, since they detested each other."

"A great many people appear to have disliked Jonathan McCarthy, that is certain."

"Granted, granted. Shaw's tongue may be wicked, but he always addresses himself to the issues. McCarthy was a parasite, preying on art and artists, which is not the same thing." He started to rise, gave another gasp, and fell back in his chair, doubled over and clutching at his side as though he wished to remove it in one savage haul. His pince-nez slid from his nose and dangled wildly by its black ribbon, inches from the floor.

"You are seriously ill!" I cried, rushing forward. For several moments he was unable to answer but lay gasping in his chair, like a fish out of water. I opened his tie for him and removed his collar. I perceived the kitchen Ellen Terry had spoken of and hastened to it for some water, which I brought back to him. He swallowed it in awkward gulps.

"Thank you."

"You are too ill to continue this interview," I stated, drawing a black look across the table from Holmes.

Sir Arthur sat up slowly. Something that resembled a smile stretched itself taut across his face. "Ill? I am dying. These kidney stones are working their way with me and will shortly make an end." He shrugged feebly and replaced his pince-nez. "When the pain disappears, I go to Monte Carlo and relax; when it returns, I work to forget it. I am in London, working; ergo, it is back."*

"Can you continue talking?" Holmes enquired reluctantly.

"I can and I will, provided you establish the importance of your questions." Sullivan rallied and sat straighter in his chair, re-fastening his collar with nervous little fingers.

"Do you not find the fact that both murders occurred within the space of twenty-four hours a telling coincidence?"

"Inspector Lestrade didn't appear to find it so. He didn't even mention the McCarthy affair when we talked this morning."

---

* Sullivan succumbed to his ailment five years later.

"The police have their own ways of functioning," Holmes stated tactfully. "And I have mine. I may tell you flatly that the deaths are related."

"How so?"

"They were achieved by the same hand."

Sullivan smiled faintly. "I have read Dr. Watson's accounts of your cases with the liveliest interest," he confessed, "and have always found them agreeably stimulating. Nevertheless, you will forgive me if, in this instance, I do not deem your word sufficient proof."

Holmes sighed, realising that Sullivan was no fool. He would have to play more of the cards in his hand.

"Were you aware, Sir Arthur, that Jessie Rutland was Jonathan McCarthy's mistress?" The composer blanched as though his fatal ailment had flared up again.

"That's impossible!" he retorted with heat. "She was no such thing."

"I assure you that she was." Holmes leaned forward earnestly, his eyes bright. "Our informant, whom I am not yet at liberty to disclose, assures me that she was. His accuracy in several other small matters forces me to trust him in this, the more so as it provides an otherwise missing link between these two crimes."

"What small matters?"

"For one thing, he states flatly that a leading member of the Savoy company uses drugs because Mr. Gilbert makes him so nervous."

"That is a damned lie." But he spoke without conviction and subsided into thoughtful silence. Holmes surveyed him coolly for a few moments, then leaned forward again.

"A moment ago you violently resisted the idea of Jonathan

McCarthy as Jessie Rutland's lover. It wasn't merely because you despised the man. You *knew* better, didn't you?"

"It seems pointless now."

The grey eyes of Sherlock Holmes grew brighter than ever; they burned like twin beacons.

"I give you my word it is of the utmost moment. Jessie Rutland is dead; we cannot restore her to life or confer upon her any advantages, save, possibly, a decent funeral. But there is one thing we can do, and that is to bring her murderer to book."

It was now Sullivan's turn to study Holmes, and this he did for what seemed like a solid minute, glaring at him through his pince-nez, without moving, his hand pressed to his side. "Very well. What do you want to know?"

The detective breathed an imperceptible sigh of relief. "Tell us about Jack Point."

"Who?"

"Forgive me, that is the name by which McCarthy referred to him in his engagement calendar. He appears to have made a practise of substituting characters from your operas for the real names of people. The appointment in his diary for the night of his death was with Jack Point. Point is the hapless jester who loses his love in *Yeomen of the Guard*, is he not?"

"He is! He is!" Sullivan was impressed by the detective's familiarity with his work. "So you think Jessie had a second lover?"

"You've as good as told me she had, Sir Arthur."

Sullivan frowned, reached into his breast pocket, and withdrew a cigarette case. He extracted a cigarette, tapped it several times in a nervous tattoo against the box, then allowed

Holmes to light it for him, throwing his head back gratefully as he blew out a cloud of smoke.

"You must understand first that Gilbert runs the Savoy," he began. "He runs it like a military outpost, with the strictest discipline, on stage and off. You may have observed that the men's and women's dressing rooms are on opposite sides of the stage. Congregation betwixt them is strictly forbidden. Conduct of the company while in the theatre—and to a very great degree outside of it—must satisfy Gilbert's mania for propriety.

"If his attitude seems to you gentlemen somewhat extreme, let me say that I understand and sympathise with what he has been trying to accomplish. The reputation of actresses has never been a very good one. The word itself has for many years been accepted as a synonym for something rather worse. Mr. Gilbert is attempting at the Savoy to expunge that particular synonym. His methods may seem severe and ludicrous at times, and—" he hesitated, tapping an ash—"individuals may suffer, but in the long run, I believe, he will have performed a useful service.

"Now, as to Jessie Rutland. I engaged her three years ago and never had any cause to regret my decision. She was, I knew, an orphan, raised in Woking, who had sung in various church choirs. She had no family nor income of her own. Gaining a position at the Savoy meant everything to her. For the first time in her life, she not only earned a decent wage, she had a home, a family, a place to which she belonged, and she was grateful for it."

He stopped, momentarily overcome, whether by mental or physical anguish it was impossible to say.

"Go on," Holmes ordered. His eyes were closed and the

tips of his fingers pressed together beneath his chin—his customary attitude when listening.

"She was a dear child, very pretty, with a lovely soprano—a little coarse in the middle range, but that would have improved with time and practise. She was a hard worker and a willing one, always ready to do as she was told.

"My contact with the theatre is generally of the slightest. I engage the singers after auditioning them, and as the songs are written, I play them over for the company and soloists until they are learned. And I conduct on opening nights if I am able." He smiled grimly. "Mr. Grossmith is not the only member of the company who has used drugs to get through a performance."

"I am no stranger to them myself, Sir Arthur. Please continue."

"Normally, Mr. Cellier rehearses the chorus and soloists. It was a surprise to me, therefore, when several weeks ago, Jessie approached me after a rehearsal in which I had gone over some new material with the chorus, and asked if she might speak with me privately, as she was in need of advice. She was clearly distressed, and looking at her closely, I perceived that she had been weeping.

"My first impulse was to refer her to Gilbert. He is much more popular with the company than I—" this stated with a wistful air—"for though he sometimes tyrannises them and plays the martinet, they know he loves them and has their interests very much at heart, whereas I am a relative stranger. When I suggested this course of action to her, however, she started to cry again, saying that it was impossible.

" 'If I confide in Mr. Gilbert, I am lost!' she cried. 'I will lose my place, and *he* will be harmed, as well!' " The composer sighed and dusted an imaginary speck of ash off his sleeve. "I am a busy man, Mr. Holmes, with many demands upon my time, both musical and otherwise." He coughed and put out his cigarette, his eyes avoiding our own. "Nevertheless, I was touched by the girl's appeal and I agreed to listen to her story. We met the next afternoon at a little teashop in the Marylebone Road. We were not likely to be recognised there, or if we were, it would be difficult to place any sordid construction on our presence.

" 'Tell me,' I said, when we had given our order. 'Tell me what has upset you.' 'I will not take up your time with preliminaries,' said she. 'Recently I made the acquaintance of a gentleman to whom I have become most attached. He is quite perfect in every way, and his behaviour towards myself has never been less than proper. Knowing the stringent rules governing conduct at the Savoy, we have behaved with the utmost circumspection. But, oh, Sir Arthur, he is so very perfect that even Mr. Gilbert must have approved! I have fallen in love!' she cried, 'and so has he!' 'But my dear,' I responded warmly, 'this is no cause for tears. You are to be congratulated! As for Mr. Gilbert, I give you my word of honour he will dance at your wedding!'

"At this point, Mr. Holmes, she began to cry in the midst of the restaurant, though she did her best to conceal the fact by holding a small cambric handkerchief before her face. 'There can be no wedding,' she sobbed, 'because he is already married. That is what he has just told me.' 'If he has deceived you in this fashion,' I retorted, much surprised, 'then he is utterly unworthy of your affections and you are well rid of him.' 'You don't understand,' said she, regaining her composure, 'he has not deceived me—as you mean. His wife is an invalid, confined to a nursing home in Bombay. She—' "

"One moment," Sherlock Holmes broke in, opening his eyes. "Did she say 'Bombay'?"

"Yes."

"Pray continue." His eyes closed again.

" 'His wife can neither hear nor speak nor walk,' she told me, 'as she was the victim of a stroke five years ago. Nevertheless, he is chained to her.' She was unable to suppress a trace of bitterness as she spoke, though I could not at the time —nor can I now—find it in my heart to reproach her for it. 'He feared to tell me of his plight,' she went on, 'for fear of losing me. Yet when he saw the direction our affections were taking, he knew he must disclose the truth. And now I don't know what to do!' she concluded and pulled forth her handkerchief yet again while I sat across the small table from her and pondered.

"Mr. Holmes, you can imagine how I felt. The woman had placed me in a most delicate position. I am part owner of the Savoy and in theory, at least, sympathise with Mr. Gilbert's aspirations for its company; thus, my duties clearly lay in one direction. But I am a human being and, moreover, a man who has experienced a very similar problem,* and so my emotions and personal inclinations lay in quite another."

"What did you advise?"

He looked at the detective without flinching. "I advised her to follow her heart. Oh, I know what you will say, but we are only here once, Mr. Holmes—at least, that is my conviction—and I believe we should seize what chance of happiness we can. I told her I would not reveal her secret to Mr. Gilbert, and I was as good as my word, but I warned her that I

* Sullivan's mistress was an American, Mrs. Ronalds, who was separated but not divorced. They remained devoted to one another throughout much of his life.

could not shield her from the consequences should he learn of her intrigue from another source."

"I begin to understand a little," said Holmes, "though there is much that remains obscure. Did she say anything at all concerning her young man that would enable us to identify him?"

"She was most careful to avoid doing so. The closest she came to an indiscretion was to let slip that the wife's nursing home was in Bombay. I am quite certain she made no other reference."

"I see." Holmes closed his eyes briefly and tapped his fingertips together. "And how much of all this did you tell the police this morning?"

The composer blushed and dropped his eyes.

"Not a word?" Holmes was unable to conceal a trace of scorn. "The woman cannot now be compromised, surely. She has no place to lose."

"But I, *I* can be compromised," the other responded softly. "If it emerges that I knew of a liaison at the Savoy and failed to mention it to Gilbert—" He sighed. "Relations between us have never been very cordial, and of late they have become more strained than usual. He has never got over the fact of my knighthood, you know. But we need each other, Mr. Holmes!" He laughed shortly and without mirth. "The ironic truth is that we cannot function apart. Oh, I grant you 'The Lost Chord' and 'The Golden Legend,' but when all is said and done, I have the hideous knowledge that my forte is *The Mikado* and others of that ilk. He knows it, too, and knows that it is for our Savoy operas, if anything, that we shall be remembered. I have not long to live," he concluded, "but while I breathe, I cannot afford to antagonise him further."

"I understand you, Sir Arthur, and I apologise for having seemed to pass judgement. One final question."

Sullivan looked up.

"Do you know Bram Stoker's wife?"

The question took him by surprise, but he recovered and shrugged. "His wife is a good friend of Gilbert's, I believe. That is all I can tell you."

Holmes rose. "Thank you for your time. Come, Watson."

"I trust you will be discreet—if possible," Sullivan murmured as we moved towards the door.

"Discretion is a part of my profession. By the way—" Holmes hesitated, his hand on the knob. "I saw *Ivanhoe*."*

Sullivan looked at him over the rim of his pince-nez. "Oh?"

"I quite liked it."

"Really? That's more than I did." He stared moodily at the table top before him as Holmes opened the door.

Bram Stoker was standing there.

"Did you observe his boots?" the detective murmured softly after we had passed.

---

* *Ivanhoe* was Sullivan's sole excursion into the realm of grand opera. It was not generally accounted successful.

TEN

THE MAN WITH BROWN EYES

Sherlock Holmes refused to elaborate on his observation regarding Bram Stoker's boots, the man's eavesdropping, or Ellen Terry's reaction to his enquiry after Stoker's Soho flat. Indeed, he declined to volunteer any thoughts upon leaving the Lyceum.

"Later, Watson," said he as we stood on the kerb before the theatre. "Things are not so simple as I had first supposed."

I was about to ask him what he meant by this when he took me by the sleeve.

"I must spend the afternoon in some research, Doctor. Might I prevail upon you to assist me in a small matter?"

"Anything you like."

"I want you to find Bernard Shaw and learn the meaning of his eccentric behaviour last night."

"You begin to attach some importance to my theory, then?"

"It may be," he answered, smiling. "At all events, I think it would be as well to have all the threads of this tangled skein in our hands. It is almost lunchtime, and I fancy you will come upon him at the Café Royal. I know he likes to take his meals there. Good luck." He squeezed my arm and started rapidly down the street.

"Where shall we meet?" I called after him.

"Baker Street."

When he had rounded the corner, I wasted no time but hailed a cab and hastened directly to the Café Royal, a snow-bound mile from the Lyceum. Indeed, all the events in which we found ourselves immersed at present had taken place within the space of a single square mile, a thought which made me pause as I considered it. The world of the theatre proved to be more insular than any I had heretofore encountered. All denizens of that world appeared to know one another at least slightly, creating an atmosphere so domestically intimate that in it a single sneeze would likely be overheard by a thousand people.

The Café Royal was crowded when I entered, and, it seemed to me, in a collective state of some confusion. Nervous clusters of people whispered intently together, huddling 'round tables and glancing apprehensively over their shoulders.

"Doctor!"

I peered about at the agitated throng and beheld Bernard Shaw, seated at a table with another man, whose coarse appearance disturbed me at once. He was short and squat, with eyes too closely set on either side of a prizefighter's pug nose, and his head sat awkwardly atop a thick, muscular neck, which threatened to burst the confines of his collar and tie.

"This is Mr. Harris," the critic informed me as I joined them, dropping into a chair opposite. "He's one of our leading publishers. We are here commiserating. The whole place is," he added sardonically, looking about. "And speculating."

"About what?"

They looked at one another briefly.

"About Oscar Wilde's folly," boomed Mr. Harris in a voice designed to be heard across the room. My face must have betrayed my confusion.

"You recall my running out of Simpson's last night, Doctor, I've no doubt?" enquired Shaw.

"I could hardly help remarking upon it at the time."

He grunted and stirred his coffee with a disinterested motion, leaning his cheek upon an open palm. "It was the beginning of a horrible night. In the first place, some maniac assaulted me outside the restaurant."

"Assaulted you?" I could feel the blood quickening in my veins and the hairs rising on the back of my neck.

"Some kind of practical joke, but it served to delay me when I thought speed counted most. I was trying to prevent the arrest of the Marquess of Queensberry. I rushed right here—to this very booth!—and sat with Frank here, doing my best to dissuade him."

"Wilde?"

He nodded.

"We bent his ear," the publisher agreed in a stentorian bellow, "but it was no use. He sat through it like a man in a trance."*

Harris's accent was impossible to place, partially owing to

---

* According to Harris, who is not reliable, and Shaw (who is), Lord Alfred Douglas was also present at this interview. "Bosie," in later years, confirmed this himself. For authoritative biographies of Shaw, Wilde, and Gilbert and Sullivan the reader is urged to consult the works of Hesketh Pearson.

the volume at which he spoke. It sounded alternately Welsh, Irish, and American. Later I learned that his background was much in dispute.

"He cannot prove he has been libelled?" I asked.

"It's worse than that," Shaw explained. "According to the law—which, as Mr. Bumble noted, is an ass—he leaves himself open for Queensberry to prove he hasn't."

"The Marquess was arrested this morning," Harris concluded in a dull rumble.

They returned glumly to their coffee, leaving me to ponder this. I wondered if I dared turn the conversation backwards and decided to attempt it: "What of your assault? I take it you were not injured?"

"Oh, that." Shaw wiggled his fingers airily. "Some kind of practical joke. I was seized from behind, forced to swallow some disagreeable concoction and then released. Can you imagine such nonsense? Right in the heart of London!" He shook his head at the thought of it, but his mind was clearly elsewhere.

"Did you get a look at the man? I assume it was one man?"

"I tell you I was paying no attention, Doctor! I simply wanted to be let go and do what I could to prevent Wilde's destroying himself. In that I failed," he added with a sigh.

"It is a foregone conclusion, then, that he will lose the case?"

"Utterly foregone," replied Harris. "Oscar Wilde, the greatest literary light of his time—" I noticed Shaw winced slightly at this—"and in three months—" Harris held up his fingers—"in three months, less, perhaps, he will be in total eclipse. People will fear to speak his name except in derision." He intoned all this as though delivering a sermon; clearly, he did not know how to speak below a roar. Yet for all his vocal posturing, I sensed a very real distress on his part.

"I should not be surprised if some of his works are proscribed," Shaw added. "Maybe all."

At the time I could not understand how grave the issue was. But in three months Frank Harris's prophecy had fulfilled itself utterly and Oscar Wilde was sent to prison for two years, his glorious career in ashes.

Ignorant of the facts surrounding the case, my mind returned to the matter at hand, and looking up at me, Shaw perceived my train of thought. "Well, but how's the murder?" he enquired with a rueful smile, as much to say, "Here's a more cheerful topic."

"It's two murders, as I expect you'll discover in this afternoon's editions," I said and told them of the events at the Savoy Theatre, pointing out to Shaw that if he had not bolted from the restaurant the previous evening, he should have known of them earlier.

They listened to my recital, open-mouthed.

"Murder at the Savoy!" Harris gasped when I had done. "What is happening? Is the entire fabric of our community to be rent by scandal and horror within the narrow space of four days?" Somehow he managed to convey the impression of relishing the prospect. He was certainly a contradictory character.

"It begins to resemble something of Shakespeare's," Shaw agreed slowly, his sharp tongue for once at a loss. "Corpses and what-not strewn over the entire West End."

"Does either of you gentlemen know Bram Stoker?"

They looked at me, confused by the turn the talk had taken.

"Why d'ye want to know?" Harris asked.

"I don't, but Sherlock Holmes does."

"What about him?"

"That is the question I am putting to you."

Shaw hesitated, regarding me and then exchanging glances with his publisher.

"He's an odd one, all right," Harris allowed, playing with his coffee spoon. "His name isn't Bram, of course. It's Abraham."

"Indeed. What else?"

"He was born in Dublin or thereabouts, I believe, and has an older brother who is a prominent physician."

"Not Dr. William Stoker?"

Shaw nodded. "The same. He's due for a knighthood this spring."

"And what of Bram?"

He hunched his shoulders, then dropped them. "Athletic champion of Dublin University."

"What was his occupation before entering Irving's employ?"

The Irishman chuckled and looked something like his usual elfin self.

"All roads lead to Rome, Doctor. He was a drama critic."

"A critic?" I dimly perceived a pattern to Holmes's suspicions.

"And sometime author—of the frustrated variety."

"Did he know Jonathan McCarthy?"

"Everyone knew Jonathan McCarthy."

"And his wife is a friend of Gilbert's."

Shaw's and Harris's eyes widened.

"Where did you come to learn that?" asked Shaw.

I stood up and did my best not to appear smug. "I have my methods."

"You're not leaving, surely," Harris protested. "You've had nothing to eat."

"I'm afraid my business takes me elsewhere. Thank you, gentlemen. I hope the affair with your friend does not end as badly as you fear."

"It will end worse," Shaw muttered, shaking my hand without conviction.

Leaving them, I hastened to Baker Street, eager to impart the results of my interview to Holmes, but he had not returned. I spent a dreary afternoon pacing about the place, energetically trying to make sense out of our data and to reconcile the pieces of our puzzle into a coherent whole. At times I thought I had mastered the thing, only to recollect an item of importance which I had omitted in my latest calculations. Finally, bored with fruitless speculation, I set about putting away the scores of books which still littered our floor, reasoning that my companion had for the moment lost interest in them.

I fell asleep at some point during my exertions, for the next thing I recall was being roused from an armchair reverie by the familiar knock of our landlady.

"There's a gentleman asking to see Mr. Holmes," she informed me.

"He isn't here, Mrs. Hudson, as you know."

"Yes, Doctor, but he says his business is most urgent, and he asked me to bring him to you."

"Urgent, is it? Very well, show him up. Stay, Mrs. Hudson, what's he like?"

The good woman frowned, then regarded me cannily. "He says he's an estate agent, sir; certainly he's well fed and wined —if you take my meaning." She tapped the side of her nose suggestively with a forefinger.

"I do indeed. Very well."

I had not long to wait before there was a second rap on the door, preceded by much huffing and puffing on the stair.

"Come in."

The door opened to admit a gentleman of advancing years and enormous girth; he must have weighed close to nineteen stone, and his every move was accompanied by gasps of effort.

"Your—very—humble—ah, servant, Doctor," he wheezed, presenting his card with a feeble flourish. It identified him as Hezekiah Jackson, of Plymouth, estate agent. The place fitted his accent, which was Devonshire in the extreme. I glanced and took in the beefy, corpulent, puffing countenance of Mr. Jackson. His bulbous nose was almost as red as a beet and the veins running over its tip as pronounced as a map of the Nile delta. They declared Mr. Jackson to be a tippler of no mean proportions. His wheezing breath tended to confirm that declaration, as it was liberally laced with alcohol. His brown eyes had a glazed, staring look as they endeavoured to take in their surroundings. Perspiration glistened on his cheeks and forehead, dribbling down from his close-cropped white hair. In another age he would have been the King of Misrule.

"Mr. Jackson?" said I. "Pray have a chair."

"Thank you, sir, I don't mind if I do." He looked around, swaying on his feet, for a seat large enough to accommodate his bulk. He chose the stuffed leather by the fire, which Holmes preferred, and squeezed into it so heavily that it creaked alarmingly. I shuddered to think of the detective's response should he return and find it exploded by this obese character.

"I am Dr.—"

"I know who you are, Doctor. I know all about you.

Sherlock's told me a good deal about you." He said it in a knowing tone which I found vaguely disquieting.

"Indeed. And what can I do for you?"

"Well, I think for a start you might have the courtesy to offer me a drink. Yes, a drink. It's devilish cold out there." He said this with the greatest conviction as he sat before me, sweating like a stuck pig.

"What can I give you?"

"Brandy if you have it. I 'most always take a little brandy at this time of day. It keeps up the strength, you know."

"Very well. Tea is about to be laid on if you prefer."

"Tea?" he gasped. "Tea? Great heavens, Doctor, do you wish to kill me? Being a medical man, I felt sure you knew about tea. The great crippler—that's what tea is. More men my age drop dead as a result of reckless and intemperate consumption of tea than from almost any other single cause save the colic. You were unaware of that fact, sir? Dear me, where have you been? Do you read no other pieces in the *Strand* magazine than your own? Do you honestly suppose I'd be the living picture of health that I am if I took tea?"

"Brandy it is, then," said I, suppressing an overpowering impulse to laugh and fetching a glass for him. Holmes certainly knew the queerest people, though what his connection with this aged toper was, I couldn't for the life of me fathom.

I handed him the drink and resumed my chair. "And what is your message for Mr. Holmes?"

"My message?" The brown eyes clouded. "Oh, yes, my message! Tell Mr. Holmes—this isn't very good news, I'm afraid—tell him that his land investments in Torquay are all wet."

"Wet?"

"Yes, wet, I'm afraid. Dropped into the sea, they have."

"I was unaware that Mr. Holmes had invested in land in Torquay."

"Everything he had," the estate agent assured me gravely, picking up his glass and burying his nose in it.

"What?"

He nodded, shaking his massive head from side to side in a despairing attitude. "Poor man. For years he's been instructing me to buy up property overlooking the sea—seems to have been an idea with him to build some kind of hotel there—but now, you see, it's all gone to smash. You've heard about the storm we've been endurin' there these past four days? No? Well, sir, I don't mind telling you I've lived in those parts all my life and never seen anything like it. Plymouth almost destroyed by floods—and huge chunks of land toppling right into the channel. The map makers'll have to get busy, make no mistake." He buried his enormous nose in the brandy once more as I digested this information.

"And do you mean to tell me that Mr. Holmes's land—all of it?—has been washed into the ocean?"

"Every square inch of it, bless you, sir. He's ruined, Doctor. That's the melancholy errand that brings me up to town."

"Great Scot!" I leapt to my feet in agitation as the full force of the catastrophe made itself felt. "Ruined!" I sank into my chair, stunned by the suddenness of it all.

"You look as though you could do with a drink yourself, Doctor, if you don't mind my saying so."

"I think perhaps I could." I rose on unsteady legs and poured a second brandy while the fellow broke into a low laugh behind me.

"You find this amusing?" I demanded sternly.

"Well, you must admit it *is* rather humourous. A man invests every cent he owns in land—the safest possible investment, you'd say—and then it falls right off into the water. Come now, sir, admit in all honesty that there is a kind of humour to it."

"I fail to see anything of the kind," I returned with heat. "And I find your indifference to your client's plight positively revolting! You come here, drink the man's brandy, calmly report his financial reverses, and then laugh about them!"

"Well, sir, put that way—" The fellow began some clumsy show of remorse, but I was in no mood for it.

"I think you'd better go. I shall break the news to him myself—and in my own way."

"Just as you say, sir," he replied, handing me back the brandy glass. "Though I must confess, I think you're taking a very narrow view of all this. Try to see the humour of it."

"That will do, Mr. Jackson." I turned on my heel and replaced the glass on the sideboard.

"Quite right, Watson," said a familiar voice behind me. "I think it time to ring for tea."

ELEVEN

THEORIES AND CHARGES

"Holmes!"

I spun 'round and beheld the detective sitting where I had left the estate agent. He was pulling off his huge nose and stripping his head of white hair.

"Holmes, this is monstrous!"

"I'm afraid it was," he agreed, spitting out the wadding he had held in his cheeks to inflate them. "Childish, I positively concur. It was such a good disguise, however, that I had to try it on someone who knew me really well. I could think of no one who fitted that description so conveniently as yourself, my dear fellow."

He stood and removed his coat, revealing endless padding beneath. I sat down, shaking, and watched in silence as he divested himself of his costume and threw on his dressing gown.

"Hot in there," he noted with a smile, "but it worked wonders for me. Still, I'm afraid there are a few loose ends which my new data fail to tie up. By all means, let's have tea."

He rang downstairs, and Mrs. Hudson shortly appeared with the tray, much astonished to find Sherlock Holmes in residence. "I didn't hear you come in, sir."

"You let me in yourself, Mrs. Hudson."

Her comments at this piece of intelligence are not relevant here. She departed, and Holmes and I pulled up chairs.

"Your eyes!" I cried suddenly, the kettle in my hand. "They're brown!"

"What? Oh, just a minute." He bent forward in his chair, so that he was looking at the floor, and pulled back the skin by his right temple, cupping his other hand beneath his right eye. Into his palm dropped a little brown dot. As I watched, nonplussed, he repeated the operation with his left eye.

"What in the name of all that's wonderful—" I began.

"Behold the ultimate paraphernalia of disguise, Watson." He stretched forth his hand and allowed me to view the little things. "Be careful. They are glass and very delicate."

"But what are they?"

"A refinement of my own—to alter the one feature of a man's face no paint can change. I am not the inventor," he hastened to assure me, "though I venture to say I am the first to apply these little items for this purpose."

"For what purpose are they intended?"

"A very specific one. Some twenty years ago a German in Berlin discovered that he was losing his sight due to an infection on the inside of his eyelids that was spreading to the eyes themselves. He designed a concave piece of glass—rather larger than these and clear, of course—to be inserted between the lid and the cornea, where they were held in place by surface tension. They retarded the disease and saved his sight.* I

---

* Precisely right. Contact lenses are over one hundred years old.

read of his research and modified the design slightly, with the results that you have seen."

"But if the glass should break!" I winced at the thought.

"It isn't likely. Provided you don't rub your eyes, the chances of anything hitting the lenses directly are remote. I use them rarely—they take some getting used to, and I find I cannot wear them for more than a few hours. After that they begin to hurt, and if a speck of dust should enter the eye, I find myself weeping as though at a funeral."

He took the little circles back and placed them in a small box evidently designed to contain them.

"You may be doing yourself an irreparable injury," I warned, feeling obliged, as a medical man, to point out some of the obvious pitfalls to him.

"Von Bülow wore them for twenty years without ill effect. In any event, I consulted your friend Dr. Doyle about them. He is so caught up in his literary whirl that we forget he is also an ophthalmologist. He was extremely helpful in his suggestions for the modifications I had in mind. Zeiss ground them for me," he went on, pocketing the box, "though I fancy they can't have imagined why. Now—" he filled his pipe and held out his teacup—"what of Bernard Shaw?"

Doing my best to adjust to these successive shocks, I poured out the tea and recounted in a few words the tale of my meeting at the Café Royal. Save for asking an occasional pointed question, he heard me out in silence, puffing steadily on his briar and sipping his tea.

"He thought it a practical joke, then?" was his comment regarding Shaw's account of the mysterious assault. "What a whimsical turn of mind he must have."

"I don't feel he thought about it much at all—or wanted

to." I found myself defending the critic. "He was in such a hurry to reach Wilde."

"Hmm. I wonder who else has been pressed to sample this tonic."

"You don't think it a practical joke, then?" I asked, knowing perfectly well that he did not.

He smiled. "Most impractical, wouldn't you say?"

"And what did you discover this afternoon?" I demanded in turn.

He rose and began a perambulation of the room, his hands thrust deep into the pockets of his dressing gown, smoke emanating from his pipe, as from the funnel of a locomotive. He did not appear to notice that I had cleared the floor for him.

"First I paid a visit to Mr. Stoker's clandestine flat in Porkpie Lane," he commenced. "I ascertained (without his knowing it) that he cannot account for his whereabouts during the time of either murder. I learned, as you did, his true Christian name and his former calling as a drama critic. Next I called upon Jessie Rutland's former lodgings (off the Tottenham Court Road) and spoke with the landlady. She was guarded but more helpful than she knew."

"This fits in perfectly with a theory I have been developing all afternoon!" I cried, jumping to my feet. "Would you care to hear it?"

"Certainly. You know I am endlessly fascinated by the workings of your mind." He took the chair I had left.

"Very well. Jessie Rutland meets Bram Stoker. He does not reveal his name or true identity but pretends instead to have recently returned from India, where he has left his invalid wife. He even smokes Indian cigars to bolster this impression. He lets a room in Soho to pursue his intrigue, but somehow

Jonathan McCarthy, an old rival from the drama desk (who patronises the Savoy), discovers his game and threatens the girl with exposure unless she succumbs to his attentions. Fearing for herself and also for her lover, she agrees. Stoker learns of her sacrifice and contacts McCarthy, who feels free to change his game and ask for money. They agree to a meeting to discuss the price of discretion. During their conversation—which begins leisurely enough, over brandy and cigars—tempers flare, and Stoker, seizing the letter opener, drives it home. He was perfectly capable of this," I added excitedly as more pieces of the puzzle began falling into place pell-mell, "because he was not only athletic champion of Dublin University, but brother to the well-known physician, William Stoker, from whom he had very likely received a cursory but adequate introduction to anatomy. As you yourself have pointed out, he is the right height and wears the right shoes."

"Brilliant, Watson. Brilliant," my companion murmured, relighting his pipe with a warm coal from the fire. "And then?"

"He leaves. McCarthy is still breathing, however, and he forces himself to the bookshelf. The copy of Shakespeare in his hand was meant to indicate the Lyceum, where the specialty is the Bard. Irving is even now producing *Macbeth.* Stoker, in the meantime, has begun to panic. He knows that when Miss Rutland learns of McCarthy's death—as assuredly she must—there will be no doubt in her mind as to the identity of his murderer. The thought of another living soul with his secret begins to gnaw at him like a cancer. What if the police should ever question her? Could she withstand their enquiries? He decides there is only one solution. The Savoy is no great distance from the Lyceum. He slips backstage and leaves the theatre through the Old Beefsteak Club Room, and runs quickly to the Savoy, where he accomplishes the second crime during the rehearsal of *The Grand Duke,* which he knows is in progress. Then he retreats hastily to the Lyceum again, with no-one the wiser. There! What do you think of that?"

For a time he did not respond, but sat puffing at his briar with his eyes closed. Were it not for the continuous stream of smoke, I should have wondered if he was awake. Finally he opened his eyes and withdrew the pipe stem.

"As far as it goes, it is quite brilliant. Really, Watson, I must congratulate you. I marvel, especially, at the many uses to which you have put that volume of *Romeo and Juliet.* Why did McCarthy not choose *Macbeth,* then, if he wished —as you say—to point a finger at the Lyceum?"

"Perhaps he couldn't see by then," I hazarded.

Holmes shook his head with a little smile. "No, no. He saw well enough to turn over the leaves of the volume he selected. That is merely one objection to your theory, despite the fact that there are some really pretty things in it. It appears to explain much, I grant you, but in reality it explains nothing."

"Nothing?"

"Well, almost nothing," he amended, leaning over and tapping me consolingly on the knee. "You mustn't feel offended, my dear chap. I assure you I have no theory whatsoever. At least none that will accommodate your omissions."

"And what are they, I should like to know?"

"Let us take them in order. In the first place, how did Jessie Rutland meet Bram Stoker—so that no one we have questioned knew of it? Male company is severely discouraged at the Savoy, as you know. Where, then? At Miss Rutland's former lodgings that reverend dame, the landlady, spoke quite highly of Miss Rutland and said she had but once seen her boarder in the company of a man—and it was not a man with a beard. She would not be more specific, but that information appears to rule out either of the two men in question. Now, as to friend McCarthy's engagement calendar. Can you see him, in a mood however jocular, referring to Bram Stoker as a lovelorn jester? Is there anything particularly hapless about Stoker, or feeble? Or amusing? I think not. Say, rather, does he not strike the casual observer as menacing, sinister, and quite powerful? And having said that, are you prepared to explain how our Miss Rutland could fall in love with him, any more readily than you reject the idea of her falling in love with the critic? And granting for the moment that she *did* love Stoker and he returned her affection, how are you prepared to explain McCarthy's incautious behaviour in bringing such a man to his own home, where there were no witnesses to ensure his safety? According to your theory, he had seduced the lady and then proposed to extort money from her true love. Was it wise to leave himself alone with a man he had so monstrously wronged? Would he not consider it flying in the face of Providence? Jonathan McCarthy may have been depraved—the evidence suggests it—but there is nothing in the record to support the notion that he was foolhardy."

He paused, knocked the ashes from his pipe, and began to refill it. The action appeared to remind him of something.

"And what of the Indian cigars? Do you seriously contend they were smoked to convince Miss Rutland that Stoker was recently returned from India? I cannot believe her knowledge of tobaccos was sufficient for her to make such fine distinctions. You and I, you may recall, were obliged to visit Dunhill's for a definite identification. For that matter, in the insular world of the theatre, how long could Stoker (if indeed it was he) hope to maintain his Indian deception amongst people who knew him so well? You heard today that his wife is a friend of Gilbert's. How long before Jessie Rutland, working at the Savoy, should stumble upon his true identity? And if, by some odd twist of reasoning, the cigars *were* smoked to contribute to the illusion, why bring them to McCarthy's flat? By your account, the critic knew perfectly well who he was. Indeed, how could he get in touch with him if he didn't? And what about the letter threatening us, its message pasted on Indian stock? Isn't it rather more likely that Jack Point—as I shall continue to call him—is indeed recently returned from India and that this accounts for his choice of tobacco and letter paper? Finally, your theory fails to explain the most singular occurrence in the entire business."

"And what is that?"

"The little matter of the tonics we three were forced to down outside Simpson's last night. Even allowing for Stoker's physical strength and his capacity for *outré* behaviour, what can he have hoped to accomplish by making us drink whatever it was we swallowed? Until we find out, this affair will remain shrouded in mystery."

His logic was so overwhelming that I was reluctantly obliged to succumb. "What will you do now?"

"Smoke. It is quite a three-pipe problem. I am not sure, but it may be more."

With this, he settled himself down amongst a pile of cushions on the floor and proceeded to smoke three additional pipes in rapid succession. He neither moved nor blinked but sat stationary, like the caterpillar in *Alice*, contemplating I knew not what as he polluted our rooms with noxious fumes.

Familiar with this vigil, I occupied my time by trying to read, but even Rider Haggard's fine stories could not engage my attention as the dark settled over London. They seemed tame indeed when compared with the mystery that confronted us—a mystery as tangled and complex as any I could recall in the long and distinguished career of my friend. Holmes had been correct when he spoke of the liquid we had been forced to swallow as the key to the business. Try as I might, however, I could scarcely remember what it tasted like, and my inability to recall anything of the persistent host who served it—save for his gloves—teased me beyond endurance.

Holmes was in the act of filling a fourth pipe—his disreputable clay—when his ritual and my impatience were brought to a simultaneous end by a knock on the door, followed by the entrance of a very cocksure Inspector Lestrade.

"Found any murderers lately, Mr. Holmes?" he demanded with a mischievous air as he removed his coat. The man's idea of subtlety was elephantine.

"Not lately." The detective looked up calmly from the centre of his mushroom-like arrangement of cushions.

"Well, I have," crowed the little man.

"Indeed? The murderer of Jonathan McCarthy?"

"And the murderer of Miss Jessie Rutland. You didn't know these crimes were related, did you? Well, they are—they positively are. Miss Rutland was the mistress of the late critic, and they were both dispatched by the same hand."

"Indeed?" Holmes repeated, turning pale. It would cut him to the quick, I knew, should this fool manage to solve the two murders before himself. His vanity and professional pride were at stake. Everything he stood for in the way of criminal detection demanded that his methods not be beaten by any so haphazard and clumsy as those of Scotland Yard.

"Indeed?" he echoed a third time. "And have you found out why the murderer should smoke Indian cigars?"

"Indian cigars?" Lestrade guffawed. "Are you still going on about them? Well, if you must know, I'll explain it to you. He smoked them because he's an Indian himself."

"What?" we exclaimed together.

"That's right, a sambo, a Parsee. His name is Achmet Singh, and he's been in England just under a year, running a used-furniture* and curio shop in the Tottenham Court Road with his mother." Lestrade walked about the room, chuckling and rubbing his hands together, scarcely able to contain his self-satisfaction and glee.

If Sherlock Holmes felt chagrined by the policeman's news, he did his best to conceal the fact. "Where did he meet Miss Rutland?"

"His shop is just down the road from her boarding house. The landlady identified him for me, saying he used to call for her there and take her out walking. The woman was so scandalised by the thought of her lodger taking up with a brown devil that she didn't open up to you about it." He laughed again. "At least I assume it was you she was talking to earlier in the day." He gestured with his hands, delineating a corpulent belly, laughing some more. "That's where being official police comes in handy, Mr. Holmes."

"May I ask what he was doing with tobacco if he is a Parsee?"

" 'What's he doing in England?' you might as well ask! But if he came here to mingle with white folk, he'll 'ave taken to

---

* "Used furniture" and "second-hand furniture" are accepted British synonyms for our American "antiques."

some of our ways, no doubt. Why, the fellow was even attending evening classes at the University of London."

"Ah. A sure sign of a criminal mind."

"You can jeer," the inspector returned, undisturbed. "The point is—" he placed a forefinger emphatically on the detective's chest—"the point is that the man cannot account for his time during the period when either murder took place. He had the time and the motive," the policeman concluded triumphantly.

"The motive?" I interjected.

"Jealousy! Heathen passion! You can see that, surely, Doctor. She dropped him and took up with that newspaper chap—"

"Who invited him to his home, where the Parsee drank brandy," Holmes offered mildly.

"Who knows if he drank a drop? The glass was knocked on its side with the drink still in it. He might have accepted the offer of a glass simply as part of his plan to gain admittance to the place."

"He went there, of course, knowing a murder weapon of some sort was bound to be ready to hand—"

"I didn't say the plan was murder," Lestrade countered. "I didn't say anything about premeditated murder, did I? He may simply have wanted to plead for the return of his white woman." Lestrade stood up and took his coat. "He's almost the right height. He's right-handed, too."

"And his shoes?"

Lestrade grinned broadly. "His shoes, Mr. Holmes, are three weeks old and were purchased in the Strand."

TWELVE

THE PARSEE AND PORKPIE LANE

After Lestrade had gone, Sherlock Holmes sat motionless for a considerable period of time. He looked to be in such a brown study that I did not like to disturb him, but my own anxiety was so great that I was unable to remain silent for very long.

"Hadn't we best speak with the man?" I asked, throwing myself into a chair before him. He looked up at me slowly, his countenance creased with thought.

"I suppose we had," he allowed, getting to his feet and assembling his clothes. "It is as well in such circumstances to go through the motions."

"Do you think, then, that they can have apprehended the guilty party?"

"The guilty party?" He considered the question, thrusting some keys into his waistcoat pocket and taking a bull's-eye lantern from behind the deal table. "I doubt it. There are too many explanations, and phrases such as 'almost the right height' give away the holes in their case. However, we'd best take a look, if only to find out what didn't happen." He came forward with the gravest expression I had ever beheld on his face. "I have an inkling about this that bodes ill, Watson. Lestrade has built up a neat circumstantial case in which the hideous spectre of racial bigotry plays a large and unsubtle rôle. Achmet Singh may not be guilty, but the odds are against him."

He said no more on the subject but allowed me to ponder his view of the situation during a silent cab drive to Whitehall. There was no great difficulty in our being admitted to interview the prisoner, Lestrade's visit having included an invitation to see the man for ourselves.

The moment we were shown to Singh's cell, Sherlock Holmes breathed a sigh of relief. The man we studied through the small window of his cell door was diminutive in stature and wiry of build. He appeared neither large enough nor strong enough to perform the physical feats counsel would have to attribute to him. Moreover, he wore a pair of the thickest spectacles I had ever seen and was reading a newspaper held only an inch or so from his nose.

Holmes nodded to the guard, who unlocked the door.

"Achmet Singh?"

"Yes?" A pair of dark brown eyes squinted up at us from behind the glasses. "Who is that?"

"I am Sherlock Holmes. This is Dr. Watson."

"Sherlock Holmes!" The little fellow came forward eagerly. "Dr. Watson!" He made to seize our hands but thought better of it and drew back, suspiciously. "What do you want?"

"To help you if we can," said Holmes kindly. "May we sit down?"

Singh shrugged and vaguely indicated his meagre pallet. "There is no help for me," he responded in a trembling voice. "I cannot account for my time, and I knew the girl. Also, my shoes are the right size and purchased in the wrong place. Finally, I am coloured. What jury in the world could resist such a combination?"

"A British jury will resist it," I said, "provided we can show that the prosecution cannot prove its case."

"Bravo, Watson!" Holmes sat down on the cot and motioned for me to do the same. "Mr. Singh, why don't you tell us your version of events? Cigarette?" He made as if to reach for a case in his pocket, but the other declined it with a distracted wave of his hand.

"My religion denies me the consolations of tobacco and liquor."

"What a pity." Holmes could scarcely conceal a smirk. "Now tell me what you know of this business."

"What can I tell you, since I did not kill poor Miss Rutland and do not know who did?" Tears stood in the miserable wretch's eyes, magnified pathetically by his thick lenses, which almost seemed to double his sorrow.

"You must tell us what you can, however unimportant it may seem to you. Let us begin with Miss Rutland. How did you come to know her?"

The prisoner leaned up against the brick wall next to the door and directed his voice to the corner: "She came into my shop, which is just 'round the corner from her room. I deal in curios from the East, as well as second-hand English furniture, and she liked to look at the things there when she had some time to herself. I would answer her questions about the pieces she liked and tell her what I could of their origins. Slowly we began to discuss other matters. She was an orphan, and my mother had passed away not long before. Aside from my customers and her friends in the theatre, we neither of us knew many people." He paused and swallowed painfully, his

Adam's apple protruding from the tightened muscles in his scrawny neck, as he turned and faced the detective across the cell. "We were lonely, Mr. Holmes. Is that a crime?"

"Indeed, it is not," said my companion gently. "Go on."

"Then we began to go for walks. Nothing more, I give you my word!" he added hastily. "Only walks. In the evening before the weather turned cold and she had to leave for the theatre, we strolled. And we continued our conversations."

"I understand."

"Do you?" He emitted a laugh that resembled nothing so much as a sob. "That is good. Inspector Lestrade does not. He places a rather different construction on my behaviour."

"Do not concern yourself with Inspector Lestrade for the moment. Pray continue your narrative."

"There isn't any more. Wherever we walked, people stared at us and whispered as we passed. At first we paid no attention. We were so lonely, our loneliness lent us the courage to defy conventions."

"And then?"

He sighed and his shoulders shook. "And then we began to notice. It frightened us. We tried to ignore our fears for a time, but we were too frightened even to mention them to one another. And then—" He hesitated, confused by his own recollections.

"Yes?"

"She met another man." His low voice made it difficult to catch the words. "A white man. It pained her to tell me," he continued, tears rolling freely down his cheeks now, "but our awkwardness together increased. Our fears grew greater. There were little incidents—a word overheard as we walked by a knot of tradesmen—and she became more terrified and reluctant to go with me when I came to call for her. Still, she did not know how to tell me of her fears or of the man she had met. I do not think she wished to tell me." He paused. "So I told her. I said our being seen together so frequently was beginning to excite comment in the neighbourhood and I thought it better that such talk be stopped lest it injure her reputation or get back to the theatre. She tried not to show her relief when I said these things, but I could see a great weight had been lifted from her shoulders. She was a good person, Mr. Holmes, kind and generous to a fault, and it was not her way to abandon a friend. It was then that she told me about the man she had met. The white man," he repeated in a tone so helpless that it wrenched my heart to listen to it.

"What did she say about him?"

"Why, nothing but that she had met him and come to love him. The rules at the Savoy are terribly strict regarding such things, and she was forced to be discreet. Also, I think she did not wish to pain me with the details. That is why we never ventured into other neighbourhoods than our own," he added. "Because it would have meant ruin for her at the theatre had she been recognised in my company." He looked up at us from the kneeling posture to which he had succumbed. "That is all there is to tell."

"What are you studying at the university?"

"Law."

"I see." Holmes went over and shook his hand. "Mr. Singh, I beg of you to be of good cheer. The matter stands against you for the time being, but I shall see to it that you never appear in the dock."

For some moments the Indian studied him searchingly from behind his thick spectacles. "Why should it matter to you whether I stand there or not? I do not know you and cannot possibly pay you for any trouble you take on my be-half."

Sherlock Holmes's grey eyes grew moist with an emotion I had seldom seen there. "To pursue the truth in this world is a trouble we should all undertake gladly on our own behalf," said he.

The Parsee looked at him, swallowing and unable to speak, the tears still streaming down his face.

"The man's vision is hopelessly astigmatic," Holmes observed as we emerged from the gloomy building. "Did you notice how he was forced to read his paper?" My friend's customary detachment of voice and facial expression had been forcibly restored. "To imagine that he can even see clearly across a table the size of the one in McCarthy's flat is as difficult as it is to envisage someone of his size striking a single fatal blow from that distance with a blunt-tipped letter opener."

"What do you propose, then?"

He looked at his watch in the light of the street lamp. "A little past eight," he noted. "The theatres are busy. Would you care to accompany me on an excursion, Doctor?"

"An excursion? Where?"

"Number Fourteen Porkpie Lane, Soho."

"To Bram Stoker's flat?"

"Yes."

"We are going to burgle it?"

"If you've no objection."

"None whatever. But why, if you reject my theory, does the place interest you?"

"We have no choice in view of recent developments—" he gestured with a crooked thumb in the general direction of the jail—"but to eliminate even the outside suspects in this matter. I can emerge with no theory of my own, and Stoker taunts us like an apparition. Perhaps we can exorcise his influence on our thinking. For this purpose I have brought a bull's-eye and some keys which may be useful to us. Are you coming? Good. Cab!"

The cab took us into a part of the West End with which I was not familiar. We threaded our way at first through well, if garishly lit neighbourhoods, listening to raucous laughter and tinny music, and then passed into an area where even the occasional street lamp provided scant illumination. Looking about in the gloom, I felt little inclined to remain in one place and did not like the thought of being stranded there. Not many folk were about in this quarter of the town; at any rate, not many were visible, but I sensed them behind windows, around corners, and in the menacing shadows of buildings. Our cab was obviously a novelty in the vicinity, a distinction keenly felt by the driver, whom I could hear muttering an unceasing string of maledictions above us. The horse's hooves echoed eerily on the deserted cobblestones.

Number 14 Porkpie Lane was a three-storey affair which looked positively squeezed between its neighbours, two seedy constructions on either side of it. Somewhat taller, they leaned towards one another over the roof of number 14, creating a vise-like impression.

"Which is it?" I asked, looking up at the queer structure.

"On the second storey, in the middle. The window's dark, as you can see. It has a little ledge beneath it."

"Someone thought of putting a balcony there once."

"Very likely."

We descended from the cab and made arrangements with the unwilling driver to come back in an hour and fetch us home. He was not loath to go, and I could not blame him, for the setting was not in any way appealing. I only hoped he would prove as good as his word and return.

We waited in the shadows of the nearest edifice until the horse had clattered 'round the corner. Then, looking carefully about, Holmes produced a latchkey from his pocket and held it up to the faint light.

"A very useful item, this," said he softly. "I had it from Tony O'Hara, the sneak thief, when I nabbed him. You recall the case, Watson? It was a sort of parting gift, an entire ring of these little beauties. Each will tackle a great many simple locks of the same make. If one fails, you have only to move 'round the ring."

"You chose only two this night," I pointed out as he inserted the key in the front door lock and began to fiddle and twist with it. "How did you know which to bring?"

"By examining the locks this afternoon."

"I had no idea you were so adept at breaking and entering."

"Quite adept," he replied cheerfully, "and always ready in a good cause. It is always the cause that justifies little felonies such as these." His eyes twinkled in the dark. *"L'homme c'est rien, l'oeuvre c'est tout.* Come along, Watson."

The lock had yielded to his gentle ministrations, and now the door opened before us, the small passage on the other side of it leading instantly to a rickety flight of stairs. We ascended without hesitation, judging that the less time we spent exposed to view, the safer we should be. I looked about as we climbed, wondering what sort of place it was.

A step or two behind me on the stair, the detective read my thoughts. "It's a sort of boarding house of the kind that caters to transient characters," he informed me. "Keep moving."

It took rather more time to open the door to the flat, but after some delicate manipulations, this obstacle was also overcome and we found ourselves in the private sanctuary of Bram Stoker.

Holmes opened the bull's-eye, and we surveyed the small room.

"Not suffused with romance," he commented drily, holding the lantern high above his head and turning slowly. The room, though shabby, was nonetheless neat and spare. There were only three articles of furniture to be seen: a desk, chair, and small day bed. On the desk was a lone inkwell and a blotter. The cracked and peeling walls boasted not a single picture nor decoration of any sort.

"Scarcely a trysting place," I agreed, looking at Holmes.

He grunted by way of reply and moved towards the desk. "I begin to see the logic of it, Watson. Our Mr. Stoker's secret mistress is the muse of literature. But why all the circumspection?" He sat down before the desk, setting the lantern on top of it, and began pulling open drawers. I advanced behind him and looked over his shoulder as he drew forth bundles of paper covered with small, neat, surprisingly feminine handwriting.

"Have a look at some of this." He passed me a sheaf, and I began to read, standing next to him for want of a chair or other source of light. The man had apparently copied out a series of letters, extracts from diaries and personal notes written or exchanged among people named Jonathan Harker, Lucy Westenra, Dr. Abraham Van Helsing, Arthur Holmwood, and Mina Murray.

"This must be some sort of novel," Holmes intoned softly, bent over a portion of it.

"A novel? Surely not."

"Yes, a novel, written in the form of letters and journals. Does nothing strike you about the name Jonathan Harker?"

"I suppose it vaguely resembles Stoker's real name."

"Vaguely? It contains precisely the number of syllables, and they are distributed between Christian and surnames in exactly the same manner. Stoker and Harker are almost identical, and Jonathan and Abraham are culled from the same source, the Bible. Harker must be his literary self."

"Why, then, is there a Doctor *Abraham* Van Helsing?" I asked, showing him the name. He read it, frowning.

"Name games, name games," he murmured. "Obviously that part of my assumption was incorrect—or at any rate incomplete." He continued reading, turning over the pages of the manuscript in an orderly fashion, his lips pursed with concentration.

"Look at this," he said after the space of a few minutes' silence. I returned from an idle tour of the room and read over his shoulder again:

> On the bed beside the window lay Jonathan Harker, his face flushed and breathing heavily, as though in a stupor. Kneeling on the edge of the bed, facing outwards, was the white-clad figure of his wife; by her side stood a tall, thin man, the Count. His right hand gripped the back of her neck, forcing her face down on his bosom. Her white nightdress was smeared with blood, and a thin stream trickled down the man's bare chest, which was shown by his torn, open dress. The attitude of the two had a terrible resemblance to a child forcing a kitten's nose into a saucer of milk to compel it to drink.*

* This passage and the characters' names make it abundantly plain that the manuscript in question was an early draft of *Dracula*, begun in 1895 by Stoker and published in 1897. Ellen Terry's mention of "when it happened the first time" undoubtedly refers to the publication of Stoker's short stories, *Under the Sunset*. Henry Irving was extremely possessive about Stoker's time.

"Great heavens!" I exclaimed, looking up and passing a hand before my eyes. "This is depraved."

"And this." He set down another passage before me:

". . . and you are now to me, flesh of my flesh, blood of my blood, kin of my kin; my bountiful wine press for a while." He then pulled open the shirt with his long, sharp nails, and opened a vein in his breast. When the blood began to spurt out, he took my hands in one of his, holding them tight, and with the other seized my neck and pressed my mouth to the wound, so that I might either suffocate or swallow some of the —oh, my God, what have I done?

"Holmes, what sort of mad work is this?"

"No wonder he writes in secrecy," the detective remarked, looking up. "Have you noticed anything else?"

"What do you mean?"

"Only that our Mr. Stoker knows how to induce swallowing." I looked at the two passages again, and we stared at each other, horror written on our faces.

"Can we have been forced to drink blood?" I whispered in awed tones.

Before he could answer, we were both made aware of the clip-clop of horse's hooves entering the lane.

"The cab's not due back yet," Holmes observed, snapping shut the bull's-eye and plunging the room into darkness. He peered through the shutters into the street. "Great Scott! It's *he!*"

"The cabbie?"

"Stoker!"

THIRTEEN

THE MISSING POLICEMAN

"Hurry, Watson." Rapidly Holmes assembled the papers and replaced them in the drawers from which he had taken them. As we heard the cab door slam in the stillness, he leapt to the door of the flat and locked it from within.

"But, Holmes—"

"The balcony, man! Quick!"

In less time than it takes to report, we threw open the window and passed out on to the precarious ledge, closing the shutters behind us as Stoker's heavy tread became audible on the stair.

"Don't look down," were my companion's last instructions as we flattened ourselves against the building wall and awaited further developments.

We had not long to wait. Within seconds of our gaining tenuous positions of safety, the door to the flat was reopened and Stoker entered the room. He closed and locked the door behind him, then proceeded to his desk, lit the gas, and pulled open the drawers. He took out pens, fresh paper, and what he had already written, spent some minutes ordering his materials, but did not appear to notice anything amiss. Without further preamble he settled down to work on his ghastly manuscript.

How long we stood on that slender shelf, clutching the bottom of the window frame for support, it is difficult to say. The moon had risen, pinning us like specimens beneath an observation light. We dared not move, for we were so near the clandestine novelist that our merest sound was certain to excite his suspicions. As the time passed and we prayed for the return of our cab, our hands, even in their gloves, began to lose sensation. The stillness around us was broken only by an occasional cough from within.

After what seemed a year, the silence was abruptly shattered by the hoofbeats of another horse. Holmes and I exchanged looks, and he signed for me to peer under the shutters. I did so and was able to discern the bending author in pursuit of his story, happily indifferent to any disturbance outside his mad world. I looked again at Holmes, indicating with a blink of my eyes that all was well, and he gestured with a free hand, explaining that we must jump on to the roof of the cab as it stopped underneath.

The poor cabby entered the alley nervously and looked about. Holmes signalled from our perch above and waved him over, placing a finger on his lips in a theatrical plea for silence. The man appeared quite dumbfounded by the sight of us hanging, as it were, from the moon but responded to the detective's repeated gesticulations and moved the vehicle hesitantly forward. When he had arranged the cab's position perfectly, we lowered ourselves gingerly to the roof before him, making but little noise in the process.

When we had landed, Holmes clapped the cabby on the back in a grateful embrace. "Baker Street," he urged quietly, and we returned to our lodgings, leaving the fiendish Mr. Stoker to his queer literary efforts.

"Your theory has had another hole punched in it," Holmes remarked as we climbed the seventeen steps to our rooms. "Bram Stoker's secret lair is used for his writing, not his rendezvous, given that his pastime is one of which his family and employer disapprove."

"I can see why," I acknowledged. "But what about the passages in the book—the ones in which folk are compelled to drink—?"

"I was thinking about them on our way back," he returned, stopping on the stair. "You will find that if you wish to induce swallowing, there is only one way to go about it. No, Watson, I am afraid matters have come to a very serious pass. We might wish Bram Stoker to be our man, but he is not—no more than is that miserable wretch Lestrade has arrested. The only difference between them," he added, opening the door, "is that if we cannot find the true murderer, Achmet Singh will hang. Hullo! Who is here? Why, it's young Hopkins!"

It was indeed the sandy-haired policeman, who was just being shown to a chair by our landlady as we entered. He rose awkwardly at once and explained that Mrs. Hudson had told him he might wait for us there.

"Quite right, Mrs. Hudson," Holmes assured her, interrupting her flow of oratory on the subject. "I know that you don't like policemen standing about in your parlour."

The long-suffering woman referred briefly to the strange goings-on of late (by which she meant, I knew, Holmes's appearance in disguise that afternoon) and withdrew.

"Now, then, Hopkins," Holmes began as soon as the door had closed, "what brings you to Baker Street at an hour when most off-duty policemen are at home, resting their feet?

I perceive that your route here has been a circuitous one and that you have taken great pains to avoid being seen."

"Heavens, sir, how can you tell that?"

"My dear young man, you have divested yourself of every vestige of your police uniform, which means you probably stopped at home first. And then, look at your trouser leg. There must be seven different splashes there, each evidently from a different part of town. I believe I recognise some mud from Gloucester Road, the cement they are using at the Kensington—"

"I have had to be extremely circumspect." The youth blushed and looked uncertainly from one to the other of us.

"You may speak before Dr. Watson here as before myself," Holmes promised smoothly.

"Very well." He sighed and took what was palpably a difficult plunge. "I must tell you gentlemen straight off that my appearance here tonight puts me in a very awkward situation—with the force, I mean." He eyed us anxiously. "I've come on my own initiative, you see, and not in any official capacity."

"Bravo," Holmes murmured. "I was right, Hopkins. There is hope for you."

"I very much doubt if there will be at the Yard if they learn of this," the forlorn policeman replied, his honest features clouding further at the thought. "Perhaps I'd best be—"

"Why don't you pull that chair up to the fire and begin at the beginning?" Holmes interrupted with soothing courtesy. "There you are. Make yourself quite at home and comfortable. Would you care for something to drink? No? Very well, I am all attention." To prove it, he crossed his legs and closed his eyes.

"It's about Mr. Brownlow," the sergeant commenced hesitantly. He saw that Holmes's eyes were shut and looked at me, perplexed, but I motioned for him to go on. "Mr. Brownlow," he repeated. "You know Mr. Brownlow?"

"The police surgeon? I believe I passed him on my way downstairs at Twenty-four South Crescent yesterday morning. He was on his way for McCarthy's remains, was he not?"

"Yes, sir." Hopkins ran a tongue over his dry lips.

"A good man, Brownlow. Did he find anything remarkable in his autopsy?"

There was a pause.

"Did he?"

"We don't know, Mr. Holmes."

"But he's submitted his report, surely."

"No. The fact is—" Hopkins hesitated again—"Mr. Brownlow has disappeared."

Holmes opened his eyes. "Disappeared?"

"Yes, Mr. Holmes. He's quite vanished."

The detective blew air soundlessly from his cheeks. With automatic gestures his slender hands began nervously packing a pipe which had been lying near to hand. "When was he last seen?"

"He was in the mortuary all day at work on McCarthy—in the laboratory—and he began acting very strangely."

"How do you mean strangely?"

The sergeant made a funny face, as though about to laugh. "He threw all the assistants and stretcher-bearers out of the laboratory; made all of 'em take off all their clothes and scrub down with carbolic and alcohol and shower. And you know what he did while they were showering?"

The detective shook his head. I found myself straining to catch the sergeant's low tones.

"Mr. Holmes, *he burned all their clothes.*"

My companion's eyes grew very bright at this. "Did he, indeed? And then disappeared?"

"Not just yet. He continued to work on the corpse by himself, and then, as you know, Miss Rutland's remains were carried in and he went briefly to work on them. He grew excited all over again and again summoned the stretcher-bearers and his assistants together and made them take off all their clothes once more, scrub with carbolic and alcohol, and shower." He paused, licked his lips and took a breath. "And while they were showering—"

"He burned their clothes a second time?" Holmes enquired. He could not suppress his excitement, and he rubbed his hands together with satisfaction, puffing rapidly on his pipe. The young man nodded.

"It was almost funny. They thought he'd started to play some sort of prank on them the first time, but now they were furious, especially the bearers. They all had to be wrapped in blankets from the emergency room and in the meantime, Mr. Brownlow'd barricaded himself inside the laboratory! They brought Inspector Gregson down from Whitehall, but Mr. Brownlow wouldn't open the door to him, either. He had a police revolver with him in there and threatened to shoot the first man across the threshold. The door is quite solid and has no window, so they were obliged to leave him there all afternoon and into the night."

"And now?"

"Now he is gone."

"Gone? How? Surely they had sense enough to post a man outside the laboratory door."

Hopkins nodded vigourously. "They did, but they didn't think to post one outside the back of the laboratory."

"And where does that door lead?"

"To the stables and mews. The laboratory receives its supplies that way. The door is bigger and easier to lock, so that they never thought to challenge it. You see, Mr. Holmes, it never occurred to any of us that his object was to *leave* the laboratory. Quite the reverse. We assumed his purpose was to make us leave, and remain in sole possession. Besides, they could hear him talking to himself in there."

Holmes closed his eyes and leaned back once more in his chair.

"So he left the back way?"

"Ay, sir. In a police van."

"Have you checked at his home? Brownlow's married, I seem to recall, and lives in Knightsbridge. Have you tried him there?"

"He's not been home, sir. We've men posted by it, and neither they nor his Missus have seen hide nor hair. She's quite worked up about it, needless to say."

"How very curious. I take it none of this activity at the mortuary has had the slightest effect on the consensus at the Yard that Achmet Singh is guilty of a double murder?"

"No effect whatsoever, sir, though I venture to suppose there must be a connection of some sort."

"What makes you suppose that?"

Young Hopkins swallowed with difficulty. "Because there's one other thing I haven't told you, Mr. Holmes."

"And that is?"

"Mr. Brownlow took the bodies with him."

Holmes sat forward so abruptly that the sergeant flinched.

"What? Miss Rutland and McCarthy?"

"That is correct, sir." The detective rose and began pacing about the room as the other watched. "I came to you, sir, because in my limited experience, you appear to think much more logically about certain matters than—" he trailed off, embarrassed by his own indiscretion, but Holmes, deep in thought, appeared not to notice.

"Hopkins, would our going over to the laboratory and having a close look at things there place you in an awkward position?"

The young man paled. "Please, sir, you mustn't think of doing it. The fact is, they're all of a dither down there and don't want anyone to know what's happened. They've got it in their heads this thing could make them a laughing stock— the idea of the police surgeon burning all those clothes and then absconding with two corpses. . . ."

"That is one way of looking at it," Holmes agreed. "Very well, then. You must answer a few more questions to the very best of your ability."

"I'll try, sir."

"Have you seen the laboratory since Brownlow abandoned it?"

"Yes, sir. I made it my business to have a look."

"Capital! Really, Hopkins, you exceed my fondest hopes. Now tell me what was left there?"

The sergeant frowned in concentration, eager to continue earning the detective's effusive praise. "Nothing much, I'm afraid. Rather less than usual, in fact. The place had been scrubbed clean as a whistle and it fairly reeked of carbolic. The only thing out of the ordinary was the pile of burnt clothes in the chemical basins where he'd set fire to them. And he'd poured lye over the ashes."

"How did you know what they were, in that case?"

"Some of the buttons still remained, sir."

"Hopkins, you are a trump." Holmes rubbed his hands together once more. "And have your sore throat and headache quite vanished?"

"Quite, sir. Yesterday Lestrade said it was probably just—" He stopped and gaped at the detective. "I don't recall mentioning my illness."

"Nor did you—which doesn't alter the fact of your recovery. I am delighted to learn of it. You haven't left out anything? A little nip of something on the side?"

Hopkins looked at him uncertainly. "Nip? No, sir. I don't know what you mean, I'm afraid."

"Doubtless not. Lestrade feels fit, too, now, does he?"

"He is quite recovered," the sergeant answered, giving up all hope of learning the detective's secrets. Holmes scowled and cupped his chin in thought.

"You are both luckier than you know."

"See here, Holmes," I broke in, "I seem to see what you are getting at. There's some matter of contamination or contagion involved—"

"Precisely." His eyes gleamed. "But we have yet to discover what is in danger of proliferating. Watson, you saw both bodies and conducted a cursory examination of each. Did their condition suggest anything in the nature of a disease to you?"

I sat and pondered while they watched, Holmes barely able to conceal his impatience.

"I believe I stated at the time that both the throats were prematurely stiff, as though the glands were swollen. But any number of common ailments begin with a sore throat."

Holmes sighed, nodded, and turned once more to the policeman. "Hopkins, I very much fear a discreet visit to the back of the mortuary laboratory is inevitable. The stakes are too great that we should hesitate to trifle with the dignity of the metropolitan police. We must see how one man carried out two corpses. We already begin to know why."

"To dispose of them?" I asked.

He nodded grimly. "And it would be as well to put out a general alarm for that missing police van."

"That has already been done, Mr. Holmes," said the young sergeant with some satisfaction. "If it's in London, we'll lay hands on it."

"That is exactly what you must none of you do," Holmes returned, throwing on his coat. "No one must go near it. Watson, are you still game?"

FOURTEEN

THE WEST END HORROR

Moments later we stood in the company of the anxious sergeant on the stretch of pavement before 221b, in search of a cab. Instead of a hansom, however, I beheld a familiar figure dancing down the street towards us in the glare of the lamplight.

"Have you heard the latest outrage?" Bernard Shaw cried without so much as shaking hands. "They've pinned the whole thing on a Parsee!"

Sherlock Holmes endeavoured to inform the volatile Irishman that we were aware of the turn events had taken, but at that moment Shaw recognised Hopkins and turned upon that unfortunate young man the full force of his sarcastic vitriol.

"Out of uniform, eh?" he commenced. "And well you should be if murder is being contemplated. I wonder you've the face to appear in public at all with your hands so red! Do you seriously believe, Sergeant, that the British public, which I agree is gullible beyond credence, is going to swallow this particular connivance? It won't go down, believe me, Sergeant, it won't. It's too big to pass the widest chasm of plausibility. This isn't France, you'd do well to remember.* You can't divert *our* attention with a xenophobic charade!"

In vain, as we waited for our cab, did Hopkins attempt to stem the tidal wave of rhetoric. He pointed out that it was not he who had arrested the Indian.

"So!" the other eagerly seized the opportunity for a literary analogy. "You wash your hands with Pilate, hey? I wonder there's room at the trough for so many of you, lined up alongside with your dirty fingers. If you suppose—"

"My dear Shaw," Holmes remonstrated forcefully, "I don't know how you can have learned of Mr. Singh's arrest—the newsboys are hawking it, very likely—but if you have nothing better to do than rouse mine honest neighbours at a quarter past twelve, I suggest you come along with us. Cabby!"

"Where to?" Shaw demanded as the cab pulled up before us. His voice lacked any trace of contrition.

"The mortuary. Someone appears to have made off with our two corpses."

"Made off with them?" he echoed, getting in. This intelligence succeeded in doing what Sergeant Hopkins could not, and the critic fell silent as he tried to determine its significance. His shrill imprecations were reduced to a stream of mutterings as we threaded our way to the mews behind the mortuary laboratory. A street or so before the place, Holmes ordered the driver to stop and we descended from the cab. In hushed tones, the cabby was instructed to wait where he was until we should return.

There was no one about as we entered the mews, though the voices of the ostlers were audible from the police stables

---

* We have no way of knowing what precisely was meant by this remark. In my opinion it refers to the trial of Captain Dreyfus.

across the way. We proceeded cautiously on foot, our path being lit by the yellow lights of windows overhead. Sergeant Hopkins looked fearfully about as we advanced, being more apprehensive about discovery than ourselves, for obvious reasons.

"This door leads to the laboratory?" Holmes enquired softly, pointing to a large, wooden, portcullis-like affair, whose base was some four feet off the ground.

Hopkins nodded, stealing an anxious glance over his shoulder. "That's it, Mr. Holmes."

"You can see the wheel marks where the wagon was backed up to it." The detective knelt and indicated the twin tracks, plainly visible in the meagre light from above. "Of course the police have examined it," he added with a weary sigh, pointing to all the footprints running in every direction all 'round the place.

"It looks like they danced a Highland fling here," I commented, sharing his indignation.

He grunted and followed the wheel marks out of the dirt to where they disappeared on the cobblestones. "He went left; that's all we can say," he reported gloomily, returning to the door where we waited. "Once he departed the mews there's no telling where he was bound."

"Perhaps we should fetch Toby," I suggested.

"We haven't the time to get to Lambeth and back, and besides, what could we offer him as a scent? He's not as young as he used to be, you know, and the stench of carbolic would be insufficient. Blast! Every second gives this thing—whatever it is—more time to spread. Hullo, what's this?"

He had been speaking bent over and almost touching the ground as he inspected it inch by inch. Now he dropped to his knees once again, directly beneath the laboratory door, and rose with something held gingerly in his right hand. "The noose around Achmet Singh's neck begins to loosen, or I am much deceived."

"How so?" Shaw enquired, stepping forward.

"Because if the prosecution contends that the Parsee smoked these Indian cheroots, they will be hard put to explain the presence of this one outside the mortuary whilst Singh himself is incarcerated in a private security cell at Whitehall."

"Are you certain it is the same cigar?" I hazarded, not wishing to question his abilities and yet, for the sake of the prisoner, feeling obliged to do so.

"Quite sure," he returned without seeming to take umbrage. "I took great pains to recognise it should I ever see one like it again. It's in an excellent state of preservation, as you can see. Notice the distinctive square-tipped ends. Our man simply threw it aside when the other opened the laboratory door for him."

"The other?"

Holmes turned to Hopkins. "I take it Mr. Brownlow did not smoke Indian cheroots?"

"No, sir," the youth replied. "In fact, to my knowledge, he did not smoke at all."

"Excellent. Then there was another man here, and it is that other man who concerns us. Brownlow was not talking to himself but conversing with our quarry."

"But what of Mr. Brownlow?" Hopkins demanded, his honest features revealing his perplexity.

"Hopkins—" the detective put a hand upon his shoulder— "the time has come for us to part company. Your position here becomes increasingly delicate as this night progresses. If you will be guided by me, I suggest that for your own good

you go home and get a good night's rest. Say nothing to anyone of what you have seen and heard here tonight, and I, for
my part, will endeavour to keep your name out of it—unless,
of course, Achmet Singh comes to the foot of the gallows, at
which point I will have no alternative but to take drastic
steps."

Hopkins wavered, torn between his own curiosity and his
sense of discretion. "Will you tell me what you find, at least?"
he implored.

"I am afraid I cannot promise that I shall."

The sergeant hesitated a moment or so longer and then departed with evident reluctance, his personal impulses outweighed by the obligations of loyalty he felt he owed to his
superiors.

"A bright young fellow, that," Holmes observed when he
had gone. "And now, Watson, every minute counts. Whom
do you know who could tell us about tropical diseases?"

"Tropical diseases?" Shaw interjected, but Holmes waved
him to silence and waited for my answer.

"Ainstree* is generally regarded as the greatest living authority on the subject," I replied, "but he is in the West
Indies at present, if I am not mistaken."

"What have tropical diseases to do with this?" Shaw
demanded, raising his voice.

"Let us return to the cab, and I will explain. Only keep
your voice down, like a good fellow.

"I think we had best pay a call on Dr. Moore Agar, of
Harley Street," he resumed when we had regained the cab.
"Watson, you've frequently recommended him when I've
been suffering from overwork and fatigue."

---

* Watson had urged Holmes to consult Ainstree in his capacity as tropical
disease expert in *The Adventure of the Dying Detective* (1887).

"I did not envisage your calling upon him after one in the morning," I hastened to point out. "In any case, the man's not a specialist in tropical diseases."

"No, but he may be able to direct us to the leading available authority."

"In heaven's name," Shaw exploded as the cab rattled off for Harley Street, "you still haven't said why we need a specialist in tropical diseases!"

"Forgive me, but I hope to make all plain before the night is out. All I can say at present is that Jonathan McCarthy and Miss Jessie Rutland were not killed to prevent their living but rather to prevent their dying a more horrible and more dangerous death."

"How can one death be more dangerous than another?" Shaw scoffed in the dark recesses of the cab.

"Very easily. Different kinds of death pose different hazards to those who continue living. All bodies become sources of infection if they are not disposed of, yet a body that dies a natural death or even one that has been stabbed is less dangerous to other people than a corpse that has succumbed to some virulent disease."

"You mean these two were slain violently in order to prevent their suffering the ravages of some malady?" Shaw exclaimed.

"Just so. A virulent disease that would have made off with them as surely as a bullet, given time. Their corpses were stolen from the mortuary laboratory to prevent further contagion, and we three, who were most prominently exposed to them, were forced to imbibe some sort of antidote."

"Antidote!" the critic cried out, his voice rising an involuntary octave. "Then that practical joke outside Simpson's—"

"Saved our lives, I shouldn't wonder."

"If your theory is correct," Shaw returned gruffly. "But what is the malady we are speaking of?"

"I have no idea and hesitate even to venture a guess. Since all the evidence points to someone recently returned from India, I take the liberty of postulating some tropical disorder, but that is the best I can do with such insufficient data.

"The bodies were no doubt stolen, also, to prevent an autopsy from revealing what would have killed them had the murderer permitted them to live."

"What of Brownlow, then? Did he collaborate with Jack Point?"

"He opened the door to him, that much seems certain. The evidence suggests he had come upon the truth—why else scrub down the laboratory, force the stretcher-bearers to shower, and burn their clothes?"

"Where is he now, then?"

Holmes hesitated. "I very much fear that Mr. Brownlow is dead. If the murderer's purpose was to contain a spreading epidemic, the police surgeon, by virtue of his occupation, was more exposed to contamination than any of us."

Next to me I could see Holmes's jaw tighten, and in his expression I beheld that which I had never seen before in all the years I had known him. I beheld fear.

It was almost two o'clock when the cab deposited us before Dr. Moore Agar's imposing residence in Harley Street. Remarking that our intrusion was not likely to be rendered less irritating to Dr. Agar by our waiting, Holmes proceeded up the steps and rang the night bell vigourously several times. It took some moments before a light appeared in one of the overhead windows, followed shortly thereafter by another on the floor above. In another few moments the door was opened by the housekeeper, an elderly woman, half asleep, who stood upon the threshold in her nightcap and dressing gown.

"I am extremely sorry to disturb you," the detective informed her briskly, "but it is absolutely essential that I speak with Dr. Agar at once. My name is Sherlock Holmes." He handed her his card.

She gaped at us, her eyes blinking away sleep.

"Just a moment, sir, please. Won't you gentlemen step into the hall?"

We were obliged to stand there while she closed the door and went upon our errand. Sherlock Holmes paced furiously in the confined space of the vestibule, gnawing at his knuckles.

"It is staring us in the face, I know it," he cried in exasperation, "but I cannot fathom it, cannot for the life of me!"

The inner door of the hall opened and the housekeeper admitted us, somewhat more alert now, and showed us to Dr. Moore Agar's consulting room, where she turned up the gas and closed the door. This time we had not long to wait. Almost at once the doctor himself—tall, spare, and distinguished—swept into the room, tying the belt of his red silk dressing gown but otherwise appearing wide awake.*

"Mr. Holmes, what is the meaning of this? Are you ill?"

"I trust not, doctor. I have come to you in a crisis, however, for a piece of information upon which the lives of many may well depend. Forgive me if I do not take time for introductions, though I suspect you already know Dr. Watson."

"Tell me what you need to know, and I will try to help you," Agar informed him without standing on ceremony. If

---

* In *The Adventure of the Devil's Foot* (1897) Watson says that one day he will recount the dramatic first meeting of Holmes and Dr. Agar. This would appear to be it.

he was in any way discomfited by the lateness of the hour or
perturbed by our unannounced arrival, he gave no outward
sign of it.

"Very well. I need the name of the leading specialist in
tropical diseases here in London."

"Tropical diseases?" He frowned, passing a graceful hand
across his mouth as he considered the request. "Well, Ainstree
is the man who—"

"He is not at present in England," I pointed out.

"Ha. No, indeed not." The physician suppressed a yawn
that was meant to attribute his lapse of memory to the
hour.

"Let me see, then—"

"Every minute is of the utmost urgency, Dr. Agar."

"I understand you, sir." He thought a moment longer, his
blue eyes unblinking; then suddenly he snapped his fingers.
"It comes to me now. There is a young man who might be
able to assist you. His name escapes me, but I can look him
up in my study and it won't take but a minute. Wait here."

He took a piece of paper from his desk and disappeared
from the office. Holmes continued to pace restlessly, like a
caged animal.

"Just look at this place," Shaw growled, taking in the plush
surroundings with a sweep of his small arm. "Fancy bound
books and gadgets galore! The medical profession could easily
compete with the theatre as a house of illusion if it wanted to.
Does any of this paraphernalia really assist in curing folk of
their ailments, or are these all a collection of stage props designed to impress the patient with the majesty and power of
the shaman?"

"If the patient is cured by illusion, that is no less a cure," I
protested, whereat Shaw regarded me with a curious stare. I

confess that once again I was nettled by the fellow's caustic observations, but Holmes, seemingly oblivious to the exchange, continued to pace about the room.

"So," Shaw went on, "if a man contracts the plague and goes to see a physician about it, by your argument, a roomful of books and instruments, such as these—"

"Plague!"

Holmes spun around, his face dead white, his hands shaking. "Plague," he repeated in an almost reverential tone. "That is what we are dealing with."

Never had a single word struck such terror in the very roots of my soul.

"Plague?" I repeated faintly, suppressing a shudder of dread. "How can you know?"

"Watson, invaluable Watson! You held the key in your own hands from the first! Do you remember the line you quoted from Act three, Scene one, of *Romeo and Juliet*?: 'A *plague* on both your houses!' He was being literal! And what did they do when the plague came to London?"

"They closed the playhouses," Shaw interjected.

"Precisely."

At this moment the door opened and Agar returned, a folded piece of paper in his hand.

"I have the name you asked for," he informed the detective, holding forth the paper.

"I know already what name it is," Holmes responded, taking it. "Ah, you have included his address. That is most helpful. Ah, yes, before me all the time, and I was blind to it! Quick, Watson!" He stuffed the paper into the pocket of his Inverness. "Dr. Agar—" he grabbed the astonished physician's hand and pumped it in passing—"a thousand thanks!" He tore from the room, leaving us no alternative but to pursue him.

The cab was waiting for us as ordered, and Holmes leapt in, yelling to the driver, "Thirty-three Wyndham Place, Marylebone, and don't spare the horse!" We had barely time to clamber in after him before the vehicle was tearing through the nocturnal city of London with an echoing clatter of hoofbeats.

"All the time, all the time," was the insistent litany of Sherlock Holmes, intoned again and again as we raced through the deserted streets on our fateful errand. "When you have eliminated the impossible whatever remains, however improbable, must be the truth. If only I had heeded that simple maxim!" he groaned. "Watson, you are in the presence of the greatest fool in Christendom."

"I believe we are in the presence of the greatest lunatic," Shaw broke in. "Pull yourself together, man, and tell us what's afoot."

My companion leaned forward, his grey eyes flashing like lighthouse beacons in the dark.

"The game, my dear Shaw! The game's afoot, and such a quarry as I've never been faced with yet! The greatest game of my career, and should I fail to snare it, we may all very well be doomed!"

"Can you not speak more plainly, in heaven's name? I think I've never heard such melodrama outside of the Haymarket!"

Holmes sat back and looked calmly about him. "You don't need to listen to me at all. In a very few minutes you shall hear it from the lips of the man we are seeking—if he is still alive."

"Still alive?"

"He can't have toyed with the disease as much as he has done without succumbing to it sooner or later."

"Plague?"

Holmes nodded. "Sometime in the mid-fourteenth century three ships carrying spices from the East put into port in Genoa. In addition to their cargo they carried rats, which left the ship and mingled with the city's own rodents. Shortly dead rats began appearing in streets everywhere, thousands of them. And then the human populace began to die. The symptoms were simple: dizziness, headache, sore throat, and then hard black boils under the arms and around the groin. After the boils—fever, shivering, nausea, and spitting blood. In three days the victim was dead. Bubonic plague. In the next fifty years it killed almost half the population of Europe, with a mortality rate of ninety percent of all it infected. People referred to it as the Black Death, and it must easily rank as the greatest natural disaster in human history."

"Where did it come from?" We found ourselves talking in whispers.

"From China, and from thence to India. The Crusaders and then the merchants brought it home with them—it destroyed Europe and then disappeared as suddenly as it erupted."

"And never returned?"

"Not for three hundred years. In the mid-seventeenth century, as Shaw recalled, they were forced to close the playhouses when it reached England. The great fire of London appeared to have ended it then."

"But it's not been heard from since, surely."

"On the contrary, my dear Watson, it has been heard from —and only as recently as last year."

"Where?"

"In China. It erupted with an old vengeance: sprang out of Hong Kong and is at present decimating India, as you know from the papers."

It was difficult, I owned, to associate the bubonic plague that one read of in the newspapers with something as primitively awesome as the Black Death—and even more difficult to envisage another onslaught of the fatal pestilence here in England.

"Nevertheless, we are now facing that possibility," Sherlock Holmes returned. "Ah, here we are. Hurry, gentlemen!" He dismissed the cab and dashed up the steps of number 33, where we discovered the door to be unbolted. Cautiously Holmes pushed it open. Almost at once our nostrils were assailed by the most terrible odor.

"What is it?" Shaw gasped, reeling on the front step.

"Carbolic."

"Carbolic?"

"In enormous concentration. Cover your noses and mouths, gentlemen. Watson, you haven't your revolver with you? No? What a pity. Inside, please." So saying, he plucked forth his own handkerchief and, pressing it to his face, moved into the house.

The lamps were off, and we dared not light the gas for fear of disturbing the occupants, though how anyone should have passed a decent night in that pungent atmosphere, I could not imagine.

Gradually, making our way back along the first floor, we became aware of a rasping, rhythmic sound, rather like the pulse-beat of some piece of machinery in need of an oil can.

Instinctively we made our way towards that pumping sound and found ourselves in a darkened room.

"Come no nearer!" a voice rasped suddenly, very close by. "Mr. Holmes is it? I have been waiting for you." I was aware of a shrouded figure, slumped in a chair somewhere across the room by the windows which faced the street.

"I hoped we would find you in time, Dr. Benjamin Eccles."

Slowly the figure moved in the dark and, with a groan of effort, managed to turn up the gas.

FIFTEEN

JACK POINT

It was indeed the theatre doctor who was revealed to us by the faint light of the lone lamp.

But so changed! His body, like that of a wizened old monkey, sat shrunk in its chair, and I should scarcely have recognised the face as human, let alone his, had Holmes not identified him for us. His countenance was withered, like a rotten apple, covered with hideous black boils and pustules that split and poured forth bile like dirty tears. The stuff ran down his bumpy face and made it glisten. His eyes were so puffed and bloodshot that he could hardly open them; the whites, glimpsed beneath the lids, rolled horribly around. His lips were cracked and parched and split, with bleeding sores. With a chill shock shooting through my bones, I realised that the rasping, pump-like sound we had been listening to was his own laboured breath, wheezing like the wind through a pipe organ—and the knowledge told me that Dr. Eccles had not another hour to live.

"Come no closer," the apparition repeated in a husky whisper. "I am going fast and must be left alone until I do. Afterwards you must burn this room and everything in it, especially my corpse—I've written it down here in case you came too late—but whatever you do, do not touch the corpse! Do you understand? Do not touch it!" he croaked. "The disease is transmitted by contact with the flesh!"

"Your instructions shall be carried out to the letter," Holmes answered firmly. "Is there any way we can make you more comfortable?"

The putrescent mass shook slowly from side to side, a black, swollen tongue lolling loosely from what had once been a mouth.

"There is nothing you can do for me—and nothing I deserve. I am dying of my own folly and merit all the pain my wickedness has brought me. But God knows I loved her, Mr. Holmes! As surely as a man ever loved a woman in this world, I loved Jessie Rutland, and no man since time started was ever forced to do for his love what fate made me do for mine!" He gave a choked sob that wracked all that remained of his miserable frame, and it almost carried him off then and there. For a full minute we were obliged to listen to his dreadful sounds, until at length they subsided.

"I am a Catholic," said he, when he could speak again. "For obvious reasons, I cannot send for a priest. Will you hear my confession?"

"We will hear it," my companion answered gently. "Can you speak?"

"I can. I must!" With a superhuman effort the creature hoisted himself straighter in his chair. "I was born not far from here, in Sussex, just over forty years ago. My parents were well-to-do country folk, and though I was a second son, I was my mother's favourite and received an excellent education. I was at Winchester and then at the University of Edinburgh, where I took my medical degree. I passed my examinations with flying colours, and all my professors agreed that my strength lay in research. I was a young man, however, with a head crammed full of adventurous yearnings and ideas. I'd spent so much time studying, I craved a little action before settling down to my test tubes and microscope. I wanted to see a little of life before I immured myself within the cloistered walls of a laboratory, so I enrolled in the course for army surgeons at Netley. I arrived in India in the wake of the mutiny, and for fifteen years I led the life I dreamed of, serving under Braddock and later Fitzpatrick. I saw action in the Second Afghan War and, even like yourself, Dr. Watson, I was at Maiwand. All the time I kept notebooks and recorded the things I found in my travels, mainly observations on tropical disorders I encountered in my capacity as army doctor—for I was determined, eventually, to follow my true calling and take up research."

He stopped here and again broke into a series of heaving coughs, spitting blood upon the carpet. There was some water in a glass and a carafe just out of reach on the table beside him, and Shaw made to move it nearer.

"Back, fool!" he gasped. "Can you not understand?" With an effort of will he seized the glass and greedily gulped down its contents, the water gurgling through his distended intestines, so that all could hear it.

"Five years ago I left the army and settled in Bombay to pursue research at the Hospital for Tropic Diseases there. I had by this time married Edith Morstan, the niece of a captain in my regiment, and we took a house near my work, preparing ourselves for a happy and rewarding future together. I don't know that I loved her the way I came to love Jessie, but I meant to do right by her as a husband and a father, and I did it, too, so far as it was within my power. Up until that time, Mr. Holmes, I was a happy man! Life had smiled upon me from the first, and everything I had touched had turned to gold. As a student, as a soldier, as a surgeon, and as a suitor my efforts were always crowned with success."*

He paused, remembering his life, it seemed. Something very like a smile played upon what remained of his features and then vanished.

"But overnight it all ended. As suddenly and arbitrarily as though I'd been allotted a store of good fortune and used it all up, disaster overtook me. It happened in this way. Within two years of my marriage, my wife, whose heart condition I had known of from the first days of our courtship, suffered an attack that left her little more than a living corpse, unable to speak, hear, see, or move. It came like a thunderbolt from the blue. I had seen men die or lose their limbs in battle, but never before had catastrophe blighted me or mine. There was nothing for it but to put her in the nursing home run in conjunction with the hospital—she who only the day before had been my own dear girl.

"At first I visited her every day, but seeing that my visits made no impression on her and only served to rend my own heart, I reduced their frequency and finally stopped going altogether, satisfying myself with weekly reports on her condition, which was always the same, no better or worse than before. The law precluded any question of divorce. In any event, I had no desire to marry again. It was the last thing in my mind as I continued my work in the hospital laboratory.

"For a time my life took on a new routine, and I came to

* Eccles's life almost parallels Watson's in many ways, but in none so astonishing as his wife's maiden name. Could Edith Morstan have been a cousin to Mrs. Watson?

assume that I was finished with disaster. But disaster had only begun with me! My father wrote to say he was not well, but I hesitated to return home, fearing to leave my wife. Thus, he died without seeing me again, and my elder brother succeeded to his estate. After my father's demise, my mother wrote, begging me to return, but again I refused, saying that I could not leave Edith—and soon my mother died, herself. I think she died of double grief—my father's death coupled with my refusal to come home.

"And then last year, as if all that had gone before it were but a foolish prelude, a light-hearted glimpse at things to come, there came the plague from China. It tore through India like a veritable scourge of God, sweeping all before it. By the millions people died! Oh, I know you've read it in the papers, but it was quite another thing to be there, gentlemen, I assure you! All the Asian subcontinent turned into one vast charnel house, with only a comparative handful of medical men to sort out the situation and fight it. In all my experience as a physician I had never before beheld the like. It came in two forms: bubonic, transmitted by rats, and pneumonic, which infects the lungs and is transmitted by humans. By virtue of my previous research in the area of infectious diseases, I was one of the first five physicians named to the Plague Board, formed by Her Majesty's government to combat the epidemic. I was put in charge of investigations into the pneumonic variety of plague and set to work at once.

"In the meantime, the plague raced through Bombay itself, killing hundreds of thousands, but my ill luck stayed with me and my wife remained untouched. Do not misunderstand me. I did not wish her to die like this—" he gestured feebly to himself—"but I knew what a burden her life was, and I prayed for her to be stricken and put out of her misery. May God forgive me for that prayer!" he cried fervently.

He paused again, this time for breath, and sat there panting and wheezing like some ghastly bellows. Then, summoning reserves of strength I did not expect remained in him, he leaned forward, seized the carafe, and drank from it, holding it unsteadily to his face and dribbling much water down his chin and on to his open collar. When he had done, he let it fall to the floor, where the carpet prevented its breaking.

"The Plague Board decided to send me to England," he resumed. "Someone had to continue research while others actually fought the disease. I had had some slight luck with a tincture of iodine preparation, provided it was applied within twelve hours of exposure, and the board wished me to experiment with the possibilities of vaccination based upon my formula. It was decided that the work could better be continued in England, as the ravages of the malady itself severely limited facilities and equipment, as well as making it more difficult to ensure absolute control over the experiments.

"This decision was by no means painful to me. On the contrary, it salved my conscience with a real excuse to quit that pestilent place, which contained so many bad memories for me, including a wife I could neither cure nor destroy. For years I had contemplated abandoning my life in India, and now the legitimate opportunity had been afforded me. All due precautions were taken, and I brought samples of pneumonic plague bacillus with me to St. Bartholomew's Hospital here in London, where an emergency laboratory was placed at my disposal. I continued my investigations with a vengeance, studying the plague, its cause and cure, relying heavily on the work of Shibasaburo Kitasato, director of the Imperial Japanese Institute for the Study of Infectious Diseases, and Alexandre Yersin, a bacteriologist in Switzerland. Last year both these men isolated a rod-shaped bacterial micro-organism called *Pasteurella pestis*, vital to the progress of my work.

"I laboured long and hard to integrate their findings with my own but found that when evenings came, I could stand it no longer. My mind was stagnating for lack of recreation or other occupation. I knew virtually no-one in London and did not care to speak with my brother, so it was hard for me. And then I heard of the post vacated by Dr. Lewis Spellman, the theatre physician on call in the West End, who was retiring. I visited Dr. Spellman and ascertained that the work was not really difficult and would serve to occupy my evenings in a pleasant and diverting fashion. I had never known any theatre people, and I thought the job would certainly provide me with some human contact, sadly lacking in my life of late.

"Upon Dr. Spellman's recommendation I was given the post some months ago, and it made a considerable difference in my life. The work was scarcely exacting, and I was seldom called upon to treat more than an untimely sore throat, though I once had occasion to set a fractured arm suffered by an actor during a fall in a duel. All in all, it was a distinct contrast to the desperate search I was engaged in at Bart's. I would scrub myself down at the end of every day, using the tincture of iodine solution, and eagerly proceed upon my theatrical rounds. When I had finished my tour of an evening, I returned here to my lodgings, pleasantly enervated and mentally refreshed.

"It was in this way that I came to meet Jessie Rutland. It had been years since I thought of a woman, and it was only by degrees that I noticed and became attracted to her. In our conversations I made no mention of my wife or her condition, as the subject never came up. Later, when it was relevant, I feared to tell her of it.

"That was the beginning, gentlemen. All was perfectly correct between us, for we had not acknowledged the depth of our feelings and we were both aware of the rules governing contact between the sexes at the Savoy.

"Yet, slowly we came to love each other, Mr. Holmes. She was the sweetest, most generous creature under a bonnet, with the most loving and tender disposition. I saw in her love the chance for my soul's salvation. It was then that I told her of my marriage. It caused me agony for weeks beforehand, but I decided I had no right to keep the facts from someone I loved so dearly and so made a clean breast of it."

He stopped to catch his breath, the whites of his eyes winking madly at us, rolling about in their sockets.

"She was very distraught at first, and I thought my worst fears were confirmed. For three days she refused to speak to me, and during that time I thought I must become lunatic. I was ready to do away with myself when she relented and told me that she loved me still. I cannot tell you into what transports of joy that knowledge put me. I felt there were no obstacles that could not be overcome, nothing I could not accomplish with her at my side and her love in my heart!

"But Fate had not yet done with me. Just as it had done in the past, it struck not at me directly but through the woman I loved. A man—an ogre, I should say—approached Jessie without my knowing of it and told her he knew of our intrigue. He had made enquiries of his own and said he knew I was married. He twisted our love into something sordid and terrifying. His whispers were without shame and without remorse —and she succumbed to them. She acted partly for my sake, as well as for her own, in submitting to his lecherous fancy, for he had played upon her fears in that respect, and she told me nothing of what she had done, lest she compromise us both and add my ruin to her own.

"But she couldn't keep secret her emotions, Mr. Holmes. That intuitive bond that exists between two people in love had already sprung up between us and without knowing what had happened, I knew something was wrong. With many sighs and tears I pried the tale of her humiliation from her, promising beforehand that whatever I heard, I would take no action.

"But it was no use my making such a promise! What she told me was too monstrous to be believed, let alone endured. There was something so incredible about such casual, yet total malevolence that I had to see it for myself.

"I went to his house and spoke with him—" he paused, coughing slightly and shaking his head. "I had never met such a man in all my travels. When I confronted him with his shameful deed, he laughed! Yes, laughed to hear me throw it to his face and said I didn't know much about the ways of the theatre! I was so taken aback by the colossal effrontery of the thing that I found myself pleading with him—yes, *begging* him—to return to me my life, my world. And still he laughed and patted me jovially on the shoulder, saying I was a good fellow but warning me to stay clear of actresses, as he escorted me to the door of his flat!

"For the entire night I walked the streets of London, venturing into places I didn't know then and couldn't name now as I forced myself to digest my own damnation. During that interminable odyssey something snapped in my mind and I became mad. It was as though all my ill luck had resolved itself into one crystalline shape and that shape belonged to

Jonathan McCarthy. On his shoulders I heaped my catalogue of misfortune and travail—my wife's illness, my parents' deaths, the plague itself, and finally, that for which he was truly responsible, the debauch of the woman I loved. She, who was all in the world that was left to me. To picture her in the arms of that bearded Lucifer was more than flesh and blood could bear, and a horrible thought came to me in the early hours of that morning as I stumbled about the city. It had all the perverse logic of the truly insane. If Jonathan McCarthy were Lucifer, why should not I let him wrestle with the scourge of God? I chuckled madly at the notion. Gone were thoughts of science, responsibility, my work; the implications of my fantasies, even, did not exist. All my sinews were bent upon vengeance—horrible and terrible retribution that knew neither reason nor restraint.

"It scarcely matters how I did it; what matters is that I exposed Jonathan McCarthy to pneumonic plague. I know how you are looking at me now; I know full well what you must think of me, gentlemen—and in fact, as the hours ticked by afterwards, I came to share your opinion of the deed. No man was worthy of such a death. Having come to my senses, it was now borne in upon me with a rush—the full impact of what I had done. The terrible forces I had unleashed must be contained before they could wreak havoc on a scale unknown in modern times. All England, possibly all of Western Europe, had been threatened by my folly.

"My conversion to sanity lasted roughly twelve hours. At the end of that time I rushed to McCarthy's flat to warn him of his danger and do what I could for him—but he was not there. In vain I searched all London for the man, stopping at the theatres and restaurants I knew were frequented by members of the literary profession. No-one had seen him. I left a message at his flat finally, and he sent word that he would see me that night. I had no choice but to wait for him while every hour took him further and further from my power to save him and increased the danger to the world. My tincture of iodine solution I had now perfected for induction by mouth, but it still depended on being administered within the first twelve hours.

"I found him at home that evening, as he had promised, and in halting but urgent sentences, I told him what I had done."

Eccles began to cough again and spat great quantities of blood as we watched, our handkerchiefs still pressed to our mouths and noses to avoid the stench of carbolic and putre-faction, our minds numb with horror. He fell back in his chair, exhausted, when he had done, his breath coming more painfully now with every inhalation. Were it not for the noise he made breathing, we should have thought him dead.

When next he spoke, his words were slurred as though he could not form them with the muscles remaining at his dis-posal: "He laughed at me *again!* Oh, he knew what my real work was, but he didn't think me capable of such an action. Jack Point, he called me and laughed when I tried to make him swallow my tincture of iodine solution with a little brandy. 'If I am infected,' he chuckled, 'you must be sure and call upon Miss Rutland with your potion. She'll be in a worse way by far!' He laughed again, long and hard this time, until I knew and understood why I had been unable to find him for the past twelve hours. And when I *did* comprehend, com-prehend that my actions and his had doomed all three of us—and perhaps millions, besides!—I seized a letter opener from his desk and stabbed him with it."

He sighed with a noise like kettledrums, and I knew the sands of his clock were running quickly out.

"From then on, events unfolded with the inevitable precision of a machine built to destroy itself. Jessie was doomed. My antidote would have no effect by the time I reached her. The only question was whether I could prevent her suffering. I waited for her in her dressing room and sent her to heaven when she walked into my arms. I did it as mercifully as I could—" real tears were rolling down his cheeks, now in addition to the pus—"and then I walked 'round to the front of the theatre and entered as though on my evening tour. Stunned, as though that were the truth, I performed an autopsy on the woman I had just slain, while the bloodstained scalpel nestled in my bag under all your noses."

He covered his face with swollen black hands that now resembled claws, and he seemed unable to continue, overcome not only by the ravages of his disease but by his own emotions.

Sensing this, Sherlock Holmes spoke quietly: "If you find it difficult to talk, Doctor, perhaps you will allow me to take up the story as I understand it. You have only to say 'Yes' or 'No' or merely shake your head if you prefer. Is that agreeable to you?"

"Yes."

"Very well." Holmes spoke slowly and distinctly so that he might hear and understand every word before responding: "When you came through the theatre to perform your autopsy, you discovered Dr. Watson and myself already at the dressing room, exposing ourselves to contamination. From our presence there, you could not but infer that we were already involved with the case."

"Yes."

"Mr. Gilbert and Mr. D'Oyly Carte stayed outside the dressing room during our examination; hence, they ran no risk, but Watson and I, as well as you, were now in danger. You heard me say we were going to Simpson's, and you followed us there, waiting for us outside with your antidote."

"Yes."

"While watching us through the window, you perceived that we were joined by a third gentleman—" he gestured to Shaw but Eccles, his eyes closed now, could not see him— "and, wishing to take no chances, you gave him the antidote to drink, as well, as we left the restaurant, happily one by one, which simplified your task."

"Yes. I didn't wish to kill anybody."

"Anybody else, you mean," the detective amended sternly.

"Yes."

"Then you sent a note, warning us out of the Strand."

"I didn't know how else to stop you," Eccles gasped, struggling to open his eyes and face his confessor. "There was nothing for it but to threaten. I would never have done anything."

"As long as we didn't expose ourselves to the plague. For those, like Brownlow, who did, you had no choice."

"No choice. His job killed him, for I knew he must discover my secret. Having been a doctor in the army, I knew that only the coroner would have direct contact with the corpse of a murdered man, and I counted on him to deal with his assistants and stretcher-bearers. Certainly, I could never have managed to deal with them all. But he settled my mind on that score. And we scrubbed down the lab together."

"Then you left together?"

He nodded, his head moving like a drugged man. "I knew

when he recognised the symptoms he would dismiss the others and make them scrub. That left only him. My time was limited now, as well. I had already begun to turn into this." He gestured feebly with a talon to himself. "I went 'round to the back of the laboratory and spoke to him through the door, telling him that I knew of his predicament and could help him."

"You helped him to his maker."

Eccles did not move but sat like a grotesque statue of mouldy clay. Suddenly, he began to sob and choke and scream all at once, struggling to rise from his chair and clutching wildly at his abdomen.

"Oh, God have mercy on their souls!" He opened his mouth again, wanting to say more, but sank slowly to the floor in a crumpled heap. There was silence in the room as the light of dawn began to filter through the curtains, as though to dispel the end of a nightmare.

"He prayed for *them*," Shaw murmured, the handkerchief still pressed to his face. "The human race surprises me sometimes in a way that confounds my philosophy." He spoke in an unsteady voice and leaned against the door frame, as though about to faint.

"*In nomine Patris et Filii et Spiritu Sancti*," said Sherlock Holmes, drawing the sign of the Cross in the foetid air. "Has anyone a match?"

And so it was that in the early morning hours of March 3, 1895, a fire broke out at 33 Wyndham Place, Marylebone, and mingled with the rosy red and gold-tongued flames of dawn. By the time the fire brigades reached the spot, the house was almost consumed, and the body of the lone occupant was found burned beyond all possible recognition or preservation. Sherlock Holmes had poured kerosene over it before we walked out of the door and into the new day.

EPILOGUE

Achmet Singh walked across the narrow confines of his cell towards Sherlock Holmes and peered at him from behind his thick spectacles.

"They tell me I am free."

"And so you are."

"You have done this?"

"The truth has set you free, Achmet Singh. There is some concern for it yet in this reeling world."

"And Miss Rutland's killer?"

"God has punished him more harshly than any jury would have done."

"I see." The Parsee hesitated, indecisive, and then, with a mighty sob, fell upon his knees, seized the detective's hand, and kissed it.

"You—Sherlock Holmes—breaker of my shackles—from my heart's depths I thank you!"

Indeed, he had much for which to be grateful, though he would never know *how* much. Securing his release from prison and having the charges against him dropped was one of the more difficult feats of Sherlock Holmes's long and surprising career. He was obliged to make Inspector Lestrade appear ridiculous in public—something he was at pains never to do—and he did it with the full knowledge and cooperation of the inspector, first swearing him to secrecy and then divulging the entire truth behind the closed doors of the latter's office. They sat closeted together for over an hour while the detective explained the implications of what had happened and the need to prevent the truth from becoming generally known, lest the panic which would inevitably follow prove worse than the plague itself. The detective managed to suppress all reference to Sergeant Hopkins's nocturnal initiative, and the inspector, preoccupied with the meat of the case, never thought to ask how Holmes had learned of Mr. Brownlow's disappearance with the corpses before knowledge of it was made public.

In addition, we spent an anxious week waiting to see if Benjamin Eccles had accomplished his mission and truly managed to murder everyone who had contracted pneumonic plague and to dispose of their bodies. There was some question as to the health of the Savoy chorus, and both Gilbert and D'Oyly Carte were ordered intensive medical examinations, which, happily, failed to reveal a trace of the disease.

Bernard Shaw, as most people know, continued working as a critic but remained true to his promise and kept writing plays until they made him wealthy and famous. His curious attitude towards social reform and personal wealth persisted as long as we knew him. He and the detective remained eccentric friends to the last. They saw one another less as Shaw grew more in demand, but they maintained a lively corre-

spondence, some of which is in my possession and which includes the following exchange of telegrams:

TO SHERLOCK HOLMES:
ENCLOSED PLEASE FIND TWO TICKETS TO OPENING
NIGHT OF MY NEW PLAY, *Pygmalion*. BRING FRIEND
IF YOU HAVE ONE.

G. B. S.

TO BERNARD SHAW:
UNABLE TO ATTEND OPENING NIGHT OF *Pygmalion*.
WILL ATTEND SECOND NIGHT IF YOU HAVE ONE.

HOLMES*

Holmes and I returned to Baker Street later that day, feeling as though we'd just come back from the moon, so long
had we been gone and so singular had been our experiences
while away. The last few days seemed like aeons.

For a day or so we sat around our rooms like automatons,
unable, I think, to fully digest the terrible events in which we
had taken part. And then, bit by bit, we fell into our old
ways. Another storm blew silently outside our windows, and
Holmes found himself again immersed in his chemical experiments. Finally his notes on ancient English charters were
once more in his hands.

It was a month later when he threw down the paper at
breakfast one morning and looked at me across the table.
"We must definitely go to Cambridge, Watson, or I shall not

---

* For years this exchange was erroneously attributed to Shaw and Winston Churchill.

accomplish anything constructive with my research.* How does tomorrow strike you?"

He stalked into his bedroom, leaving me to the coffee and paper, where I discovered his motive for leaving town so abruptly.

Speculation was rife that Oscar Wilde would shortly be charged with offences under the Criminal Law Amendment Act of 1885.† The subject of Wilde brought back memories of our adventure the previous month.

I followed Holmes into his room, the paper in my hand and on my lips a question that had never occurred to me. "Holmes, there is something that puzzles me about Dr. Benjamin Eccles."

"A great deal, I shouldn't wonder. He was a complicated individual. As I have said before, Watson, a doctor is the first of criminals. He has brains, and he has knowledge; should he care to pervert either, there is great potential for mischief. Will you hand me that brown tie? Thank you."

"Why, then, did he allow himself to die?" I asked. "Had he taken his own antidote with the zeal he pressed it on others, he might have survived."

---

* For details of Holmes's Cambridge experience the reader is urged to consult the case labeled by Watson *The Adventure of the Three Students*. According to Baring-Gould's chronology, this case began on April 5, 1895, almost immediately after the news about Wilde appeared in the papers. This significant jibing of dates goes a long way—in my opinion—towards certifying the authenticity of *The West End Horror*, added to which fact, Holmes's work in Cambridge is not generally conceded to be his best, which also makes sense if we consider that he was operating under something of an emotional strain.

† Wilde was charged on April 6, 1895. His first trial ended in a hung jury on May 1. On May 20 a second trial was held, and on May 25, 1895, Wilde was found guilty and sentenced to two years' imprisonment with hard labor.

My companion paused before replying, taking a coal from the fire and lighting his pipe with it. "We shall probably never know the truth. It may be that he had taken the potion before and in so doing had exhausted its curative properties. Or it may be that he had no wish to live. Some people are not only murderers but judges, juries, and their own executioners, as well, and in those capacities they mete out punishments far more severe than their fellow creatures could devise." He rose from a bootlace. "Do you think it too early in the day for a glass of sherry and a biscuit?"

ACKNOWLEDGEMENTS

It is again time to pay off a happy debt and thank a number of people for their help, inspiration, encouragement, and critical acumen in preparing the manuscript of *The West End Horror*.

First and foremost, this book could not have been thought of but for the genius of Sir Arthur Conan Doyle. Without his immortal creations, Sherlock Holmes and Dr. Watson, nothing in the way of this story could have been written. It is a tribute to the enormous popularity of Doyle's characters that people are interested in reading stories about them even though their creator is not around to keep supplying them.

After Doyle, I must acknowledge the help and inspiration I found in the works of W. S. Baring-Gould, whose Holmesian chronology I freely accept and whose theories I continue to find charming and provocative.

Probably the foremost living authority on Sherlock Holmes and his world is Mr. Michael Harrison, whose books on the subject I have pored over to advantage, and whom I had the great privilege of meeting. In addition to the use of his books, Mr. Harrison generously allowed me to pick his brain by offering to inspect the manuscript itself and tell me when I was going either astray or too far, two predilections of mine. He made innumerable comments and suggestions, all of great assistance in achieving literary and historical authenticity, and most of which I adopted without hesitation. Where my book remains inaccurate, the blame must fall not upon Mr. Harrison but on my own stubborn insistence on some point or other. Also, I am indebted to Mr. Michael Holroyd for drawing my attention to several crucial questions in the text.

After these four gentlemen, a host of friends and critics crowd the list, some of them Sherlockian enthusiasts, others merely literate. In no particular order I extend my thanks to Craig Fisher, Michael and Constance Pressman, Bob Bookman, Leni Kreitman, Brooke Hopper, Ulu Grossbard, Michael Scheff, Jon Brauer, and Miss Julie Leff, who put up with a great deal of nonsense. My father, of course, has put up with it much longer, and he deserves thanks here, too.

In addition to those who provided literary assistance, I wish to thank Herb Ross, my collaborator on the film version of *The Seven-Per-Cent Solution,* who managed to keep my interest in things Holmesian alive for many months longer than I thought possible; my lawyers, Tom Pollock, Andy Rigrod, and Jake Bloom, whose contributions to the book are not to be underestimated; and my editor, Juris Jurjevics, who is such a good audience.

The Nuclear Years

"AND What's New With You?"

—from *Herblock's Here and Now* (Simon & Schuster, 1955)

THE
NUCLEAR
YEARS

The Arms Race and Arms Control, 1945-70

Chalmers M. Roberts

PRAEGER PUBLISHERS
New York · Washington · London

PRAEGER PUBLISHERS
111 Fourth Avenue, New York, N.Y. 10003, U.S.A.
5, Cromwell Place, London S.W.7, England

Published in the United States of America in 1970
by Praeger Publishers, Inc.

© 1970 by Praeger Publishers, Inc.

Library of Congress Catalog Card Number: 70–112978

Printed in the United States of America

For Lois, who has shared the nuclear years with me, and for David, Patricia, and Christopher, in the hope that, through wisdom born of knowledge, their generation and succeeding generations may escape a nuclear holocaust.

Contents

Preface

"We must have some international sanity to cope with this thing."

I find that sentence in a letter I wrote to my wife on November 7, 1945, just after having visited Hiroshima. Ten days and twenty-four years later, I watched in the Yellow Room of the Finnish Government's banquet hall Smolna, in Helsinki, as representatives of the United States and the Soviet Union gathered to open the Washington-Moscow strategic arms limitation talks, which have come to be known as the SALT talks, despite the redundancy. I cite these matters to give the reader what he is entitled to: some reason to feel that the author of this book has, at the least, a considerable acquaintance with the events that have shaped the nuclear years.

As to almost all other Americans, the Bomb was a total surprise to me when President Truman revealed to the world its development and its first use on August 6, 1945. As a junior officer in the U.S. Army Air Corps (now the Air Force) working in the Pentagon in Far East Intelligence, I had been privy to many military and diplomatic secrets. But of the Bomb I knew nothing. Soon after the end of World War II, I went to Japan (where I had lived and worked in 1938 and 1939) as a member of the U.S. Strategic Bombing Survey to interrogate Japanese officers and officials. On October 27, I visited Nagasaki, where the second bomb had been exploded on August 9, and on November 7, I visited Hiroshima.

Reading now the letters I wrote home about those two experiences, some three months after the Bomb had been used the first two times (the only times, thus far, in war), I vividly recall the horror of it.

First impressions generally lack scientific accuracy, but they can sear the mind. "The people who were there may have been vaporized for thousands were instantly killed," I wrote. "The blast effect was terrific. [Hiroshima] is far worse than Nagasaki because it is flat and the blast traveled further before it ran into mountains. . . . The appearance of devastation is terrific, trees are stripped, poles are down and rubble, rubble, rubble is everywhere. . . . Most of the city's doctors were killed the first day. . . . They say that people protected against the rays by three feet of concrete were not affected by direct radiation, though possibly by indirect radiation. Burns killed the bulk of those who died, of whom there is no firm or accurate figure."

The Hiroshima and Nagasaki bombs were, by today's standards, relative miniatures, dropped from aircraft. Each of them packed about 20 kilotons of explosive force, the equivalent of 20,000 tons of TNT. Since the advent of the H-bomb, nuclear weapons have made the quantum jump to megatons. Rival American and Soviet intercontinental missiles today carry from 1 to 25 megatons in their single warheads. The largest single nuclear explosion to date was that of a 1961 test in the Soviet Union, a blast of 60 megatons —the equivalent of 60 million tons of TNT—3,000 times the force of the bombs used against Japan.

Like most Americans in 1945, I accepted the use of the Bomb against Japan as a means of saving American lives that we thought would otherwise have been lost in an invasion. And, too, like most of those in the armed services, I doffed uniform as quickly as possible to return to peaceful pursuits.

Not until 1953 did I have reason to begin to grapple with the problems the Bomb had posed. That year I began to write about nuclear weapons when I first was assigned by the *Washington Post* to be its diplomatic reporter. My job has since led me to

numerous international conferences, including all the Soviet-American summit meetings of national leaders, at which nuclear weapons more and more were at issue.

This book grew from an effort to summarize for the *Washington Post,* on the eve of the SALT talks, the history of the nuclear years, both the arms race and the efforts to control or curb it. The book is meant to be a short history for those who wish to re-explore the past quarter-century, or who are too young to remember it.

Naturally, I owe much to others: first, to the editors of the *Washington Post,* who have given me the opportunity to follow this fascinating, though so often disheartening, and increasingly complex story for so many years; second, to my colleagues at the *Washington Post,* Murrey Marder, now the newspaper's diplomatic reporter, and Howard Simons, long the paper's science reporter and now assistant managing editor, both of whom have shared many of the stories of these years with me, and to Herbert Block, whose pen (over the signature of Herblock) has so well illuminated the problems of the age; also, to many in the U.S. Government and in other governments who have been so helpful to me in the past seventeen years; and, finally, to the many others who have written in this field.

Washington, D.C.
March, 1970

The Nuclear Years

From Hiroshima to the SALT Talks

Bernard M. Baruch, a veteran of the disastrous Versailles Peace Conference after World War I, pulled his chair up to the table, adjusted his pince-nez, and began to read:

> We are come to make a choice between the quick and the dead. That is our business. Behind the black portent of the new atomic age lies a hope which, seized upon with faith, can work our salvation. If we fail, then we have damned every man to be the slave of Fear. Let us not deceive ourselves: We must elect World Peace or World Destruction.

The day was June 14, 1946. The place, the newborn United Nations' temporary headquarters at New York's Hunter College in the Bronx. Baruch was President Harry S. Truman's representative at the U.N. Atomic Energy Commission.

The tone of Baruch's speech had been determined a few days earlier. In his accustomed way, he had sat on a park bench in New York with two friends, discussing the remarks he was soon to make. He said he wanted to convey that the question the delegates were about to consider was a matter of life and death for the world. Later, as he was to recount in *My Own Story*,* one of his

---

* Publication data on this and all books mentioned hereafter can be found in the Bibliography.

park-bench companions, Herbert Bayard Swope, phoned to say, "I've got your opening line. It comes from the best possible source —the Bible."

Thus began the quest for man's control of the cataclysmic power he had unleashed when he learned to split the atom. What follows is a review of the efforts, now in their twenty-fifth year, to control some or all aspects of nuclear weapons with the hope of curbing their growth in power and their proliferation in numbers and types—or even, in some Utopian future, of eliminating them.

The post-World War II history of nuclear arms control and disarmament effort falls into four broad phases:

1945–52: The era of the Baruch Plan and its aftermath in the period of the American nuclear monopoly and the beginning of a Soviet nuclear force.

1953–60: The era of assessment by the post-Stalin leadership in the Soviet Union and by the Eisenhower Administration in the United States, when both nations plunged forward with their respective nuclear developments.

1961–67: The era of limited agreements, chiefly after the Soviet-American confrontation at the nuclear brink over Cuba, after which the Soviet Union rushed to reach at least nuclear parity with the United States.

1968–70: The era when the two superpowers, finding themselves in rough nuclear parity but with new developments threatening to upset what Winston Churchill had popularized as the "delicate balance of terror," warily circled each other and finally agreed to try negotiating about control of the most critical weapons each possessed.

In the quarter-century since the first atomic bomb exploded, both the nuclear arms race and the effort to control it have achieved lives of their own. Technological developments have forced endless changes in political negotiating positions, but it is still a fact that no nuclear weapon has been exploded in anger since Hiroshima and Nagasaki in 1945.

The 1962 Cuban missile crisis led Nikita Khrushchev to remark, when it was over, that "there was a smell of burning in the air." However, it was widely said at the time that both the superpowers had learned something of crisis control. The Moscow-Washington use of the hot line during the Arab-Israeli Six Day War in 1967 showed a mutual sense of restraint.

But weapons development has raced on, the delicate balance of terror has been shaken, if not upset, and new possibilities of nuclear war, including a contest between the Soviet Union and China, have emerged. Efforts to control the nuclear arms race remain inescapable for both the United States and the Soviet Union.

Over the years, the Kremlin has had at its command a group of men both skilled in negotiations and increasingly well informed in arms control problems. Since 1946, when Andrei Gromyko made the first Russian response to Baruch's appeal, only seven men have been the chief negotiators for Russia, and they have been well backstopped at the conference table.

In contrast, U.S. expertise has waxed and waned. There have been three high points: the early Baruch period, the era when Harold Stassen was Eisenhower's disarmament man, and the period since the Arms Control and Disarmament Agency was created by President John F. Kennedy. The American personnel turnover, in part due to changes in administrations, has been far greater than that of the Soviet Union.

In the end, although it is the experts who provide the formulas, it is the political chiefs who make agreement possible. What is critical, therefore, is, on the one hand, a President's dedication, and, on the other, the determination of at least a Kremlin majority.

One striking factor in the history of the nuclear years is how much the political men who make the decisions about such negotiations are not only beholden to, but also captives of, the scientists and technicians who expand nuclear knowledge. Each new weapons development has made it more difficult to find a politically propitious moment to forge an agreement. The problem in arms

control is to find that rare moment when, in William C. Foster's words, "the technological stars and planets" are "in favorable conjunction, so to speak"—and are matched to a workable degree by a conjunction of Soviet-American interests in the political sphere.

There has been from the beginning of the nuclear age, and there is today, what Robert S. McNamara, when he was Secretary of Defense, called the "action-reaction phenomenon which fuels the arms race." By that he meant that what one side does in weapons development, out of sheer inventive genius, out of fear of the other nation's development, or out of ignorance of such developments, tends to make the second side react. That this phenomenon is recognized in Moscow as well as in Washington can be seen from the words of Soviet Premier Alexei Kosygin: "The United States must realize that in both physics and politics each action causes a corresponding counteraction."

Both McNamara and Kosygin might have added that the action-reaction phenomenon is expressed in political terms as well as in weapons development. It has never been possible to isolate arms control from the international political environment, especially from the mood of Soviet-American relations.

It is because of such action-reaction that the following account is replete with offer and rejection, proposal and counterproposal, thrust and parry, both in serious effort and in propaganda intent. Positions long and stubbornly held have been suddenly reversed and well-meant offers have been altered or withdrawn, all because of some new action-reaction in the realm of weapons development or in the field of international political relationships.

A second factor of great importance that runs through the history of arms control efforts is the internal dispute over the issue within the government in Washington and, similarly, within the Kremlin.

American Presidents, once in office, find the role of nuclear peacemaker irresistible. But they also find that the men who work for them and with them are often bitterly divided on how

to achieve that end—especially in trying to judge the risks involved in any form of nuclear arms control. This has been true in the Truman, Eisenhower, Kennedy, Johnson, and Nixon administrations. Far less is known about what goes on in the Kremlin than about what happens in the American Government. But enough is known to say with certainty that there have been, and probably are today, counterpart disagreements in the Soviet hierarchy. In addition, Soviet decision-making has been seriously affected by rival views on the central issue of whether to deal generally with the United States even before confronting the problem of any particular arms control proposal, and, if so, how.

Both the United States and the Soviet Union in recent years have had their influence in areas outside their own boundaries greatly eroded, even though they remain supreme in the field of nuclear weapons. No government in Washington or Moscow will take very much of a risk, as the record demonstrates. Each has a fear of the unknown and finds it easier to stand pat. Yet each is driven by economic pressures and by ever-recurring glimpses of the nuclear sword of Damocles to try and try again for some new agreement to curb the arms race.

Each President and each Kremlin leader has had to accept the fact, as J. Robert Oppenheimer once put it, that the two superpowers "may be likened to two scorpions in a bottle, each capable of killing the other, but only at the risk of his own life." Abandonment of efforts to control the already terrifying conventional arms race became unthinkable once the Soviet Union as well as the United States had nuclear weapons. Now five nations have nuclear weapons and more are capable of making them. And the scientists, who do not wait for the political leaders, have already moved the arms race into a new, more deadly, and more expensive stage by the development of rival multiple warhead systems for intercontinental ballistic missiles (known by the acronym MIRV) and by creation of rival systems for anti-ballistic-missile defense (ABM).

Because of what this could mean for the safety, perhaps even

the survival, of the Soviet Union and the United States, the two superpowers have at long last begun to discuss how they might limit, control, and possibly reduce both offensive and defensive strategic nuclear arms. What makes two governments keep trying to reach agreements to limit the nuclear arms race? The answer can only be the sheer terror of nuclear war. In 1950, the man whose formula $(E = mc^2)$ first made the bomb possible, Albert Einstein, appeared on American television to discuss the decision to produce the hydrogen bomb. He said:

> If these efforts should prove successful, radioactive poisoning of the atmosphere, and, hence, annihilation of all life on earth, will have been brought within the range of what is technically possible.
>
> A weird aspect of this development lies in its apparently inexorable character. Each step appears as the inevitable consequence of the one that went before.
>
> And at the end, looming ever clearer, lies general annihilation.

The end foreseen by Einstein has not yet arrived. Men in both Washington and Moscow are still trying to see that it does not.

The cynics and the discouraged will say that little or nothing has been accomplished in a quarter-century of effort and thus nothing of substance can now be expected. It is true that what has been arrived at is only a series of essentially peripheral agreements. But it also is true that what is being discussed at the strategic arms limitation talks, for the first time with any real seriousness, goes to the heart of the arms race.

I. The Baruch Plan Era

I consider the problem of our satisfactory relations with Russia as not merely connected with but as virtually dominated by the problem of the atomic bomb.

Secretary of War HENRY L. STIMSON
September 11, 1945

On a March day in 1945, Senator Arthur H. Vandenberg, the Michigan Republican who was an important minority member of the Senate Foreign Relations Committee, sat beside the cluttered White House desk of President Franklin D. Roosevelt. He spotted on the desk a copy of his own January 10 Senate speech, with a heavy line drawn under the words "If World War III unhappily arrives, it will open new laboratories of death too horrible to contemplate."

The President, seeing that Vandenberg had noted the underlining, gestured toward the manuscript of the speech and remarked, "Senator, you have no idea how right you are, but I think you'll discover before the year is over." Roosevelt had returned the month before from the Yalta Conference with Joseph Stalin and Winston Churchill. Already a sick man, he was to die a month later, but, at the time of his conversation with Vandenberg, he had begun to create what came to be the United Nations. In his thinking, the possibility and the meaning of an atomic bomb had become a critical factor in the future peace of the world.

The first test of an atomic bomb took place in secrecy at Alamogordo, New Mexico, on July 16, 1945. The first bomb exploded in war fell from the bomb bay of a B-29 on Hiroshima, Japan, on August 6, and the second, on Nagasaki, three days later. Scientifically, the bomb was based on the phenomenon of nuclear fission, which had been universally known since 1939. Soviet scientists were among those who recognized the possibility of the nuclear chain reaction, although the Soviet effort, we now know, did not get under way until 1942. In the United States, several scientists, chiefly refugees from Nazism, worried that German scientists would provide Hitler with an atomic bomb, and so set about to induce President Roosevelt to build such a weapon first. A letter, drafted by Leo Szilard, dated August 2, 1939, and signed by Albert Einstein, himself a refugee in the United States, was sent to FDR, suggesting the possibility of an atomic bomb. This letter, after some delay, led to the creation of the supersecret, multibillion-dollar Manhattan Project, out of which came the world's first nuclear weapons.

When FDR died, one of his Cabinet members, Henry L. Stimson, stayed on for some months to help the new President, Harry S. Truman. Senior statesman Stimson had been Herbert Hoover's Secretary of State and was Roosevelt's Secretary of War during World War II. He prepared a memorandum on the atomic bomb and its relations to foreign policy, which led President Truman, once Japan had surrendered on August 14, 1945, to begin a search for ways to harness this newfound power. The Stimson memorandum was first discussed by Truman's Cabinet on September 11, 1945, the last meeting Stimson attended before he retired from public life.

Stimson clearly saw what lay ahead, as evidenced by a passage from his memorandum:

> Those relations [with the Russians] may be perhaps irretrievably embittered by the way in which we approach the solution of the bomb with Russia. For if we fail to approach them now and merely continue to negotiate with them, having this weapon rather osten-

tatiously on our hip, their suspicions and their distrust of our purposes and motives will increase.

Stimson was pleading for direct Soviet-American discussions, excluding other nations, with the possible exception of Great Britain. It should be recalled that the United States and the Soviet Union had been wartime allies, albeit at times wary of one another and that the majority of Americans, though far from all, devoutly hoped that this relationship would continue after the end of World War II.

But political differences such as that over the fate of Poland had begun to embitter Soviet-American relations in the final weeks of FDR's life, and Truman's impatience with Moscow was evident soon after he became President. At the Potsdam Conference in July, 1945, Truman had hinted to Stalin of the success of the Alamogordo test, word of which reached the President during the meeting. On his return from Potsdam and after the bomb had been dropped on Hiroshima, the President, in a report to the nation, declared:

> The atomic bomb is too dangerous to be loose in a lawless world. That is why Great Britain and the United States, who have the secret of its production, do not intend to reveal the secret until means have been found to control the bomb so as to protect ourselves and the rest of the world from the danger of total destruction.

The news of the achievement of nuclear fission burst for the first time upon all but a handful of people on August 6, 1945, the day the bomb fell on Hiroshima. On August 16, the War Department made public what amounted to a primer on the principles of the process that had made the bomb possible. This was the Smyth Report, named for its author, physicist Henry D. Smyth, who had helped make the bomb and was then serving as a member of the Atomic Energy Commission (he is currently U.S. representative to the International Atomic Energy Agency in Vienna). The problem of the bomb and what to do about it

became a matter of wide public discussion, in and out of Congress and the White House.

Stories appeared saying that Truman wanted to share the bomb with the Russians. An argument began over whether the wartime Manhattan Project, which had created the bomb, should now be placed under civilian or military control. Senator Vandenberg called for the creation of what became the Joint Committee on Atomic Energy; it remains today a major power center in the United States on atomic matters.

At the insistence of British Prime Minister Clement Atlee, who had taken over from Churchill in the midst of the Potsdam Conference, a tripartite meeting of Truman, Atlee, and W. L. Mackenzie King of Canada was held in Washington in November. Both the Canadian and the British governments had been associated with the Manhattan Project.

At the conclusion of the meeting, the three leaders produced a declaration of their willingness, as representatives of the only nations then possessing "the knowledge essential to the use of atomic energy [to] proceed with the exchange of fundamental scientific literature for peaceful ends with any nation that will fully reciprocate." But to do so, the statement went on, would be perilous unless "it is possible to devise effective reciprocal and enforceable safeguards acceptable to all nations [which] would contribute to a constructive solution of the problem of the atomic bomb."

In Moscow on December 27, 1945, the Soviet Union agreed with the United States and Great Britain to recommend that the newly created U.N. General Assembly establish a commission "to consider problems arising from the discovery of atomic energy and related matters." The establishing resolution called on the proposed commission, among other things, to come up with proposals "for the elimination from national armaments of atomic and of all other major weapons adaptable to mass destruction" and for effective safeguards against "the hazards of violations and evasions." At Soviet insistence, the resolution also stated that the

Security Council, where the Russians had a veto, should be the U.N. body to "issue directives" to the proposed commission, and that the commission should be accountable to it. It was the Soviet Union's first move to protect its own interests in this new age of atomic weapons.

The tripartite declaration and the establishment of the U.N. Disarmament Commission put pressure on the Truman Administration to come up with a plan quickly. The September 21 Cabinet meeting, at which the Stimson Memorandum was discussed, had gotten nowhere. As Dean Acheson, then Under Secretary of State, said in his memoirs, *Present at the Creation*, "The discussion was unworthy of the subject. No one had had a chance to prepare for its complexities." As acting Secretary of State at the time, Acheson was aware of the problems: the internal American struggle, now clearly visible, over civilian versus military control of atomic energy and the need for an American international position in the wake of the Stimson Memorandum.

The domestic issue was resolved in favor of civilian control. President Truman signed the McMahon Act, named for Senator Brian McMahon, a Connecticut Democrat, August 1, 1946, and thus created the civilian Atomic Energy Commission (AEC), which continues to this day to oversee the production of nuclear material for weapons and for peaceful uses.

The international issue was less successfully resolved. On October 26, 1945, Vandenberg wrote in his diary, later published in *The Private Papers of Senator Vandenberg:*

> I am frank to say that I do not yet know what the answer is to the awful problem which we have brought upon ourselves. It seems perfectly clear that we could not hope to monopolize this secret very long. It also seems clear that atomic energy will have to be put under ultimate international control. This would obviously require a complete and absolute right of world-wide inspection and information. It would be unthinkable, for example, for us to voluntarily permit Russia to take the secret of atomic energy behind its black-

out curtain to do with it whatever Moscow pleases. . . . I sometimes wonder whether the wit of man is competent to deal with this murderous discovery.

In such a frame of mind, Vandenberg, McMahon, then chairman of the new Joint Committee on Atomic Energy, and others went to see Truman in December. They were alarmed that the new Secretary of State, James F. Byrnes, an ex-senator himself, was going to Moscow to arrange for an exchange of atomic scientists and scientific information without providing for adequate safeguards. The senators insisted on an "ironclad agreement on inspection" and Byrnes's intentions, never fully disclosed, were blocked.

In December, 1945, Byrnes named Dean Acheson to head a committee to work out a plan for the control of nuclear power, to be submitted to the new U.N. Atomic Energy Commission. A board of consultants was headed by David E. Lilienthal, then chairman of the Tennessee Valley Authority and later the first chairman of the U.S. Atomic Energy Commission. Serving with Acheson were Dr. Vannevar Bush, president of the Carnegie Institution and former director of the wartime Office of Scientific Research and Development; Dr. James B. Conant, President of Harvard University; General Leslie R. Groves, who had commanded the Manhattan Project; and John J. McCloy, former Assistant Secretary of War under Stimson. According to Acheson, "the most stimulating and creative mind" in the consultant group was that of J. Robert Oppenheimer, who had headed the project to build the bomb—and who was later, in one of the most celebrated cases of the nuclear quarter century, to have his security clearance revoked.

The committee and its consultants worked until March 28, 1946, to produce their plan, the Acheson-Lilienthal Report. Some of the flavor of the days (and nights) of labor expended on the report have been preserved in an article in *The New Yorker* of August 17, 1946, by Daniel Lang—based on an interview with

Herbert L. Marks, who was Acheson's assistant in the preparation of the report:

> Last winter, a group of seven men made a strong bid for an endurance record of a very special sort when they spent two months talking about nothing but atomic energy and how to control it. ... The study was a peculiar one because the consultants had little idea of where to start and were even more uncertain about where they were going. . . . The consultants talked atomic energy in Pullman compartments and aloft in an Army plane. Sometimes they deliberated for as long as eighteen hours a day.

These labors ended with four all-day meetings on March 7, 8, 16, and 17, at Dumbarton Oaks, the mansion in Washington, D.C., where the charter of the United Nations had been drafted. In a radio address, Acheson and Bush discussed the report, which proposed "a plan under which no nation would make atomic bombs or the materials for them. All dangerous activities would be carried on—not merely inspected—by a live, functioning international authority with a real purpose in the world and capable of attracting competent personnel." The current monopoly enjoyed by the United States, they went on to say, "is only temporary. It will not last. We must use that advantage now to promote international security and to carry out our policy of building a lasting peace through international agreement."

When Acheson turned the plan over to Byrnes, the Secretary of State told him he would recommend to Truman that Bernard M. Baruch be appointed to turn the proposals "into a workable plan" and to present the plan to the United Nations. Acheson protested. He felt, as he later wrote, that Baruch, long called adviser to Presidents, since he had been just that from the days of the Wilson Administration, was anything but a wise man. Truman, though he accepted Byrnes's recommendation, later resented Baruch's demand for wide authority and wrote that "his concern, in my opinion, was really whether he would receive public recognition." There was much pulling and hauling be-

tween Baruch and those who had drafted the Acheson-Lilienthal Report, but the essence of the report was the essence of the Baruch Plan. As it turned out, both were unacceptable to the Soviet Union, and it is now evident that any such scheme was doomed to failure.

What Baruch proposed before the U.N. Disarmament Commission on June 14, 1946, with all the histrionics and prestige that were his to employ, was a system of complete control of the entire process of producing atomic weapons, from the mining of the raw materials, uranium and thorium, to the manufacture of new weapons and, eventually, the disposal of existing ones. This control system was also to apply to the use of nuclear energy for peaceful purposes, such as the generation of electric power.

The plan was to be implemented by an International Atomic Development Authority, which would have exclusive ownership of "all atomic energy activities potentially dangerous to world security." The proposed agency would have worldwide powers of inspection and of sanctions against violators. If the Soviet Union would agree to the scheme, the United States was prepared to hand over to the new agency both the data on which its technical knowledge was based and its stockpile of atomic weapons.

The Acheson-Lilienthal Report had proposed no scheme of sanctions to punish violators. Baruch had seized on this point, insisting, as Secretary Byrnes related in *Speaking Frankly*, that any violator (the presumption, of course, was that the violator, if any, would be the Soviet Union) "should be subjected to swift and sure punishment; and in case of violation no one of the permanent members of the Security Council should be permitted to veto punitive action by the council." Truman approved, and thus the proposal for sanctions by a majority vote of the Security Council became a part of the Baruch Plan.

To the Americans who had labored so long and hard to create a plan to beat the nuclear sword into a plowshare, the offer, even with the sanction provision, seemed most generous; indeed,

there were many who objected that it was far too generous. But the Baruch Plan suffered one fatal flaw: it was founded on a misreading of Stalin's Soviet Union of 1946. To the plan's authors, the scheme was a rational proposal that rational men surely ought to accept, and the authors had high hopes that this would be the case in Moscow. But the bomb had upset the balance of power achieved by the end of World War II between the Red Army and the forces of the Western Allies. Hence, to Stalin the Baruch Plan was nothing more than an American attempt to impose on the world a nuclear Pax Americana, a device to relegate the Soviet Union forever to second-class status. Stalin saw no generous offer; rather he probably suspected that, in the end, the United States would not really relinquish its atomic weapons but would manage to force the Soviet Union to submit to international inspection, thus laying bare the terrible weaknesses of postwar Russia, and to fasten upon the world American control of the authority to exploit, and reap the profits of, the peaceful atom.

In a 1962 interview with a group of visiting American journalists, Nikita Khrushchev gave just such a retrospective Soviet view. He said the aim of the Baruch Plan was

> to set up an international control organ, which would enjoy the right of ownership of atomic raw materials and atomic plants, the right of control over all research in the sphere of atomic energy, the right to interfere in the economic life of nations. This is what the United States strove for, and not to ban nuclear weapons or to destroy them. It wanted to prevent the development of the atomic industry in other countries, leaving the monopoly of nuclear arms to the United States. We, of course, could not agree to this.

Furthermore, said Khrushchev, "What would it have meant to put the development of atomic energy under U.N. control? That would have meant to put it under control of the U.S. inasmuch as the U.N., in point of fact, is a branch of the U.S. Department of State."

In their idealistic hopes of controlling the atom, few Americans

viewed the problem from the Kremlin's standpoint. What Stalin saw in the Baruch Plan was a totally one-sided, and therefore unacceptable, proposal.

But in 1946 the world was weary of war and frightened at the monstrous blows inflicted on Hiroshima and Nagasaki only a few months earlier. There was then none of the Khrushchevian blunt talk. Instead, Stalin's response represented neither direct confrontation nor outright rejection but counterproposal and obfuscation—moves designed to play for time. American action had produced Soviet reaction.

It is important to remember that in the year following the end of World War II, Stalin's postwar foreign policy was slowly becoming apparent, although there were many in the West, especially in the United States, who did their best not to believe what they saw because of what it presaged.

W. Averell Harriman, wartime ambassador in Moscow, said many years later, "When I saw Stalin himself, at Sochi, in October, 1945, he said 'We have decided to go our own way.'" According to Harriman, Stalin believed that, with Europe prostrate, "there could be a Communist takeover in Western Europe," including France, Italy, and Germany. Many historians now doubt any such intentions on Stalin's part, given his immense problems at home in recovering from the devastation caused by Hitler's armies, but at the time there was widespread fear of a Russian invasion of Western Europe.

Stalin himself, in a speech on February 9, 1946, which appeared to be stating a policy along the lines of his remark to Harriman, took a classical Marxist view of the war:

> The war was the inevitable result of the development of world economic and political forces on the basis of modern monopoly capitalism. Marxists have declared more than once that the capitalist system of world economy harbors elements of general crises and armed conflicts and that, hence, the development of world capitalism in our time proceeds not in the form of smooth and even progress but through crises and military catastrophes.

Against this view, and his economists' predictions of a shattering American economic depression, Stalin, in his speech, called for organizing "a new mighty upsurge for the national economy, which would allow us to increase our industrial production, for example, three times over as compared with the prewar period. . . . Only under such conditions can we consider that our homeland will be guaranteed against all possible accidents."

This was disturbing news for official Washington; it was a renunciation of the wartime alliance with the United States and Britain against Hitler's Germany. It was not a view of the world in which any such scheme as the Baruch Plan could have a place. The origin of the Cold War has often been dated from Stalin's speech. (It came a month before Winston Churchill, in Fulton, Missouri, with President Truman beside him, charged that an "iron curtain" had descended in Europe, dividing East from West.) But whatever the origins of the Cold War (a matter recently raised by the so-called revisionist historians), it was and, in many respects, remains today a fact of international life. What is important here is how it influenced the actions of the United States and the Soviet Union in arms control matters.

Thus, it is not surprising, in retrospect, that only five days after Baruch's sonorous presentation of "a choice between the quick and the dead," his Soviet counterpart replied with a plan that would have annulled the atomic monopoly of the United States. Andrei Gromyko, then Moscow's Security Council representative and a deputy foreign minister (and since 1957, the foreign minister for successive Kremlin regimes), called for an international convention "prohibiting the production and employment of weapons based on the use of atomic energy." Those who signed the convention were to agree "not to use atomic weapons in any circumstances whatsoever; to prohibit the production and storing of weapons based on the use of atomic energy; to destroy, within a period of three months . . . all stocks of atomic energy weapons whether in a finished or unfinished condition."

The Soviet Union had posed the central conundrum of many

nuclear control measures: Which comes first—the commitments to disarm or the measures to ensure the observance of commitments? (as Bechhoefer succinctly put it in *Postwar Negotiations for Arms Control*).

It should be remembered that the United States rapidly demobilized its armed forces soon after the end of World War II, thus leaving the A-bomb as the chief American deterrent against any attack across Europe by what was believed to be a vast Red Army. (At that time, Western intelligence, as to both Soviet military manpower and Soviet intentions, was far inferior to what it later became.)

On August 6, Gromyko gave the *coup de grâce* to the Baruch Plan when he said that the inspection proposed by Baruch was not reconcilable with the principle of national sovereignty. This statement had been foreshadowed by remarks of Gromyko to Baruch, related to Lilienthal, who recorded them in his journal. On July 28, Baruch told Lilienthal that "Gromyko understands about the veto, etc., but that his real objection isn't the veto but rather the whole idea of permitting their country to be subjected to inspection from without."

The thinking that lay behind the Kremlin proposal of what was a simple "ban the bomb" convention was quite specifically set out in 1963 during an exchange of polemics between Moscow and Peking. An official Soviet statement contained this candid account of what had been in the Kremlin's mind in 1946:

> In the early years after the United States developed nuclear weapons, when the U.S. had a nuclear monopoly and the security of the socialist [Communist] countries was thus endangered, the Soviet Government proceeded from the consideration that the main thing was to deprive the U.S. of this advantage. That could be achieved either through a complete ban on nuclear weapons which would have been tantamount to taking them away from the only nuclear power of the day, the United States; or through developing nuclear weapons of our own which would serve to protect the security of all the socialist countries.

In fact, the Soviet Union worked both lines of that approach. In the propaganda field, Moscow played on fears of another war by promoting U.N. resolutions similar in tone to one condemning "the preparations for a new war being conducted in a number of countries and particularly in the United States and in the United Kingdom." This propaganda drive reached its peak in the March, 1950 World Congress of Partisans of Peace, which produced the Stockholm Appeal demanding "the absolute banning of the atom weapon. . . ." Literally millions around the world signed the appeal.

Privately, the Soviet scientists whom Stalin had first put to work in 1942 continued their secret effort to break the American monopoly on nuclear weapons. There is no doubt that Soviet espionage helped the effort. Klaus Fuchs, the German-born British scientist who transmitted secrets to Moscow, was among those officially present when the Nuclear Age began at Alamogordo, New Mexico, in 1945. There were others, too, whose feats of espionage were surely of help.

Publicly, Stalin deprecated the bomb. In 1946, he said that "atomic bombs are intended to frighten people with weak nerves, but they cannot decide the outcome of a war since for this atomic bombs are completely insufficient." But the next year, in private, he told Yugoslavia's Milovan Djilas that the bomb "is a powerful thing, pow-er-ful!" What was really in the Soviet mind was more candidly stated in 1945 by Foreign Minister V. M. Molotov, who declared that "it is not possible . . . for a technical secret of any great size to remain the exclusive possession of one country. . . . We will have atomic energy and many other things, too."

The Soviet effort culminated in a nuclear explosion on August 23, 1949, three years and two months after the Baruch Plan had been proposed and years before the date predicted by most American estimates. It was a long time, however, before Moscow felt it had nuclear weapons enough to deter Washington and to

create, through a near parity in nuclear weapons, an atmosphere in which negotiations to curb the arms race might be feasible.

By the time of the initial Soviet test, the Cold War was on in earnest. Europe had truly divided East from West. Churchill's iron curtain was a reality, and the Berlin blockade had already provided a test of strength. The United States had begun the Marshall Plan to rescue Western Europe, by reviving it economically, from the threat of Communism, and President Truman had proclaimed the doctrine that "it must be the policy of the United States to support free peoples who are resisting attempted subjugation by armed minorities or by outright pressures."

The Truman Administration had adopted George Kennan's policy for the "containment" of the Soviet Union. Five days before the first Soviet test, the North Atlantic Treaty came into force, and the organization created by the treaty (NATO) was born. The Korean War soon followed. The United States, fearful of a Soviet attack in Western Europe while it was engaged in Korea, rearmed West Germany and brought the country into NATO. Both events were anathema to the Soviet Union.

There simply was no conjunction of Soviet-American interests to make possible any arms control measures. It is true that on June 11, 1947, Gromyko had somewhat modified the Soviet proposals on treaty safeguards, perhaps a sign, as some in Washington said, of a victory for more moderate elements in the Kremlin. At any rate, neither these concessions nor any of the lengthy discussions at the United Nations produced anything remotely resembling agreement between the two nations. The aims of Moscow and Washington were too divergent and their nuclear disparity far too great to permit agreement. Byrnes said in 1947 that the United States sought "collective security," whereas the Soviet Union's preference was "for the simpler task of dividing the world into two spheres of influence." So it seemed to the American Government.

Thus, the Baruch Plan, in which so much effort and so much

hope had been invested, was doomed from the day it was put forward.

Truman was instantly suspicious of the Soviet refusal to agree to verification, and he wrote to Baruch, "We should not under any circumstances throw away our gun until we are sure the rest of the world can't arm against us." The U.N. Disarmament Commission did, in time, adopt what was substantially the American proposal, but the gesture was meaningless since both the Soviet Union and Poland voted against the proposal, and, when the commission report was sent to the Security Council, the Soviet veto blocked all action.

The British, meanwhile, had been cut off from American nuclear information, despite what both London and Ottawa considered a binding agreement to continue the wartime cooperation. Along with creating the Atomic Energy Commission, the McMahon Act barred the executive branch from giving any nation information that would help it build nuclear weapons. The British subsequently went into the nuclear weapons business on their own. After the initial British successes, Congress amended the McMahon Act to permit American aid to go to those nations the President found had "made substantial progress in the development of atomic weapons." This allowed President Eisenhower to aid the British. President Kennedy later said publicly that France also technically met the requirement, but neither he nor his successors granted such aid to France because of Franco-American political differences arising from President Charles de Gaulle's hostility toward NATO.

Baruch himself resigned after a few months, once it was evident no agreement with the Soviet Union was likely. His plan, however, remained the centerpiece of American nuclear disarmament policy for nine more years, well into the Eisenhower Administration.

The American discovery, by aerial sampling off Japan, that the Soviets had achieved an atomic explosion (announced shortly thereafter by President Truman) produced a major internal, and

—from *The Herblock Book* (Beacon Press, 1952)

highly secret, American debate over whether the United States should proceed to develop a thermonuclear weapon, as the H-bomb is correctly called. The principle behind such a weapon was known in the scientific world, but there were grave doubts about the possibility of its development, although modest research had gone on ever since Hiroshima had definitely proved the feasibility of the A-bomb.

The H-bomb offered a quantum jump in explosive power, but in the period of the American monopoly of the A-bomb, it had seemed superfluous. Indeed, the military had developed no requirement for it at all. But action-reaction came into play with the news of the first Soviet A-bomb test.

There ensued a bitter controversy in the American Government, in which Oppenheimer, as chairman of the Atomic Energy Commission's General Advisory Committee, was to play a major role. It was his opposition to development of the H-bomb that led to the official revoking of his security clearance at the termination of what eventually became known as the Oppenheimer case. The H-bomb debate, both in secret and, after President Truman ordered a go-ahead, in public, centered on whether such a weapon was needed, the morality of its manufacture, and the effect its development would have on relations with the Soviet Union. One of the leading proponents of H-bomb development was Lewis Strauss, then a member (and later chairman) of the Atomic Energy Commission. He favored building the bomb by a crash program if necessary to "stay ahead" of Soviet nuclear development. On Strauss's side was physicist Edward Teller, who later provided some of the key formulas that resulted in success.

But others in both the scientific and political communities in the United States wanted to try first for an agreement with the Soviet Union to avoid this jump in weaponry. One of them was Henry D. Smyth, another was the physicist Lee DuBridge, then President of the California Institute of Technology (and now President Nixon's science adviser at the White House).

On January 27, 1950, the British informed the United States

of the arrest of Klaus Fuchs, who confessed to atomic espionage. Four days later, Secretary of State Acheson and Secretary of Defense Louis Johnson told the President he should go ahead with the development of the H-bomb, but Lilienthal, then chairman of the Atomic Energy Commission, was opposed. On January 31, the President announced his decision. The bomb was to be developed. Once again, Soviet action had produced American reaction. The Strauss theme that the United States must "stay ahead" was clearly dominant in the American mood, both in and out of the Administration and in the Congress.

In the final Truman years, the government was on the defensive. Senator Joseph R. McCarthy, the Wisconsin Republican, had begun to make his spies-in-government charges and to conduct a related campaign against Acheson. The British were embarrassed by the arrest of Fuchs and his confessions of espionage. In 1951, as Acheson has recently related, the British asked the United States to test an atomic bomb for them, but the Administration was so diffident in its relations with Congress that it would not risk even asking for congressional approval. The beginning of the Korean War in June, 1950, turned the Cold War hot and presented Truman with a more pressing problem than how to continue negotiations on nuclear arms.

The last major action relating to arms control during the Truman period was Acheson's creation of a panel to work out comprehensive plans for control and reduction of both conventional and nuclear arms. Oppenheimer and Bush were both members of the group. Oppenheimer's subsequent remark about the two scorpions in a bottle was reflective of his pessimism, especially since work on the H-bomb had been expedited. (Oppenheimer, incidentally, had borrowed the famous simile from Bush, who had used it in an earlier speech.)

This final arms control effort of the Truman years led Bush to suggest an understanding with the Soviet Union that neither nation would detonate an H-bomb, even if they had developed it to the point of testing. This was the germ of the test ban

treaty that was to come to fulfillment only during the Kennedy Administration. But Bush's proposal was vetoed by the panel on which he served. It is highly doubtful that in its final months the Truman Administration would have had sufficient authority, so low by then was it in public esteem, to make such a proposal public. At any rate, it did not, and the next moves in the nuclear field were left to the Administration's successor.

II. Time of Assessment

Since the advent of nuclear weapons, it seems clear that there is no longer any alternative to peace, if there is to be a happy and well world.

President DWIGHT D. EISENHOWER
October 19, 1954

General Dwight D. Eisenhower entered the White House on January 20, and Joseph Stalin died on March 6, 1953. These two events produced re-examinations in both capitals, which, however, did not begin to be reflected at the conference table for another two years and were not fully reflected until 1957.

When the two nations were finally prepared to negotiate, it was against a different backdrop from that of the Baruch era, for the world had moved from the atomic age to the thermonuclear age. The first experimental American hydrogen bomb device had been exploded on November 1, 1952, three days before Eisenhower was elected President. The first Soviet H-bomb test came nine months later.

In the Soviet Union, post-Stalin debate on nuclear problems appears to have begun early in 1954. It was intertwined with the struggle for power in the Kremlin.

On March 12, 1954, Premier Georgi Malenkov declared that a third world war "with the existence of the modern means of destruction would mean the destruction of world civilization."

This deviation from the Leninist doctrine of the inevitability of a "frightful conflict" between Communist and capitalist states undoubtedly reflected discussions on the meaning of thermonuclear weapons and on the desirability of coming to terms with the United States.

But on February 8, 1955, Malenkov "resigned," and Foreign Minister Molotov thereupon publicly repudiated the Malenkov doctrine by saying that "what will perish" in a new war "will not be world civilization, however much it may suffer from new aggression," but the "rotten social systems" of the capitalist nations.

This critical difference in doctrinal view does not appear to have been resolved until Nikita Khrushchev's assumption of first place in the Kremlin hierarchy and his 1956 pronouncement at the Twentieth Communist Party Congress that "there is no fatal inevitability of war." Concurrent with this change was the increasing stress that Moscow placed on "peaceful coexistence" between capitalist and Communist nations. Lenin had created the peaceful coexistence theme in a time of dire necessity, but it had fallen into disuse in the period of Stalin's hostility to the West.

Khrushchev was adept at finding ideological cover for pragmatic facts. His stress on peaceful coexistence was born of necessity, a necessity he recognized in 1960 when he said in a speech that the use of nuclear weapons "would not distinguish between Communists and non-Communists, between atheists and believers, between Catholics and Protestants." By 1963, after the Cuban missile crisis with the United States and the open break with China, the Soviet Communist Party adopted the Khrushchevian logic by formally declaring, in an attempt to differentiate between Soviet and Chinese policies, that "the atomic bomb does not adhere to the class principle—it destroys everybody within the range of its devastating force."

It is now apparent that the Soviet Union moved more slowly than did the United States to an appreciation of the meaning of the nuclear age and of the necessity for control of the new weap-

ons. On assuming office, Eisenhower had made a review of the nuclear arms race and was alarmed at what he found. Seeking a positive rather than a negative approach, he had rejected a plan (dubbed "Operation Candor") to make public the grim facts about the effects of a nuclear war and instead made his famous "Atoms for Peace" speech on December 8, 1953. In it, he offered the thesis that to develop the peaceful atom would be a step toward diminishing "the potential destructiveness of the world's atomic stockpiles."

But the atoms for peace approach was no substitute for a full-scale arms control plan.* Not until March 19, 1955, did Eisenhower create the position of Special Assistant to the President for Disarmament—with Cabinet rank—and name Harold Stassen, former governor of Minnesota and then head of the foreign aid program, to fill the post. In August, after a Soviet arms control proposal, the President gave Stassen negotiating as well as planning power.

Eisenhower's appointment of Stassen was evidence of the soldier-President's determination to give serious attention to disarmament. All Presidents in the nuclear age have had added to the innate loneliness of their office the sense of responsibility that springs from their command of the nuclear arsenal. Eisenhower, who had commanded 12 million men in the most destructive war in human history, felt deeply this responsibility from the moment he entered the White House.

---

* Eisenhower's 1953 "Atoms for Peace" speech did lead, however, on July 29, 1957, to creation of the International Atomic Energy Agency (IAEA), a United Nations agency with headquarters in Vienna. Both Washington and Moscow believed that such an organization would prevent the program for the peaceful uses of atomic energy (largely for the generation of electricity) from being used as a cover for the manufacture of atomic weapons among the nations involved in the program. As a gesture of support for the plan, and also in an effort to nudge the Russians into a reciprocal act, Eisenhower in 1956 offered to make available 40,000 kilograms of U-235, the raw material of bombs, for peaceful purposes, chiefly for use in nuclear reactors to generate electricity. The IAEA has come to play a role in this growing field of the peaceful atom, but it has always been a minor aspect of the nuclear arms control problem.

In the second volume of his memoirs, Eisenhower wrote that he often felt he was struggling with both his own advisers and the Russians. Yet, as one who knew firsthand that "war is stupid, cruel, and costly," he also felt that "hope is more difficult to kill than men, and humanity is not ready spinelessly to accept the cynical conclusion that war is certain to recur, that the law of the jungle must forever be the rule of life." And so he sought arms control or at least ways of "reducing the fear of global cataclysm and the practical extinction of civilization."

But in the early Eisenhower years, fear of Communism was very real. The emphasis was on ways to defend the government against it and to prevent its spread. Eisenhower's Secretary of State, John Foster Dulles, was the chief exponent of these efforts. In the diplomatic field, he negotiated a series of treaties that he hoped would contain Communism in the Middle East and Asia, as the NATO treaty had done in Europe. In the military field, he enunciated the doctrine that the United States would rely "primarily on the capacity to retaliate, instantly, by means and at places of its own choosing," whenever there was an attack.

This became known as the "instant massive retaliation doctrine," and it dominated American thinking for most of the Eisenhower era. It was based, in part, on budget limitations, which led to what became known as "more bang for the buck," or less reliance on men in uniform and on conventional weapons and more emphasis on a growing nuclear arsenal. Fundamental to the thesis was a vast American preponderance in nuclear arms, a view that was basic to Dulles's own thinking.

Dulles saw the American mission as born of both this military predominance and an ethical or even religious superiority over the Communist world. Thus he found it impossible intellectually to accept in any sense Soviet-American parity, in arms or in diplomacy. The schism that was to open between him and Stassen sprang from this view.

Dulles's influence with the President was great, for Eisenhower shared many of the Secretary's views. For example, at the end of

his second term, Eisenhower concluded that the results of his
efforts in the arms control field had been "meager, almost negligible," and that this "failure can be explained in one sentence:
It was the adamant insistence of the Communists on maintaining
a closed society."

But that was a retrospective and much oversimplified view. In
office, Eisenhower sought to find what he called "creative proposals that might, if accepted by others, lead to progress." And
he did so, despite Dulles's often dire views of the dangers involved in dealing with the Russians. It was the President's desire
at least to try that gave Stassen his opportunities. Soon after
Stassen's appointment, for reasons not directly related to arms
control, Eisenhower agreed to a summit conference with the
Soviet, British, and French leaders. The conference was to provide
the setting for the President's major initiative in arms control.

On Thursday afternoon, July 21, 1955, at Geneva, Switzerland,
sitting at the huge, square table in the Palais des Nations, President Eisenhower laid his glasses before him, disdaining the prepared manuscript, and began:

> Gentlemen, since I have been working on this memorandum to
> present to this conference, I have been searching my heart and mind
> for something that I could say here that could convince everyone
> of the great sincerity of the United States in approaching this
> problem of disarmament.

Then, looking directly at Soviet Premier Nikolai Bulganin,
Communist Party First Secretary Khrushchev, and Defense Minister Georgi Zhukov, the President went on:

> I should address myself for a moment principally to the delegates
> from the Soviet Union, because our two great countries admittedly
> possess new and terrible weapons in quantities which do give rise
> in other parts of the world, or reciprocally, to the fears and dangers
> of surprise attack.
> I propose, therefore, that we take a practical step, that we begin
> an arrangement, very quickly, as between ourselves—immediately.

Eisenhower went on to outline an "Open Skies" proposal that called for a swap of both military blueprints and, more importantly, of flights by the planes of one nation across the territory of the other.

In the American mind, the proposal offered assurance against what the United States most feared: a surprise attack or, in the phrase of the time, a nuclear Pearl Harbor. This was the age of the manned bomber armed with nuclear weapons. Open Skies was the American reaction to the growing Soviet nuclear stockpile and the skimpy American knowledge of the Russians' ability to deliver nuclear bombs.

Although there are few revealing Soviet statements on what was then in Moscow's mind, it is not difficult to guess. On the same day the plan was presented, Khrushchev told Eisenhower that the idea was nothing more than a bold espionage plot against the Soviet Union.

From the American standpoint, Open Skies was an effort to break down, by agreement, the age-old Russian suspicion of the foreigner in (and now over) his land. After Russia became the Union of Soviet Socialist Republics, secrecy came to have a dual function. It protected Soviet military and political secrets, and it at the same time concealed Soviet economic weaknesses. But Soviet secrecy in the face of America's relative openness provided an asymmetrical advantage for the Kremlin; secrecy, plus the weapons the Soviets possessed, balanced the larger American nuclear force.

Thus, to Khrushchev in 1955, it appeared that Eisenhower was trying to rip away this advantage, whatever then may have been the degree of Soviet fear of a possible American nuclear first strike. To the President, it was Soviet obstinacy over the inspection issue, an attitude he ascribed to "fear that once they lifted the Iron Curtain their own people, discovering the goodness and richness of life in freedom, might repudiate Communism itself, and, learning of the sincerely peaceful intentions of free peoples

who had been proclaimed to them as deadly enemies, would soon reject the Communist goal of world domination."

Eisenhower's assumption is not repeated here because it was correct (it was, indeed, far to simplistic,) but because it illuminates the Soviet-American gulf in the Eisenhower era and demonstrates how little most of those in Washington understood Soviet motivation in dealing with nuclear arms control issues.

Open Skies failed because, as with the Baruch Plan, there existed neither a conjunction of political interests nor the equally necessary balance of military power to make agreement possible. The ideological gulf, of course, made the problem more difficult, but, as later agreements have demonstrated, the United States and the Soviet Union can ignore the gulf, if not put it out of mind, when each decides that an agreement is mutually advantageous.

Open Skies remained an official American offer long after there was any chance of its acceptance. It served, too, to gain points for the United States in the Moscow-Washington propaganda war, for it was an immensely popular conception in many parts of the world, whatever the experts and government leaders may have thought of its practicality.

One factor that had led Eisenhower to his Open Skies offer was a proposal by the Russians some two months earlier. From the American viewpoint, the first reflection of new thinking in the Kremlin came on May 10, 1955, when Soviet representatives, at a subcommittee meeting at the U.N. Disarmament Commission, unexpectedly offered what the West took to be the first serious Soviet effort to deal with both nuclear and conventional weapons. The Soviet document declared that "science and engineering" had produced "the most destructive means of annihilating people," a phrase that appeared to compromise the Malenkov-Molotov gap. The May 10 proposal had three key features: (1) It divided the proposed total disarmament process into stages in place of the previous insistence that everything occur at once; (2) it proposed an end to nuclear tests with a vague international supervision; and (3) it proposed for the first time that foreign control personnel

be stationed at "large ports, at railway junctions, on main motor highways and in aerodromes" in the Soviet Union (as well as in other countries) to check the proposed arms control measures.

The United States had not expected such a move and was caught unprepared. For almost two years, Stassen worked to evolve, out of conflicting views within the Eisenhower Administration, a response to the proposal that conceivably could produce agreement. Eisenhower himself later wrote that "disarmament was a subject of varying, and often sharply opposing, views among departments and agencies of the United States government and outside them." Open Skies itself had evolved from the work of a group in which Nelson A. Rockefeller, then a Presidential special assistant, played a major role. It was not sold to the top American military and diplomatic officials until the days immediately preceding its enunciation.

It is probable that the worldwide interest in Open Skies lay behind a Soviet decision disclosed in October, 1955, at the Big Four Foreign Ministers Conference in Geneva. Soviet Foreign Minister Molotov announced that his country would accept aerial photography as an inspection technique but only in what he termed "the final stages of carrying out measures directed towards the reduction of armaments and the prohibition of atomic weapons." The foreign ministers meeting, which was chiefly concerned with the problem of Germany, was a failure, but what Khrushchev and others had called "the Spirit of Geneva" continued to exist. Thus, in February, 1956, Khrushchev declared that "for the first time since the war a certain *détente* has set in [in] international tension." He went on to say that, given "equal efforts and mutual concessions" by both sides, the Soviet Union expressed "readiness to agree to certain partial measures," including an end of nuclear testing, prohibition of nuclear weapons on West German soil, and reduction of military budgets.

Khrushchev's words were based on a knowledge of thermonuclear weapons. He called for "peaceful coexistence," declaring there was "no other way out in the present situation. Indeed,

there are only two ways: either peaceful coexistence or the most devastating war in history. There is no third alternative."

On May 14, 1956, Moscow announced its intention to reduce its armed forces by 1.2 million men. Khrushchev, reacting to the advent of the H-bomb and to his anticipatory knowledge of intercontinental missiles that would deliver the bomb, determined to trim conventional weapons and manpower. He publicly ridiculed naval vessels other than submarines and extolled strategic weapons when the latter were still in the early stages of development. Many observers believe that he did so in hope of transferring badly needed funds from the military to other sectors of the Soviet economy. Whatever the exact purpose, and despite infighting in the Kremlin in which, at least for a period, Khrushchev's arguments prevailed over the advice of the marshals, there resulted considerable East-West negotiation on military manpower. At one point, there was a tentative Soviet-American agreement that the armed forces of the three great land powers—the United States, the Soviet Union, and Communist China—be set at or reduced to 2.5 million men each, with a quota of 750,000 men for Great Britain and the same for France. Washington was searching for ways to save money and was extolling nuclear weapons at the same time. In 1957, Eisenhower cut the armed forces to a 2.5-million level. But this tentative agreement never reached treaty form because of the inspection and verification issue. To this day, there has been no agreement of any kind on conventional weapons, military manpower, or a combination of the two.

In 1956, the Suez crisis and the Hungarian revolution forced arms control into the shadows, but, by March of the following year, the two sides were ready to try again. From March to November, during meetings of a subcommittee of the U.N. Disarmament Commission in London, both sides put forward new proposals. Serious negotiations got under way on the thesis, basic to Stassen's thinking, that some form of parity-of-risk had to be accepted by the superpowers.

At London, both sides adjusted their proposals in light of their

respective examinations of the balance of power in nuclear and conventional arms. Not surprisingly, the United States tried out proposals to trim Soviet strength in conventional arms while the Soviet Union sought to nullify American nuclear power.

In the many proposals and counterproposals of this era, both sides found themselves proposing what they had spurned when the other side had suggested it. This was especially true in attempts to control conventional arms and military manpower. By the time of the 1957 London meeting, however, Soviet nuclear strength had so grown that the key American efforts centered on control of nuclear weapons. More and more, talk of conventional arms and manpower was relegated to the sidelines.

The United States concentrated in this period on limiting and eventually ending nuclear testing while it still had the larger inventory and the more advanced development. It was concerned moreover with methods of protecting itself against a surprise Soviet attack, now that Moscow had produced an H-bomb, and on beginning a cutback in the production of fissionable material for weapons use. (The United States was beginning to have a surplus of such materials.)

The Soviet proposal of May 10, 1955, and the amended proposal of April 30, 1957, reflected a growing nuclear arsenal but one still considerably inferior to that of the United States. It also reflected an important political consideration—Soviet fears that the United States would arm the West Germans with nuclear weapons. The Soviet proposals called for an end to nuclear tests but without inspection (a move that would preserve secrecy), for a renunciation of the use of the bomb long before a cutoff in fissionable material production (a step that would inhibit the use of the superior U.S. Air Force), and for aerial inspection of Europe outside the Soviet Union. This last proposal had the dual virtue, from the Kremlin's standpoint, of offering a means of controlling the growing power of West Germany and of providing a response to Eisenhower's Open Skies offer.

The proposal for aerial inspection of Europe, most specifically

of West Germany, raised a storm in Bonn. Chancellor Konrad Adenauer, the good and close friend of John Foster Dulles, had to be reassured that his nation's interests would not be damaged. This reassurance was fatal to Stassen's hopes.

Stassen did manage, after months of intra-Administration and inter-Allied argument, to bring the Open Skies proposal down to negotiable terms. Suggestions came from all sides, but not until August, 1957, was a substantive American plan presented.

Stassen suggested three alternative proposals for aerial inspection, as shown in Appendix II, Map 1. The proposals were for mutual aerial inspection of (a) all of the United States and Canada on the one side and the Soviet Union on the other, roughly the same areas (Alternative 1 on Map 1); (b) an area north of the Arctic Circle that would include parts of the Soviet Union and Canada, with an extension southward to take in all of Alaska (Alternative 2); (c) a pie-shaped wedge of Europe with the North Pole at its point and the Mediterranean Sea as its southern boundary, including most of Western Europe plus the western and most populous part of the Soviet Union (European Zone).

The Soviets had, at first, proposed a European inspection zone, then a zone including about two-thirds of the United States, plus Western Siberia and Alaska (Appendix II, Map 2). The final Soviet proposal, which was not offered until after the breakdown of the London Conference, repeated the Western United States–Siberia–Alaska zone and added Europe, roughly from mid-France to the Soviet border, as well as Greece, Turkey, and Iran, all militarily associated with the United States (Appendix II, Map 3).

In the midst of the London talks, Stassen fell from grace in Washington. The situation, widely reported at the time, undermined the American position by casting doubts on who was speaking for the United States.

During the conference, Stassen had won Eisenhower's approval for what was called a "talking paper," something less firm than a proposal, that included an aerial inspection scheme and a plan to prohibit the use of nuclear weapons except in defense or retalia-

tion in case of nuclear attack. The details were less important than
the fact that Stassen foolishly "showed the gist of this paper to
the Russians," as Eisenhower later recounted it, "without prior
coordination with our allies." The result was trouble with both
the British and the Germans.

British Prime Minister Harold Macmillan complained directly
to the President that a clause in the Stassen paper that called for
devoting future production of fissionable material to peaceful
purposes would prevent Britain "from developing the nuclear
strength which she is just beginning to acquire." Eisenhower
reprimanded Stassen for the "acute embarrassment" Eisenhower
felt because the British had not been forewarned, even though,
in healing the Anglo-American breach after the Suez crisis, he
had pledged fullest future cooperation.

More important, however, was the reaction of Adenauer and
Dulles. Alarmed at the Stassen proposals, Adenauer came to
Washington to insist that disarmament should come after, not
before, the reunification of Germany. His rejection of any
German role in a European aerial inspection scheme or in a
reduction of conventional weapons confined the London Conference, in essence, to a possible agreement on ending nuclear
tests.

Stassen denied he had been reprimanded by the President, but
Dulles sent a diplomat to London as Stassen's deputy, an obvious sign of displeasure among many signs evident at the time.
Furthermore, Dulles said publicly that the assent of all of the
Allies would be necessary for any agreement. And finally, Dulles
himself went to the conference to present the Western position.
Stassen's usefulness was at an end. He held his post into 1958, but
other events by then had altered the Soviet-American relationship
in nuclear arms.

In his approach to arms control, Stassen was ahead of his time.
He fought within the Eisenhower Administration for acceptance
of the thesis that a Soviet Union armed with H-bombs, even
though it lacked the arms stockpile and delivery system available

"1945 – 46 – 47 – 48 – 49 – 50 – 51 – 52 – 53 – "

—from *Herblock's Here and Now* (Simon & Schuster, 1955)

to the United States, was a formidable potential foe and therefore should be granted a status of equality in arms control discussions. But in 1957, the uncertainties in Washington about the nature and extent of Soviet nuclear power were many, and those who refused to accept Stassen's parity thesis were powerful. Chief among them was Dulles. As he had fought against the 1955 Geneva Summit Conference because it meant political parity for for Soviet Union with the United States, so he fought against Stassen's thesis of arms control parity on the grounds that the United States was incomparably the more powerful in nuclear weaponry.

Dulles's doctrine of massive retaliation, and the Kremlin's knowledge that the United States had the means to put the doctrine into practice—whatever the Soviet judgment may have been about the American will to employ such weapons—clearly had an inhibiting effect on Moscow. This is evident from a speech Khrushchev gave in 1961, in which he declared:

> There was a time when American Secretary of State Dulles brandished thermonuclear bombs and followed a policy from "positions of strength" with regard to the socialist countries. He followed this policy with regard to all states which disagreed with the imperialist claims of the United States. That was barefaced atomic blackmail, but it had to be reckoned with at the time because we did not possess sufficient means of retaliation; and if we did, they were not as many and not of the same power as those of our opponents.

Dulles also never lost sight of his political aims in considering arms control plans. A major Dulles concern was the cohesion of the Atlantic Alliance, which meant close ties to West Germany and to his friend Adenauer.

After Stassen's fall, one of his assistants, Robert E. Matteson, delivered a speech in which, without naming names but in terms apparent to all, he discussed the rival Dulles and Stassen schools of thought. He stated that the group with Stassen's viewpoint favored a policy of relaxation of tension, which he described as

"one which would recognize the strength of the Soviet bloc and would do more to encourage the liberating tendencies within the bloc. It would accept the Soviet Union as an equal power and would encourage the gradual evolution of the Soviet system toward freedom." By contrast, the other group favored an "increased tension policy," one "which would emphasize more the weakness of the Soviet bloc, would look toward pressuring the Soviet leadership into agreements which represent concessions by the Soviets to their own interest, and would look toward striving to pressure the Soviet system into a collapse without a war."

The Dulles-Adenauer relationship was a pillar of that pressure-the-Russians approach. Eisenhower was whipsawed by the two lines of argument and came down on Dulles's side in the end. Yet Stassen's hard work and imaginative thinking had a logical appeal and, in the longer view, helped prepare the way psychologically for subsequent Soviet-American relationships.

The London Conference, whatever its prospects may have been, was effectively killed in the summer of 1957 with a demonstration that the balance of power was shifting and that the deficiency in Soviet weaponry (to which Khrushchev would allude in 1961) was coming to an end. What occurred was the introduction of a new weapons system.

The Soviet Union on August 26, 1957, announced the first test of an intercontinental ballistic missile (ICBM). Six weeks later, on October 4, came the first *Sputnik*. These two events shook American confidence in its military and scientific superiority and opened for the Russians an opportunity, eagerly seized by Khrushchev, to engage in rocket-rattling nuclear diplomacy, which at times amounted to nuclear blackmail. Less than a year earlier, at the height of the Suez crisis, the Russians had threatened to hurl nuclear rockets at Great Britain, which, with France, had invaded Egypt. The threat added to world alarm at the time, even though it was viewed in Washington as merely a form of political blackmail.

President Eisenhower, in the wake of what he later described as "the current wave of near-hysteria" induced by *Sputnik* and the ICBM, created the Gaither Committee, a group of eminent Americans headed by H. Rowan Gaither, Jr., then board chairman of the Ford Foundation. The Committee, originally formed to examine chiefly the need for an American bomb shelter program, broadened its scope, and its findings, part of which became known at the time, pictured a rapidly arming Soviet Union with a capability by late 1959 of launching 100 ICBM's against the United States. In reality, as later intelligence showed, the Russians did not have sufficient ICBM's to represent what the United States considered a serious threat until 1962.

But the psychological damage had been done, and Khrushchev exploited it to the fullest. In the United States, such projections of Soviet strength formed the basis of the "missile gap" charge that Senator John F. Kennedy used in his 1960 Presidential campaign against Richard Nixon, Eisenhower's Vice-President.

But before Khrushchev began to exploit the Soviet ICBM, and before the Democrats exploited the alleged missile gap, there was a major, secret development in the action-reaction phenomenon in the arms race.

In November, 1954, Eisenhower had been presented with a proposal to build, at a cost of about $35 million, thirty high-altitude reconnaissance planes of the type that came to be known as the U-2. Design and development were already well under way, and the President had approved production plans. Eisenhower later justified this move on the grounds that "our relative position in intelligence, compared to that of the Soviets, could scarcely have been worse." About that, there is today no quarrel.

The plane was test-flown over the United States to determine the ability of its cameras and to see whether, flying at 70,000 feet or more above the earth, it could be picked up and tracked by American radar. Its distance-shrinking cameras produced incredibly detailed photographs from fourteen miles up, and its tracking by ground radar proved imperfect. Furthermore, fighter planes

at that time could not operate at higher than 50,000 feet. The risk of flying the U-2 over the Soviet Union seemed clearly outweighed by the potential gains.

When Eisenhower returned from the Geneva summit meeting after the rejection of his Open Skies proposal, he directed that the U-2 should overfly Russia. After two flights from Weisbaden, in West Germany, the U-2, in the summer of 1956, flew its first mission over the Soviet Union. It covered both Moscow and Leningrad.

The U-2 was a well-kept secret. Its limitation was the requirement for cloudless skies between the plane and the ground, a relatively rare event in much of the Soviet Union, but the pictures it brought back were a giant step forward in American intelligence gathering. The data it gathered, however, came too late to counter the false assumptions that went into the Gaither Committee predictions.

Once the Soviet ICBM program began, the U-2 became an even more essential tool for U.S. intelligence. U-2 photographs disclosed that *Sputnik* had been launched from the Tyuratam Missile Range. The Semipalatinsk nuclear test site was identified by U-2 photographs, as was a missile air defense development site. Before the flights were discontinued in 1960, U-2's had flown between twenty and thirty times over the Soviet Union, including runs over the Kamchatka Peninsula on the Pacific Ocean.

Thomas S. Gates, Jr., Eisenhower's last Secretary of Defense, told the Senate Foreign Relations Committee that information had been obtained "on airfields, aircraft, missiles, missile testing and training, special weapons storage, submarine production, atomic production and aircraft deployment . . . all types of vital information." Allen Dulles, then head of the Central Intelligence Agency, which directed the U-2 flights, said in 1968 that the planes were "primarily for the purpose of keeping the West advised of the new Soviet battle order of its guided missiles." Such data, of course, were vital in the arms control field.

Although this intelligence strongly affected American thinking about arms control proposals, the public knew nothing of the U-2 and its photographs until 1960. What was known, and what had a far more immediate effect on the public during the Eisenhower years, was the danger of radioactive fallout from nuclear tests.

The bombs that fell on Hiroshima and Nagasaki had been detonated well above the ground, and there had been no reports of fallout and its resulting damage to humans until long afterward. A dramatic example of the dangers, however, came on March 1, 1954, at a tiny atoll in the Pacific called Bikini, where the United States was testing a hydrogen weapon. From the mushroom cloud that billowed upward for more than 100,000 feet, the heavier particles of debris fell, not to the west, as had been anticipated, but to the east. Within an hour, as Ralph Lapp and Jack Schubert recounted in their book *Radiation*, "a soft rain of whitish ash was falling fifty miles downwind. Several hours later the ashy rain began to fall a hundred miles from the bomb site."

Those most seriously radiated by the fallout were twenty-three Japanese fishermen on a tuna trawler, the ironically named *Lucky Dragon*. After the ship reached Japan and scientists discovered what had occurred, there was an international uproar. Not until February 15, 1955, did the U.S. Atomic Energy Commission report that about 7,000 square miles of territory downwind from the blast "was so contaminated that survival might have depended upon prompt evacuation of the area or upon taking shelter or other protective measures."

American testing in the atmosphere, and Soviet testing as well, continued, but public pressure to do something about the fallout menace mounted rapidly. In the 1956 Presidential campaign, Democratic candidate Adlai Stevenson called for a ban on nuclear tests, although it was not clear whether he meant all tests or was merely calling for a unilateral American halt to testing. The proposal further inflamed passions over the issue. Eisenhower, though it was then evident he would easily be re-elected, found himself

on the defensive. His Administration was attacked for seeming to claim, as its enemies declared, that "radiation is good for you." There is evidence that, prior to the Stevenson proposal, the President had nearly agreed to Stassen's suggestion to untie a test ban proposal from the larger package of American arms control measures, but the political move by Stevenson killed the idea.

By October, 1957, Japanese Prime Minister Nobusuke Kishi was writing the President about "the urgent necessity of ending all nuclear test explosions." Eisenhower, disturbed by the public outcry, told Stassen to work up a proposal for a one- or two-year test ban, during which an inspection system within the Soviet Union and the United States could be installed.

But by the time the London Conference ended a few months later, the President, at Dulles's urging, had reverted to drawing tight again the knot that bound the test ban proposal to other arms control measures. Eisenhower was now arguing that if a test ban were "to alleviate rather than merely to conceal the threat of nuclear war" it "should be undertaken as a part of a meaningful program to reduce that threat."

It was an untenable position. By 1958, with continuing American and Soviet tests further polluting the world's atmosphere, immense pressure had built up in the United States and elsewhere outside the Communist bloc for a test ban agreement separate from all other issues. Dulles, fearing that he could not withstand such pressure, seized upon proposals for convening a conference of technical experts on the practical problem of supervision and control of a test ban, an idea suggested to Khrushchev by the President on April 28, 1958. To Washington's surprise, Khrushchev, eleven days later, accepted. Dulles himself conceded that he had "broken the package."

To head the American delegation to the eight-nation Conference on the Discontinuance of Nuclear Weapons Tests, Eisenhower named James Brown Fisk, executive vice-president of Bell Telephone Laboratories and a member of the President's Scientific Advisory Committee. Dr. Fisk was assisted by Ernest O. Law-

rence, a senior nuclear scientist, who had headed the University of California's radiation laboratory, and Robert F. Backer, a former Atomic Energy Commission member. A similar gathering, a ten-nation "Conference of Experts for the Study of Possible Means Which Might be Helpful in Preventing Surprise Attack," was also agreed to by Moscow and Washington. William C. Foster, a Republican businessman and Pentagon official, who later headed the Arms Control and Disarmament Agency, led the American delegation to the ten-nation conference. He had also served on the Gaither Committee.

The test ban meeting produced a Soviet-American agreement, backed by the six other participating nations, for a worldwide network of land- and ship-based control posts. A degree of on-site inspection on the territory of the two superpowers was also agreed on. The ten-nation meeting on surprise attack, however, ended in an impasse over how to separate political from technical issues; nevertheless, it forced both sides to come to grips with a number of arms control problems.

The test ban experts, Soviet and American, came up with a plan for locating control posts with respect to earthquake areas of the world. The proposed network included 24 posts in North America, 6 in Europe, 37 in Asia, 7 in Australia, 16 in South America, 16 in Africa, 4 in Antarctica, and 60 control posts on islands and "about 10 ships." The actual number of posts, according to the report, could "be determined only in the process of actually disposing them around the globe."

The Soviet willingness to agree surprised—indeed dumbfounded—Washington. Further efforts at negotiations took place in Geneva with the United States, the Soviet Union, and Great Britain, then the world's three nuclear powers, participating. Overriding the doubters in his Administration, Eisenhower offered a year's suspension of tests during the talks. The offer was not totally gratuitous. Eisenhower later recounted that the risks of such an offer were reduced, because the suspension would not begin "until after the completion of our Hardtack series of tests

in the Pacific" and because the offer was conditioned on Soviet agreement for a similar test moratorium.

The Russians agreed to the temporary ban during the talks. It was to take effect on October 31, 1958. However, the Soviet Union conducted tests on both November 1 and 3, past the unofficial cutoff date, as the Atomic Energy Commission's monitoring system discovered. Eisenhower did not revoke the American moratorium but he did announce on November 7 that the Soviet testing had relieved the United States of its obligation. However, he agreed to stick to the moratorium and, since there were no further Soviet tests, the series apparently being completed, the ban continued.

But while the Geneva talks were trying to turn the experts' views into an agreement, results of the Hardtack series of American tests were presented. The tests demonstrated that nuclear explosions could be shielded in underground caverns in such a way that they would not register on the proposed seismic detection system. Thus, it was argued, the agreement with the Soviet Union had been based on incomplete data, since large sized nuclear tests could be conducted clandestinely. The American findings were made known at Geneva, but the Russians refused to consider them.

This development put the United States in a very difficult position before the world, especially since it was well known that there was dissent in and out of the government over a test ban on any terms. The President finally suggested a ban on atmospheric tests only, permitting the difficult-to-check underground tests by both sides to continue. This was the formula finally agreed on during the Kennedy Administration, but the time was not yet right, and Khrushchev rejected the plan.

A second attempt by the experts failed, and Eisenhower announced that the American test moratorium would end on December 31, 1959, although the United States would not resume tests without prior public announcement. There now ensued fruitless efforts to agree on a "threshold" for underground tests,

that is, the seismic magnitude above which tests would be prohibited.

Khrushchev, in rejecting the limited test ban proposal, suggested that the two sides try harder to agree on the number of annual trips of inspection teams that would be needed to check suspicious events on the territory of the two superpowers and their allies. In the course of lengthy talks, the United States slowly whittled down the number of inspections per year to twenty, eventually to eight, and hinted at less.

The kind of problem inherent in Soviet-American arms negotiations is illustrated by an incident that occurred in 1962, when the number of such on-site inspections was being argued. Khrushchev apparently concluded that the United States would agree to three. He contended that such an arrangement had been indicated to him by Arthur Dean, a law partner of Dulles and sometime arms control negotiator. Dean denied giving any such indication. The American Government had believed that, if Khrushchev raised the number of annual inspection trips to three, a compromise could then be sought between his three and the American offer of eight. Khrushchev declared that he had been double-crossed, despite American disclaimers, and the episode left bad feelings all around.

In Washington, the military largely opposed a total test ban on the grounds of necessary weapons development. Others contended that scientists would leave their laboratories if barred from experimenting, whereas Russian scientists could be forced to continue work, thus giving the Soviet Union a jump on the United States against the day when tests might be ordered again.

The test ban by now was a national issue, to be debated in the Congress. There Senator Hubert H. Humphrey, head of a disarmament subcommittee, was the leading advocate. He was aided by Senator Clinton P. Anderson, the New Mexico Democrat who had served variously as chairman and vice-chairman of the Joint Committee on Atomic Energy.

American scientists entered the political fray with a vengeance.

They were divided vehemently on the issue. Some lined up on the negative side, behind Edward Teller, widely touted as the "father of the H-bomb," while others backed the equally prestigious Hans Bethe on the positive side. British Prime Minister Harold Macmillan flew to Moscow and to Washington, trying to arrange a compromise on the on-site inspection issue. Meanwhile, France became the fourth member of the nuclear club by exploding its first bomb in the atmosphere over Algeria on February 13, 1959.

Whatever possibility of agreement existed was ended with a shattering blow that occurred in the skies over the Soviet Union on May 1, 1960, when Francis Gary Powers's U-2 was shot down by a Soviet missile near Sverdlovsk, deep in the Soviet Union. A new summit conference was about to begin in Paris. The test ban was to have been a major topic. Khrushchev was caught in a serious internal Kremlin political situation because he had been looking with favor on Eisenhower, who now reluctantly admitted ordering the U-2 flights, as a "man of peace." In Paris, Khrushchev demanded an apology he surely knew the President could not and would not give. He revoked the invitation for Eisenhower to visit the Soviet Union and announced that he would have nothing more to do with the President. Arms control and all other East-West issues were shelved, and further discussion awaited the election and inauguration of a new American President.

Eisenhower wanted to end the test moratorium but decided to leave that decision to his successor. When John F. Kennedy became President-elect, Eisenhower privately emphasized to him that "our nation should resume needed tests without delay."

In this final period of the Eisenhower Administration there was one accomplishment—the Antarctic Treaty, signed in Washington on December 1, 1959, by the United States, the Soviet Union, Great Britain, France, Japan, South Africa, New Zealand, Australia, Argentina, Chile, Belgium, and Norway. The treaty, approved by the U.S. Senate on August 10, 1960, a few months after the U-2 incident, by a vote of 66 to 21, provided for main-

taining the region around the South Pole as a nuclear-free zone, subject to inspection without a veto. Subsequent inspections were made by American officials, but not by those of the Soviet Union.

Far more important, however, was an incident that occurred in Paris when the four leaders Eisenhower, Khrushchev, Macmillan, and French President Charles de Gaulle had their only meeting before the summit conference was aborted.

At this meeting, Eisenhower defended the U-2 flights against Khrushchev's charge of espionage. De Gaulle noted that in the past few days a Soviet satellite had been passing over France and, for all he knew, might be taking reconnaissance photographs. Eisenhower recounted in his memoirs what then transpired: "Khrushchev broke in to say he was talking about airplanes, not about satellites. He said any nation in the world who wanted to photograph the Soviet areas by satellites was completely free to do so."

It was a startling statement, with momentous implications for the future.

III. First Limited Agreements

Some say that it is useless to speak of world peace . . . until the leaders of the Soviet Union adopt a more enlightened attitude. I hope they do so. I believe we can help them do it. But I also believe that we must re-examine our own attitude as individuals and as a nation, for our attitude is as essential as theirs. . . . Our problems are man-made; therefore they can be solved by man.

President JOHN F. KENNEDY
June 10, 1963

The faces around the National Security Council table, at 10 A.M. on August 31, 1961, were expressive of gloom, and with every reason. The day before, the Soviet Union had announced that it was resuming nuclear testing in the atmosphere. An intimation of the news had been picked up by American monitors, who had intercepted a message two hours before the formal announcement, and President Kennedy had called his top advisers together to decide what the United States should do.

Kennedy's New Frontier, so full of hope and glowing words, had gotten off to a shattering start. First there had been the disastrous Bay of Pigs incident. Then Khrushchev, quite likely because he had interpreted the young President's handling of that abortive effort to overthrow Cuba's Fidel Castro as a sign of

weakness, had heated up the Berlin issue. And less than three weeks before the Soviet resumption of testing, the Berlin Wall had gone up, while the United States stood by helplessly. Now, a critical arms control issue had been added to the President's problems.

Kennedy had long been interested in arms control. He had come to office determined to do what he believed Eisenhower had not done—press hard for meaningful agreements. The first statement at his first press conference, on January 25, 1961, was the inevitable announcement that the new Administration would review the test ban situation. Kennedy had named John J. McCloy coordinator of disarmament activities. McCloy, a senior states-man, former High Commissioner in Germany, a member of the Establishment, and a Republican, was the ideal appointee for a new President who had won a narrow election. McCloy had been an Eisenhower arms control adviser, well-known for his cautious views. His selection at the outset of the Kennedy Administration thus mollified those who feared that the new President might take risks in regard to national security. (McCloy remains active as head of President Nixon's advisory group to the Arms Control and Disarmament Agency.)

During his campaign for the Presidency, Kennedy had com-plained that fewer than one hundred men scattered through the government had anything to do with arms control and disarma-ment, a theme that engendered considerable public response. Partly in reaction to Kennedy's charges, President Eisenhower, in the fall of the election year, had created the Disarmament Administration within the Department of State. After his inau-guration, Kennedy asked Congress to establish a new agency to deal with all arms control matters, but not until September, 1961, did Congress create the Arms Control and Disarmament Agency (ACDA). Theodore C. Sorensen, in his book *Kennedy*, described the President as interested primarily in influencing world opinion on the disarmament issue, but Sorensen added that Kennedy in time "underwent a degree of redemption on this subject" by

coming to believe that arms control measures really might be achieved, thus releasing funds for domestic programs. The new agency's very name was indicative of congressional doubts. The ACDA represented a compromise on the part of those who hoped for the utopia of total disarmament and those who felt it more realistic to attempt to control the arms race. The ACDA absorbed the small group already at work in the State Department.

For the first time since Stassen's loss of influence in 1957, the United States gathered together a full staff of arms control experts. McCloy, whose report to Kennedy was the basis for establishing the ACDA, bowed out (but still served in an advisory capacity), and William C. Foster became the agency's first head. Adrian S. Fisher, a lawyer who had worked for both the Atomic Energy Commission and the State Department, was the able backstop, serving into the early months of the Nixon Administration.

But events did not wait for orderly development of new policies by the new Administration. On Inauguration Day, Khrushchev, who had totally severed relations with Eisenhower, cabled the new President his hopes for a "radical improvement" in Soviet-American relations. As a gesture to Kennedy, Khrushchev freed the two surviving crewmen of a U.S. Air Force RB-47 electronic snooping plane that had been shot down just north of the Soviet Union over the Barents Sea the previous July 1. Khrushchev's act, said Kennedy, removed "a serious obstacle to improvement of Soviet-American relations."

This gesture, however, had not been unexpected. Between election and inauguration, two men who became key members of Kennedy's Administration, Jerome B. Wiesner and Walt W. Rostow, had met in Moscow with Soviet officials. The occasion was one of the Pugwash conferences, named after the Nova Scotia home of Cleveland financier Cyrus Eaton, who had initiated the series of meetings that continue to this day, in the belief that unofficial East-West gatherings would help Moscow and Washington better understand each other.

Wiesner, a nuclear expert who became Kennedy's White House science adviser, was the leading advocate of arms control throughout the early 1960's. He wielded considerable influence because of his ability to grasp and evaluate facts quickly. Wiesner was perhaps the first person in a high position to sense the action-reaction phenomenon. He had been a principal backer of the Stevenson test ban proposal in 1958 and now sought to make Kennedy see the problem from the Soviet point of view. In 1958, Wiesner had been a staff expert at the surprise attack conference in the delegation led by William Foster. Rostow, an economic historian, who later became President Johnson's assistant for national security affairs and a leading advocate of the Vietnam War, was equally anxious to get the Kennedy Administration off to a good start in its relations with the Soviet Union. But he was less of an optimist than Wiesner.

The Wiesner-Rostow team, under cover of the Pugwash meeting in Moscow, urged Soviet officials to release the RB-47 fliers as an opening gesture of goodwill. Arthur M. Schlesinger's *A Thousand Days: John F. Kennedy in the White House* related that, in the course of the talks, V. V. Kuznetsov of the Soviet Foreign Office mentioned Kennedy's missile-gap campaign charges, adding that a massive American buildup would necessarily bring a Soviet reaction. Rostow countered that the purpose of any Kennedy armament program would only be to maintain the stability of the American deterrent.

In February, the new Defense Secretary, Robert S. McNamara, revealed to newsmen that after examination of the facts, he had found the missile gap to be nonexistent—as Eisenhower, to no avail, had indignantly contended all along. Nonetheless, debate over the issue persisted in the United States into late 1961. The Air Force, according to Schlesinger, contended that the Russians had 600 to 800 ballistic missiles; the Central Intelligence Agency (CIA) estimated they had 450; the Navy's estimate was only 200. The figures were not broken down as between intercontinental missiles (ICBM's) and medium-range missiles (MRBM's).

(It is now known that the Soviet Union had concentrated first on building a medium-range missile force, targeted on Western Europe.) After he pulled Soviet missiles out of Cuba in 1962, Khrushchev, on January 19, 1963, gave the only specific figures ever released of the Soviet long-range force. He said that at that time the United States was still covered by 80 to 120 missiles. If correct, all the estimates given Kennedy as late as the fall of 1961 were far too high.

But the action-reaction cycle induced by the Soviet ICBM and *Sputnik* in 1957 was still in motion, and Kennedy did nothing to halt it. A nuclear-powered submarine system with nuclear-tipped Polaris missiles that could be fired from under water had been given a go-ahead by Eisenhower in the wake of the Gaither Committee's alarming predictions. A land-based ICBM program of Minuteman missiles also was accelerated after *Sputnik*, and Kennedy approved what eventually became a force of 1,054 missiles deep in concrete silos.

The result of these programs, despite all the talk in the early Kennedy years of nuclear "overkill," was to widen the missile gap in favor of the United States. One reason for Kennedy's acquiescence, according to Schlesinger, was that the President "went along with the policy of multiplying Polaris and Minuteman . . . missiles" as a concession to the Pentagon because he had already rejected the Air Force demand for the high-altitude B-70 bomber. Some observers have speculated that, after the Bay of Pigs debacle, Kennedy felt he had to show strength and thus could not afford to oppose the development of additional missiles. Foster sought in mid-1961 to win the President's approval for a proposal to Moscow calling for a mutual percentage of cuts in missiles, bombers, and naval vessels, but Kennedy replied that it was much too soon for such a move. Six years later, McNamara said that the 1961 buildup of the two missile systems "was necessitated by a lack of accurate information," and he acknowledged that "clearly the Soviet buildup" after the 1964 ouster of Khru-

shchev was "in part a reaction to our own buildup since the beginning of this decade."

Thus, although Kennedy came to office determined to control and slow the arms race, he actually fueled it with the rapid buildup of new weapons systems. But the atmosphere of the early Kennedy years was not one to suggest a cutback in strategic weapons. Furthermore, a meeting in June, 1961, with Khrushchev in Vienna raised alarms about a new Soviet-American confrontation over Berlin and confirmed the view of the fearful that a fuller complement of missiles was essential.

At the Vienna meeting, Khrushchev and Kennedy talked fruitlessly about a test ban treaty, which was once again being negotiated at Geneva. Khrushchev declared that more than three on-site inspections would constitute espionage. More important, however, he grimly put pressure on Kennedy over Berlin. According to Sorenson, the President believed if the Soviet leader "had meant what he said about Berlin, the prospects for nuclear war were now very real—for Kennedy had meant what he said" in declaring the United States would honor its commitment to the freedom of West Berlin.

Kennedy returned to Washington to raise a public alarm and strengthen the American military establishment in preparation for a showdown over Berlin. There is little doubt now that he overreacted.

It is against this background that the National Security Council meeting of August 31, 1961, began.

By the day of the meeting, the Berlin crisis had reached such proportions that Kennedy had sent an armored column from West Germany into West Berlin to show U.S. determination to protect the city. Vice-President Lydon B. Johnson had flown to West Berlin to declare to the alarmed citizens of the beleaguered city that the United States pledged "our lives, our fortunes and our sacred honor" in support of their cause. In 1962, Khrushchev contended that the Soviet Union had been negotiating a test ban

in good faith "until the President of the United States announced a mobilization of the armed forces and started threatening us with war."

The Soviet announcement of new tests was accompanied by charges that the United States was "fanning up the arms race" and justifications that "the Soviet Union considers it its duty to take all necessary measures" to ensure its security. At the National Security Council meeting, some council members advised the President to resume American tests at once, but Kennedy demurred. He knew there would be a worldwide reaction against the Russians and he followed Vice-President Johnson's advice to "let Khrushchev take the heat for a little while."

Kennedy later announced a renewal of underground tests to begin after September 5, 1961, but not until the following April 15 did he order renewed atmospheric testing. In part, the delay was to gain maximum propaganda advantage; but in part, it was due to American unpreparedness for a new test series. The United States had been caught napping.

Soviet resumption of testing, although it hit the public with force, had been preceded by considerable evidence that such a move was coming. During a July 27, 1961, meeting in the Soviet Crimean city of Sochi, Khrushchev told McCloy that he was being pressured to resume tests by his scientists and military leaders. He also dropped a hint of an incredible 100-megaton bomb, and when the tests did resume, two days after the Soviet announcement, the explosions reached the 60 megaton range, far beyond anything tested before or since by the United States.

American officials did their best to deprecate the magnitude of the Soviet tests, although it was believed that the Kremlin was somehow trying to alter the balance of power, since the balance at the moment still was very much in the United States' favor.

Erection of the Berlin Wall actually ended the Berlin crisis by blocking the hemorrhage of East Germans into the West, but it was not evident at the time and the crisis did not end until Khrushchev publicly lifted the deadline he had proclaimed for

signing a German peace treaty with the Communist East Germans. Had the Soviet Union held to the deadline, the United States would have been in the position of having to fire the first shot if it had refused to honor East German control of the routes into West Berlin.

Far more serious than the Berlin crisis was Khrushchev's bold attempt in 1962 to overcome American nuclear superiority by secretly emplacing missiles in Cuba. It was estimated then that the Soviet Union had only 75 ICBM's; the United States had 156 ICBM's ready to fire at the time of the October Cuban crisis, plus 144 missiles aboard nine Polaris submarines. Thomas W. Wolfe analyzed the reasoning behind the Soviet move in his book *Soviet Power and Europe: the Evolution of a Political-Military Posture, 1945–64:*

> The decision to deploy a force of Soviet-manned missiles to Cuba, evidently taken sometime in the spring of 1962, appears to have resulted mainly from the cumulative frustrations of policy setbacks suffered by Khrushchev during the previous three or four years. They included not only the failure of Soviet pressure tactics to obtain concessions from the West on such specific pivotal issues as Berlin, but also the deflation of Khrushchev's hopes that a diplomacy backed by the exploits of Soviet missile and space technology would weaken the resolution of the Western alliance and erode its confidence in the protective commitments of the United States. On the contrary, Khrushchev found that, by early 1962, the parallel collapse of his Berlin offensive and of the "missile gap" myth was serving to reinforce the assurances of American officials that the West still enjoyed an ample margin of strategic superiority. Moreover, he was now in the increasingly uncomfortable position some of his own military men had feared: namely, that he had been overambitious in trying to gain more political mileage from Soviet missiles than the actual strategic balance warranted. Beyond this, of course, Khrushchev was confronted in early 1962 by growing criticism of his strategic leadership from the Chinese wing of the world Communist movement, and in Cuba, itself, Castro was pressing for some form of tangible Soviet commitment to the defense of the first Communist regime to be established in the Western Hemisphere.

Emplacement of some forty medium-range Soviet missiles in Cuba, in a single stroke, would have seriously reduced the Soviet Union's missile gap, since warning time in the United States for a missile fired from Cuba would have been almost nil. It is generally believed that Khrushchev intended, once the missiles were in place, to use them as a bargaining point in reopening the Berlin issue in the fall of 1962.

In the Cuban crisis, the United States had overwhelming conventional military superiority because of its closeness to the island, and because the Soviet Union, which lacked a comparable naval force, was so far away. In his October 22 speech to the nation revealing the crisis, the President threatened the Soviet Union with a nuclear holocaust if the Kremlin should fire a nuclear missile from Cuba. The effect of this move can still only be guessed. Kennedy said bluntly, "It shall be the policy of this nation to regard any nuclear missile launched from Cuba against any nation in the Western Hemisphere as an attack by the Soviet Union on the United States, requiring a full retaliatory response upon the Soviet Union." Thus, Kennedy put the onus of starting a nuclear war on Khrushchev. Furthermore, there is reason to believe that the worldwide alert of all American forces, both conventional and nuclear, brought home to the Kremlin leaders the real possibility of a massive strike at their nation if the missiles were not pulled out of Cuba as Kennedy demanded.

Kennedy told the nation, and the world, "We are in as grave a crisis as mankind has been in," and, for thirteen days, the whole world seemed to hold its breath. In the end, Khrushchev retreated and withdrew the missiles. Although Kennedy carefully refrained from public boasting, it was evident to all which side had backed down.

In August, before the crisis, test ban and nonproliferation treaty talks were going on between the two superpowers. Much later, it was reported that on August 25 Moscow had told Peking that it intended to reject the latest American proposal for a partial test ban. But after the crisis, the Kremlin's attitude took a new

turn. Berlin was forgotten, and peaceful coexistence with the United States was once again the theme.

In this post-crisis atmosphere, Khrushchev indicated renewed interest in a nuclear test ban treaty. For reasons of his own, he chose negotiating with the United States rather than embarking on a new nuclear arms program. He exchanged letters with Kennedy on the issue, but the two leaders were unable to break the old impasse over on-site inspection. The United States cut the number of inspections it demanded to seven—with conditions— while Khrushchev vacillated from three to two to none and back to three—also with conditions. He was evidently under pressure and getting contradictory advice from his own domestic critics, who may have been emboldened by his Cuban fiasco.

On March 21, 1963, Kennedy told newsmen that the reason he was trying so hard for a test ban was because

> personally I am haunted by the feeling that by 1970, unless we are successful, there may be ten nuclear powers instead of four and by 1975, fifteen or twenty. . . . I see the possibility of the President of the United States having to face a world in which fifteen or twenty or twenty-five nations may have these weapons. I regard that as the greatest possible danger and hazard.

By May, he was even more pessimistic when he commented at a press conference that, if there were no treaty, "perhaps the genie is out of the bottle and we'll never get him back in again."

Kennedy decided, as Schlesinger put it, that the time had come for a major address on peace, in a fresh context, to save the "dying negotiations" with the Soviet Union. He chose to do so in a commencement speech at American University on June 10, seizing on what Schlesinger described as an ungracious and sulky letter from Khrushchev in which he had agreed to a Presidential suggestion for sending a special emissary to Moscow to try to break the test ban impasse.

The Kennedy speech provided an opening for Khrushchev. The President, speaking of "the most important topic on earth:

world peace" said he did not mean a "Pax Americana." He spoke sympathetically of the huge Soviet losses in World War II, and he called on Americans to re-examine their own attitudes toward the Cold War. "We are both caught up," he said, "in a vicious and dangerous cycle in which suspicion on one side breeds suspicion on the other, and new weapons beget counterweapons."

Kennedy announced that discussions would soon begin in Moscow "looking toward early agreement on a comprehensive test ban treaty." The response came quickly. Kennedy's speech was published in the Soviet press, and soon thereafter almost fifteen years of continuous jamming of Voice of America broadcasts ended. Of more importance, during a speech in East Berlin on July 2, Khrushchev accepted what he had long rejected: a treaty banning tests in the atmosphere and in outer space but permitting underground tests, thus avoiding the inspection nettle.

Once this Kremlin policy was settled, it took only a few weeks to negotiate the remaining details so long under discussion among the United States, Great Britain, and the Soviet Union. Kennedy sent W. Averell Harriman, an old Moscow hand, to the Soviet capital as head of the American delegation, and the President personally quarterbacked every move in the negotiations from the White House. The President was determined, once a treaty was in sight, that "no quibbling over language or sniping from his subordinates would prevent it."

Kennedy hoped that Moscow could persuade China to sign such a treaty, but by then the Moscow-Peking quarrel had become far more serious than was realized in the West. Kennedy also offered American aid to France for underground testing in an equally vain effort to win the assent of President de Gaulle.

The treaty was initialed in Moscow on July 25, 1963, after ten days of intensive negotiations. To win Senate approval, Kennedy rallied public opinion through television and press conferences and made personal contact with potential senatorial opponents. The core of the Kennedy argument was that while there are "risks inherent in any treaty, the far greater risks to our security

"Let's Get A Lock For This Thing"

—from *Straight Herblock* (Simon & Schuster, 1964)

are the risks of unrestricted testing." Some opponents were won over by promises of standby readiness to resume atmospheric testing, as proposed by Democratic Senator Henry M. Jackson, who has reviewed such preparations annually ever since. The intention was that the United States would not again be caught unprepared should the Soviet Union resume testing despite the treaty.

The American public accepted Kennedy's reasoning, as did most of the Senate, which consented to the treaty on September 24 by a vote of 80 to 19, far more than the necessary two-thirds. Thus culminated long arguments and lengthy negotiations over a test ban, a plan first suggested in the United States by Vannevar Bush in 1952 as a technique to prevent the two superpowers from testing H-bombs.

Although there were many contributing factors that led to agreement on the test ban, the treaty demonstrated that there could be exceptions to a maxim once advanced by Lawrence D. Weiler, an American arms control expert who is currently counselor to the director of the Arms Control and Disarmament Agency. The Weiler maxim declared that "the trouble is not that the Soviets and Americans do not have the same positions; the trouble is that they do not have them at the same time."

Before their interests finally coincided to produce agreement, both Moscow and Washington switched positions on formulations and details. These changes generally reflected a new reading of the balance of power and of the national interest involved, or thought to be involved.

In the United States, most of the discussions, pro and con, save some dependent on secret intelligence, were carried on in the open. In the Soviet Union, it is now quite clear, a factor not even mentioned at the bargaining table was involved—Moscow's deteriorating relations with Peking.

When Harriman arrived in Moscow for the final negotiations, there was a sign of this split. A Chinese delegation headed by Teng Hsiao-ping, secretary-general of the Communist Party, had come

in what is now regarded as a last effort to resolve the growing Sino-Soviet quarrel and was ostentatiously snubbed. Khrushchev openly turned from his business with the Chinese delegates in order to meet with Harriman.

When the treaty was opened for the signatures of other countries, Khrushchev called for every nation's adherence, knowing the Chinese would not sign. He especially sought signatures of as many of the Communist nations as possible. Only a handful of small nations then politically close to China refused to join in the treaty.

China, as expected, refused to sign on the grounds that the test ban treaty was a form of Soviet-American collusion designed to prevent China from becoming an equal superpower. De Gaulle's France also refused to join, claiming that the test ban did not reduce armaments but only sought to protect the privileged position of the two superpowers. In all, 101 nations eventually signed. The treaty has had two major effects: it has ended, except for the occasional French and Chinese atmospheric tests, the nuclear contamination of the earth, which alarmed so many who were fearful of the consequences of nuclear fallout, and it has been a step toward curbing the ability of nonnuclear nations to enter the nuclear club, since testing is essential to creating a nuclear arsenal.

In the early years of Soviet-Chinese friendship, the Peking Government had closely followed the Moscow line on disarmament issues. In 1958, Peking called for an Asian nuclear-free zone, as did Khrushchev. But by 1960, the Sino-Soviet rift led China to declare that "any international agreement concerning disarmament, without the formal participation of the People's Republic of China and the signature of its delegate, cannot, of course, have any binding force on her." In 1957, after the launching of *Sputnik* and the widespread belief it induced that the United States had lost its pre-eminent position, Mao Tse-tung had gone to Moscow. There he declared that "the East wind" was now "prevailing over the West wind" and that therefore the Soviet Union should use its new power, in the form of nuclear blackmail if not out-

right force, to demand concessions from the United States. On October 15, 1957, according to what the Chinese said in 1963, the Soviet Union concluded with China an "agreement of new technology for national defense," an agreement Moscow "unilaterally tore up" on June 20, 1959. The 1963 account of this affair added that Moscow "refused to provide China with a sample of an atomic bomb and technical data concerning its manufacture."

Whether there was a firm Soviet promise to provide a sample bomb to the Chinese remains unclear. What is clear is that Moscow halted aid in all forms to Peking. In 1960, Krushchev suddenly withdrew all Soviet experts from China. Peking bitterly complained that Khrushchev had canceled the agreements "as a gift" to Eisenhower during his visit to the United States. Eisenhower later recounted that Khrushchev did bring up the subject of China, but that the conversation was both limited and inconclusive. Khrushchev's failure in the 1962 Cuban crisis brought scorn from Peking. The breach proved to be irreparable although there were efforts to seek an accommodation.

In 1964, China entered the nuclear club, declaring that it would never be the first to use nuclear weapons, a healthy position for a new nuclear power, and the Chinese have repeated this pledge after each nuclear test. The United States in 1966 attempted to lure the Chinese into signing the test ban treaty, claiming that basically the treaty was merely another form of this pledge, but Peking refused to sign, calling the treaty "a criminal concoction by the two nuclear overlords . . . to consolidate their nuclear monopoly." Peking said the proposal to link the treaty with a non-first-use pledge was an American scheme to "restrict China's development of nuclear weapons while it continues to develop them in a big way."

Another consequence of the Cuban missile crisis was the establishment of the "hot line" between Washington and Moscow, on June 21, 1963. This new communications link was a teletype —not a telephone—passing through London, Helsinki, and Stock-

holm, with instant coding and decoding by American and Soviet equipment in each capital.

Although the hot line agreement was not, strictly speaking, an arms control measure, its subsequent employment demonstrated its usefulness in preventing war between the superpowers due to misinformation, misunderstanding of intentions, or a combination of the two. Obviously what passes over the hot line is far more important than the device itself.

After ratification of the test ban treaty, Kennedy hoped to negotiate other agreements to limit nuclear weapons. But he was not to see his plans realized. Less than two months later, he was assassinated in Dallas, Texas. The new President, Lyndon B. Johnson, continued the American search for arms control agreements with the Soviet Union, but, like Truman, Eisenhower, and Kennedy before him, he found the range of possibilities limited both by the precarious balance of power and by the effect of extraneous events.

In his first months in office, Johnson had little time for arms control problems. But, in the Communist world, two events occurred that were to make the American President's concern with disarmament inevitable: the ouster of Khrushchev on October 15, 1964, and the explosion, the next day, of the first Chinese nuclear device. The two occurrences gave the problems of arms control a new dimension.

After Johnson's election in November to a full White House term, he sought to continue the Kennedy-Khrushchev post-Cuba *détente* with the new duumvirate in the Kremlin, Leonid Brezhnev and Alexei Kosygin, head of the Russian Communist Party and of the Soviet Government, respectively. McGeorge Bundy, who first served Kennedy and then Johnson as Special Assistant for National Security Affairs, was a strong promoter of arms control, as, of course, was the Arms Control and Disarmament Agency's William C. Foster.

However, the Vietnam War increasingly preoccupied the President and made doing business with the Soviet Union more

difficult, since Moscow was actively supporting North Vietnam.
In 1968, after the massive intervention of American ground forces
in Vietnam, Soviet Premier Alexei Kosygin, in an interview
published in *Life* magazine on February 2, 1968, said that "in the
light of American aggression we cannot have normal relations
with the U.S. as long as it continues the war." Johnson, however,
sought to demonstrate that despite the war the United States
could have normal, or near-normal, relations with the Soviet
Union, and this was one reason he constantly pressed for arms
agreements. Of course, like his predecessors, once he was in the
White House, he came to see the overriding need of preventing
a nuclear holocaust, which many believed might be the result if
the Vietnam War were escalated. Thus, arms control measures
did have his attention.

As part of his effort to continue a dialogue with the Soviet
Union, the President in 1965 and 1966 pressed for a formal treaty
to prohibit the use of outer space for military purposes, a more
binding document than the resolution approved on October 17,
1963, by the U.N. General Assembly. (Approval of that resolution had been made possible by President Kennedy's agreement
that it need not call for an inspection system.) Negotiations for
the outer space treaty were conducted at Geneva and at the
United Nations in New York, and an agreement was produced
on December 8, 1966. The Senate consented to the treaty on
April 25, 1967, by a vote of 88 to 0.

Johnson also sought a treaty to prevent the spread of nuclear
weapons beyond the nuclear club members, who now numbered
five, but such an agreement was far more difficult to achieve
than the essentially pre-emptive move to ban nuclear weapons
from outer space, since the two superpowers alone had the ability
to use space for military purposes.

Serious discussion of a nonproliferation agreement had begun
as far back as 1956, but the proposal then had a lower priority
than the test ban, which itself was a technique for inhibiting the
spread of nuclear weapons. However, any nation, despite having

signed this treaty, could produce the nuclear component and develop the engineering necessary to fabricate a bomb, as long as the weapon was not tested. One of the aims of a nonproliferation treaty was to close this loophole.

A treaty to halt proliferation had different appeals for different nations. To the United States, it was attractive as a method of holding the nuclear club to three, then to four, and finally to five members, thus preventing national control in such inflammable areas of the world as Central Europe, the Middle East, and the Indian subcontinent.

The Soviet Union's primary interest was, and remains, to keep nuclear weapons out of West German hands. In 1963, the Russians had all but flatly told the Chinese that giving Peking such weapons would make it impossible to prevent the Americans from doing the same for the Germans. It was an ex post facto rationale, however, for Khrushchev had already withdrawn the aid Moscow had been giving Peking on nuclear development. There is good reason to believe that no Kremlin decision has ever been regretted more than the decision to help China enter the nuclear club.

The strength of the Soviet determination to keep nuclear weapons out of the hands of West Germany, born of memories of Hitler and World War II, was demonstrated by Kosygin's remarks during a 1967 press conference in London. West Germany, he said, "will have to join the agreement on nonproliferation, whether it wants it or not." Then he added this grim warning: "We will not allow the FRG [Federal Republic of Germany] to have nuclear weapons and we will take all measures to prevent it getting nuclear weapons. We say it with utter resolution."

The problem of reaching agreement on a nonproliferation treaty was complicated and delayed by an American scheme known as the Multilateral Nuclear Force (MLF). This proposal, made in the final year of the Eisenhower Administration, called for a sharing operation by the Western Allies of a seaborne missile force. The idea was advanced chiefly to appease nonnuclear

West Germany, but there were so many objections to MLF that within a short time only the United States was still backing it. Much of the MLF argument revolved around whether the scheme would give the West Germans "a finger on the nuclear trigger." The United States said no; the Soviet Union, yes. Moscow had much support in the West for its position since the possibility of Germany having the power to fire nuclear weapons was as undesirable to Western Europe as it was to the Communist world.

Another difficulty in achieving a nonproliferation treaty was protection for nonnuclear nations. Some of the countries being asked to sign a pledge of nuclear abstention were adamantly opposed to such self-denial without compensating security guarantees.

The Indians suggested a joint Soviet-American pledge to protect them against possible Chinese attack. Both Washington and Moscow shied away from such a commitment, although Johnson attempted to find a formula, including a generalized U.N. pledge, to satisfy India and other nations with similar fears. The firmest guarantee the President came up with was a public statement made on October 18, 1964, two days after the first Chinese test: "The nations that do not seek nuclear weapons can be sure that, if they need our strong support against some threat of nuclear blackmail, they will have it."

The nonproliferation treaty became the central issue at the 1965 meetings of the Eighteen-Nation Disarmament Conference in Geneva. The ENDC, as it was called, initially was composed of five Western nations (including France, which refused, and still refuses, to take its seat), five Communist nations, and eight countries considered nonaligned to either bloc. (The ENDC in 1969 was expanded by two and then by eight more nations, after which it was renamed the Conference of the Committee on Disarmament, or the CCD.)

Created by the United Nations in March, 1962, the ENDC had resumed in 1965 after a lengthy break. In August, the United States brought a draft nonproliferation treaty, and the Soviet

Union offered its version in September. Although the two drafts had a number of similar clauses, the negotiations soon became snagged over Soviet insistence that the "loophole" detected by the Russians in the American draft for the MLF scheme be closed. The Chinese reacted in June, 1966, to signs that the Soviet Union and the United States were serious about the proposed treaty with an intensification of charges that the two superpowers were in collusion. Peking declared:

> The reason why the Soviet leaders were so impatient to strike a deal on the question of prevention of nuclear proliferation was a hasty attempt to maintain the hegemony of the two nuclear powers —the Soviet Union and the United States—through such a treaty so that they may collaborate in dominating the world and at the same time to create the false impression that the international situation has relaxed so as to slack and paralyze the anti-U.S. imperialism struggle of the revolutionary people of the world.

The struggle referred to was the Communist resistance to the United States in Vietnam, where President Johnson was escalating American involvement.

Despite, or perhaps (for the Russians) because of, China's position, and despite France's continued refusal to take part, the ENDC went on.

By October, 1966, when the Chinese Red Guard movement in Peking had reached a new high in anti-Soviet vitriol, the Kremlin leaders apparently decided to modify their position in order to obtain a treaty. The Russians had been charging the United States with stalling, but Soviet Foreign Minister Andrei Gromyko went to Washington and, on October 10, signaling a change in the Soviet position, publicly declared that "it looks like both countries . . . are striving to reach agreement to facilitate the conclusion of an international agreement" on nonproliferation.

Johnson, who had met with Gromyko at the White House the day before, responded publicly by calling the talks fruitful and adding that achieving the treaty was "the thing that I think we need to do most."

Then, on October 15, Brezhnev welcomed "certain headway which has lately taken place," adding that "such a treaty would serve as a definite obstacle on the road of the further growth of the danger of a nuclear war and would create a most favorable atmosphere for progress in disarmament talks."

Once again there was a conjunction of Moscow's and Washington's interests on a step to control the arms race, despite basically irreconcilable objectives in their individual foreign policies. The Kremlin leaders put aside their earlier, firmly stated position that participation in the Vietnam conflict was a barrier to negotiations with the United States. During 1966, they also agreed to a renewal of a cultural exchange pact and to resumption of talks, this time successful, on direct airline connections between the two nations. It may be that, with the growing Sino-Soviet quarrel, the Kremlin had decided to lessen tensions with the United States. Since the United States was willing, for its own reasons, to do the same, conditions were auspicious for agreement.

By then, too, the MLF scheme was actually, if not formally, dead. The United States indicated a willingness to let the project drop, provided the Soviet Union would not press to close a treaty loophole allowing for the possibility of an eventual Western European nuclear force. The risk of that eventuality, should the day ever come when Great Britain and France would surrender their national forces to a supranational body controlled by a politically unified Western Europe, must have seemed minimal to the Kremlin, as, indeed, it still does in both the East and the West.

By mid-1967, the Soviet and U.S. drafts of a treaty were brought into line except for one key article on the traditionally troublesome subject of inspection to determine compliance with the treaty's terms. Both superpowers originally had favored use of the International Atomic Energy Agency (IAEA) to inspect peaceful atomic plants and make sure that their output was not being secretly diverted to military use. A fact of nuclear life is

that a reactor built to produce electricity invariably produces the stuff of which nuclear bombs are made. Indeed, this fact has led many observers to conclude that the development of the so-called peaceful atom portends disaster. Others, however, are not so gloomy.

Several of the six European nations that constitute the European Atomic Energy Agency (Euratom)—chief among them West Germany and, to a lesser degree, Italy—opposed IAEA inspection on grounds of national security and of competitive business secrets, insisting that Euratom inspection was adequate. Efforts at a compromise that permitted a period of Euratom control before an IAEA takeover encountered Soviet opposition.

At the summit conference between President Johnson and Premier Kosygin at Glassboro, New Jersey, in June, 1967, the two leaders agreed anew on the need for a nonproliferation treaty. But by then the inspection issue in Western Europe was not the only problem. Serious reservations on the part of India, Japan, Brazil, Israel, and other nations threatened to prevent signatures of important nuclear-potential nations, even if the two super-powers were to agree.

Furthermore, the 1967 Six Day War between Israel and its Arab neighbors, in which Israel determined to go it alone without overt Western aid, raised the specter of a later round in which Israel might employ nuclear weapons. There have been recurring reports, repeatedly denied, that Israel has been making its own nuclear bombs, and, if true, there is fear that the Soviet Union might then supply Egypt with such weapons, although there is no Kremlin precedent for such a move. (The missiles sent to Cuba remained under exclusive Russian control throughout.) Israel has an advanced research program in the nuclear field, but very little preliminary research has been undertaken in Egypt.

China's first hydrogen bomb test, on June 17, 1967, intensified the doubts of India and Japan about the value of a nonproliferation treaty, since no absolute American, Soviet, or Soviet-American guarantee against China seemed likely.

Yet in the face of such developments, the Soviet-American conjunction of interests produced, on January 18, 1968, a complete agreement on a nonproliferation treaty text. The Russians yielded on the IAEA-Euratom dispute in the inspection clause. In an apparent effort to force West German adherence, Moscow accepted language that would eventually lead to a melding of the two inspection systems, language that the Bonn Government had already approved. A limit of twenty-five years on the treaty, rather than an indefinite period, was also accepted to mollify several nations.

It was not until later in 1968 that Moscow and Washington attempted to meet the demand of India and others for protection against nuclear blackmail by proposing that the U.N. Security Council agree to call on its members for action in case of either such a threat or an actual attack. The two superpowers offered a U.N. Security Council resolution that welcomed their own intention to "provide or support immediate assistance, in accordance with the Charter, to any non-nuclear-weapon state party to the treaty on the non-proliferation of nuclear weapons that is a victim of an act or an object of a threat of aggression in which nuclear weapons are used."

The American statement of intent to go with that resolution, amounting to a formalization of Johnson's 1964 statement, said that "any state which commits aggression accompanied by the use of nuclear weapons or which threatens such aggression must be aware that its actions are to be countered effectively by measures to be taken in accordance with the United Nations Charter to suppress the aggression or remove the threat of aggression." Yet this procedure amounted to no new binding commitment by either of the superpowers since they, along with Britain, France, and Nationalist China, retain a veto in the Security Council against any action they might disapprove at such a crucial moment in the future.

Thus the nonnuclear nations, both those with a nuclear potential and those who lived in fear of their neighbors, continued to

shy away from the treaty, offering one excuse or another. Nationalism and national interest remained strong, and these nations simply did not want to sign away the option of eventually joining the nuclear club themselves.

Furthermore, reports of a new development in the long search for a cheaper method of producing nuclear material for peaceful uses produced Soviet charges that it could lead to such weapons in Germany. In March, 1969, Great Britain, the Netherlands, and West Germany agreed to build plants in Britain and Holland, but not in West Germany, to begin to produce nuclear material by the new gas centrifuge process.

The two superpowers finally found themselves in general agreement. But neither was able to convince many of the other important nations that signing the treaty would be in their own interests.

In one of those bursts of activity that seem to occur at the end of long discussions, Soviet-American agreement on the draft treaty was finally reached at 4:25 A.M. in Geneva on January 18, 1968. But minor changes still had to be agreed to by the two superpowers before they felt confident enough to submit the treaty for the signatures of all nations on July 1. But the end of 1969, the treaty had been signed by three nuclear powers—the United States, the Soviet Union, and Great Britain—but only Great Britain had finalized the ratification process.

Another agreement attained during the Johnson years, although not directly by American action, was the Latin American Nuclear Free Zone Treaty. The idea of creating such a zone for areas like Latin America, Africa, Asia, and Antarctica, springs from a hope that such agreements would keep these areas free, at least to a major degree, of Soviet-American power rivalries by keeping them clear of the nuclear weapons of the superpowers and their allies. Such a preventative approach is similar to the agreements to ban the stationing of nuclear weapons in orbit or on the world's seabeds.

To date, however, only in Latin America has the free zone idea come to fruition and, even there, there have been difficulties. The treaty signed on February 14, 1967, at Tlatelulco, Mexico, by fourteen Latin American states was the culmination of five years of effort. Since then, eight other Latin American nations have signed, leaving only Cuba, which has refused to have anything to do with the scheme, and Guyana, whose eligibility has been in dispute.

The first of the key articles pledge the signatory nations to:

Use exclusively for peaceful purposes the nuclear material and facilities which are under their jurisdiction, and to prohibit and prevent in their respective territories:

(a) The testing, use, manufacture, production or acquisition by any means whatsoever of any nuclear weapons, by the Parties themselves, directly or indirectly, on behalf of anyone else or in any other way, and

(b) The receipt, storage, installation, deployment and any form of possession of any nuclear weapons, directly or indirectly, by the Parties themselves, by anyone on their behalf or in any other way.

The second key provision declares that the signatory nations "also undertake to refrain from engaging in, encouraging or authorizing, directly or indirectly, or in any way participating in the testing, use, manufacture, production, possession or control of any nuclear weapon." The treaty places all peaceful nuclear activities in the zone under the safeguard system of the IAEA.

The American interpretation, although it was not so stated by the signatory states, is that the treaty permits nuclear explosions for peaceful uses, such as digging a canal or harbor, but only by nations that have nuclear weapons and are asked to undertake such tasks. Brazil contended that the agreement should not inhibit Latin American countries from conducting such explosions, which it feared the treaty would do, and, with Argentina and Nicaragua, attached a protocol to the agreement. This protocol provides that, if in the future it should become technologically possible to create a nuclear explosive device that cannot be used

as a weapon, the three nations will have the right to produce such a device. Technicians say that it is impossible to do so, however, because all explosive devices, including nuclear weapons, involve the same law of physics.

The free zone treaty also calls on nations outside the area but which have territories in the area to place these areas under the same restrictions—a reference to the remaining European colonial possessions and to American-controlled Puerto Rico, the Virgin Islands, and the Guantanamo Base at Cuba. This the United States has refused to accept. Washington did win an interpretation that there would be no bar to transit of nuclear weapons through Latin American territories en route to their destinations, which makes the Panama Canal available for transportation of such weapons.

On February 14, 1968, President Johnson agreed to another protocol on the non-use of nuclear weapons, adding that the United States "calls upon the powers possessing nuclear weapons" (meaning the Soviet Union) "not to use or threaten to use nuclear weapons against the Latin American states party to the treaty." However, the State Department indicated that the United States would not be bound by its pledge if a Latin American state received assistance, even in conventional arms, from a nuclear weapons state (i.e., if Cuba received such aid from the Soviet Union) for what was termed an armed attack. The memory of the Cuban missile crisis, plus the unresolved relationship between Havana and Washington, thus clouded the free zone treaty's total application.

All these agreements, affecting outer space and Latin America, were only peripheral to the major arms control effort of the Johnson Administration—the effort to begin negotiations on curbing the strategic arms race. There was however, a cumulative effect involved. The agreements, though minor compared to the central issue of curbing the strategic arms race, have served as building blocks. This has been true both in terms of Soviet-American negotiations over the agreements and in the internal discussions

of the two governments, where each step, however small, had to be related to the whole of the problems of the nuclear years.

In retrospect, it is perhaps amazing that anything was accomplished in the arms control field, once President Johnson had escalated the war in Vietnam. To the Russians, the bombing of North Vietnam, a "fellow socialist country," was a source of great embarrassment. Furthermore, the Vietnam War accentuated, rather than diminished, the Peking-Moscow quarrel and the fight of the two Communist giants for a preponderant role in the world Communist movement. Those limited agreements which were reached in the Kennedy-Johnson period are testimony to the fact that a conjunction of interests is possible, even in periods of great strain between the two superpowers.

IV. The Mad Momentum

> What is essential to understand here is that the Soviet Union and the United States mutually influence one another's strategic plans.
>
> *Secretary of Defense*
> ROBERT S. MCNAMARA
> *September 18, 1967*

On the balmy evening of August 19, 1968, Secretary of State Dean Rusk was host to a covey of ambassadors on a cruise down the Potomac aboard the *Honey Fitz*. In a quiet corner of the ship, Soviet Ambassador Anatoly F. Dobrynin told Rusk what he had been waiting to hear.

The Kremlin had just agreed, said Dobrynin, to the summit meeting President Johnson had been seeking with Premier Kosygin. It was expected that the two leaders would meet in Leningrad, and Johnson hoped to give a spectacular start to a series of strategic arms limitation talks (SALT).

A few days earlier, Moscow had finally agreed to a date—September 30—to begin the discussions. But both the September 30 date and the summit agreement were in vain. The day after Dobrynin's message to Rusk, the Red Army invaded Czechoslovakia. In such a climate, the meetings were impossible.

The delay in strategic arms limitation talks may one day be seen as a far greater tragedy for the world than the Soviet suppression of the liberal Communist movement of Alexander Dubcek in Czechoslovakia, for, at that moment, there appeared to be

79

a conjunction of interests and technologies that could have led to an important curb on the nuclear arms race. Undoubtedly, talks that fall, a Presidential election year, would have been difficult. The Republican candidate, Richard M. Nixon, by then was speaking of the "clear and present danger" of the Soviet missile buildup and calling for restoration of American military power to permit negotiation "from strength" and rejecting the idea of Soviet-American "parity" in the arms field in favor of American "superiority." But what transpired, both in the international political field and in missile and missile-defense development, was to make the problem infinitely more complex for the day when talks finally could begin.

The missile gap charges of the 1960 Presidential campaign had led to a massive American missile buildup. In 1967, Secretary of Defense Robert McNamara conceded that when Kennedy approved the buildup in 1961, the United States was acting out of uncertainty about Soviet intentions. "If we had had more accurate information about planned Soviet strategic forces," he said, "we simply would not have needed to build as large a nuclear arsenal as we have today." He readily conceded that American action, taken as a hedge against what was then only a theoretically possible Soviet buildup, could not have failed to bring a Soviet reaction.

It is now apparent that, after the 1962 Cuban missile crisis, the Kremlin laid the foundation for closing the missile gap by developing an anti-ballistic-missile system (ABM) and ordering a buildup in intercontinental ballistic missiles (ICBM's). By his clandestine effort to emplace missiles in Cuba in 1962, Khrushchev had daringly tried to close the gap in another fashion. The missiles he was putting in Cuba would not have altered the balance of power in numbers, but, had his short-cut method succeeded, it would have seriously endangered the American sense of security and given the Russians a psychological edge. But Kennedy forced Khrushchev to withdraw the missiles, and the episode very probably was one reason for Khrushchev's ouster in

1964. When the new leadership in the Kremlin began a longer-range effort to bring Soviet missilery at least to parity with that of the United States, the action-reaction phenomenon was clearly in play again.

Some time elapsed before Washington realized the sweeping importance of the Kremlin decision, however. What first came to major attention was what the Russians were doing in the anti-ballistic-missile (ABM) field, with American worries about these developments coming to a head in 1966. It was then that the path to the SALT talks first opened.

In November, during a visit to the LBJ Ranch in Texas, McNamara and General Earle G. Wheeler, chairman of the Joint Chiefs of Staff, explored with the President the alternatives to no agreement with the Soviet Union in the arms race. The result was Johnson's decision to approach Moscow about talks on limiting ABM systems in hopes that agreement would preclude the necessity for building an American system.

McNamara at that time had just completed the Pentagon's program of "assured destruction" of the Soviet Union if the Kremlin were to order a first strike at the United States. But he had rejected a host of other military programs as unnecessary. One was an anti-ballistic-missile system, which the Army had for years been pushing—first as Nike-Zeus and later as Nike-X.

Just what had transpired in Kremlin thinking is not totally clear. But it should be recalled that, in the 1960–62 period, while Khrushchev was still in power, there was evidence of Soviet deployment of an ABM system around the city of Leningrad. This development was enough to keep alive American ABM research, and in July, 1962, an ABM missile fired from Kwajalein atoll in the Pacific successfully intercepted a missile fired from Vandenberg Air Force Base in California. The problems of the ABM were many, however, and McNamara had stuck to research and development only, despite pressure from Congress to go ahead with deployment. Then, on November 7, 1964, barely three weeks after Khrushchev's ouster, what was thought to be

a new ABM was displayed in Moscow's annual military parade. The United States and its allies gave this missile the code name Galosh. Its size suggested that it had a warhead big enough to render ineffective several American missiles descending in a cluster.

About the time of the Leningrad ABM defense reports, the United States, had begun to consider how to penetrate an anti-missile defense system. One idea was to use a single missile with several warheads. This new weapon, known as a MRV, or multi-ple-re-entry vehicle, had a nuclear buckshot effect, with a limited degree of predictable landing accuracy. Since 1962, such war-heads have been operational in the Polaris A-3 missile aboard American nuclear submarines, and by December, 1969, 28 of the 41 Polaris submarines were so equipped. Some years after the MRV development, the multiple warhead technique was refined into the multiple and independently targetable re-entry vehicle (MIRV). MIRV's are to be positioned atop Minuteman III ICBM's and on Poseidon C-3 submarine missiles. At the beginning of 1970, the American intention was to replace 510 of the 1,000 Minuteman I and II missiles with Minuteman III's and to replace the Polaris missile on 31 of the 41 missile submarines with the Poseidon C-3. First flight tests of these most advanced missiles took place in August, 1968. It appears, in retrospect, that the Soviet Union had reacted to the big American missile lead by beginning an ABM defense and that the United States, in turn, had reacted to the Soviet ABM defense by developing MRV's and later MIRV's. The Russians feared the U.S. lead might result in an American first strike capability that could wipe out the Russian missiles. The Americans feared a Soviet ABM defense system might negate the American lead and wanted a new way to pene-trate that defense lest the Russians thus achieve their own first strike capability—a capability simply to hit the other side a surprise blow, or "pre-emptive strike," of such intensity that the crippled victim cannot respond with any meaningful counterblow.

Such was the background of events against which, on Novem-

"Say, We Could Get Lost In This Thing"

—from *The Herblock Gallery* (Simon & Schuster, 1968)

ber 10, 1966, at the close of his conference with President Johnson in Texas, Secretary of Defense McNamara told newsmen that there was "considerable evidence" of Soviet "action . . . to initiate deployment of such [an ABM] system."

McNamara was talking about the Galosh, which by now was being emplaced around Moscow. The Leningrad system had come to a halt because, it was believed in the West, the Russian leaders had concluded that it would not be effective against American missiles. But Galosh was rated a far more important development, and the United States responded with McNamara announcing two decisions that had come out of the meeting at the LBJ ranch. A third he left unsaid.

The first was what he called the "possible production" of Poseidon, the new missile for Polaris submarines, the development of which had already been initiated "as an insurance program." The second was the conclusion that "it is much too early to make a decision for deployment" of an American ABM system against the coming Chinese missile threat and that "we have not arrived at a decision on any other deployment," i.e., on an ABM system to protect against Soviet missiles.

The third decision made at the LBJ Ranch did not surface for some time. It was to approach the Soviet Union in hopes of reaching agreement on a limitation of ABM deployments by both superpowers.

To get at this third objective, Johnson ordered Llewellyn E. Thompson, who was returning to Moscow for a second tour as American ambassador, to try to arrange talks on limiting ABM's. Thompson arrived in Moscow on January 11, 1967. The day before, in his State of the Union Message, Johnson had said that "the Soviet Union has in the past year increased its long-range missile capabilities. It has begun to place near Moscow a limited anti-missile defense." In his budget message on January 24, the President added that in fiscal year 1968 "we will continue intensive development of Nike-X but take no action now to deploy an anti-ballistic missile (ABM) defense" and "initiate discussions

with the Soviet Union on the limitation of ABM deployments." He added that "in the event these discussions prove unsuccessful, we will reconsider our deployment decision." Money was to be provided in the new budget for such a contingency. On January 27, Johnson wrote Soviet Premier Kosygin proposing ABM talks. But at the same time that the United States was asking the Soviet Union to forego further ABM deployment, McNamara was saying that the United States had 1,446 land- and sea-based missiles, compared to 470 for the Soviet Union. Furthermore, McNamara hinted in his annual defense posture statement, presented to Congress on January 23, that the United States was developing new missiles to penetrate the Soviet ABM system. (The term MIRV then was still classified. It was first revealed in the *Washington Post* on January 29.) In that statement, McNamara also announced that acceleration of Poseidon development and production and deployment of the Minuteman III had been going forward during the past year. The Poseidon would be produced and deployed in the coming year, he said, and the number of Minuteman III missiles would be increased.

These signs of American determination to continue a nuclear lead and to counter the Soviet ABM must have been among the reasons for a long period of internal discussion and delay in the Kremlin in agreeing to the talks proposed by Johnson. Action-reaction, again.

Pressures within the Johnson Administration and from Congress to go forward with an ABM program, if there could be no agreement to limit rival ABM's, were accentuated by disagreement within the American intelligence community over what came to be known as the Tallinn Line. This was a line of Soviet radars stretching across the northwestern (as viewed from the United States) approaches to the Soviet Union and in several other places. Argument raged over what the Tallinn Line was for almost two years before there developed a clear majority view that the system was designed to protect against bombers, not missiles.

On February 10, 1967, when he was visiting London, Kosygin was asked at a press conference about the American proposal for talks. In his answer, he justified a "defensive" weapons system this way: "Maybe an anti-missile system is more expensive than an offensive system, but it is designed not to kill people but to preserve human lives." Five days later, *Pravda* spelled out the Soviet position by saying that Kosygin had declared (although he had not) that "the Soviet Government was ready to discuss the problem of averting a new arms race, both in offensive and defensive weapons."

When Thompson was finally able to see Kosygin on February 18, it was quickly agreed that any talks would cover both offensive and defensive strategic nuclear weapons. Beyond that, Thompson could not get the Russians to move. On March 2, Johnson announced that he had had a reply from Kosygin saying that Moscow was willing to discuss "means of limiting the arms race in offensive and defensive nuclear missiles."

But the Soviet agreement to talk was only in principle. No date was suggested. Meanwhile, Moscow kept increasing its missile force, closing the gap with the United States. It was becoming evident in Washington that the Kremlin was building toward parity.

By the spring of 1967, McNamara, Air Force Secretary Harold Brown, and others were quietly trying out the idea that parity, or something close to it, would really make no difference, since the United States had so many nuclear weapons in one form or another that it would have the "assured destruction capability" necessary to deter a Soviet first strike. At a congressional hearing, Brown said that "our plans are that five years from now we will have just about as many missiles as we have right now." He added that the Russians

have known that. They have known it for a couple of years, and they keep on building. Now we can afford to let them build for a while, if they feel they want to catch up. But there is evidence that

if we stop, they don't necessarily stop. They haven't stopped. I think that in our position we can afford to let this go on for a while, without overresponding.

During the same period, Soviet military leaders were boasting of their ability to knock down any incoming American missiles. "If missiles fly," said one general, "they will never arrive in Moscow. Detecting missiles in time and destroying them in flight are no problem today."

At the Glassboro summit conference in June, Johnson pressed Kosygin for a date to start the talks, and McNamara pressed his case on the disadvantage to both superpowers in deploying ABM systems. But Kosygin said he could not then set a date. The President concluded that this answer reflected a disagreement in the Kremlin—probably related to what he sensed was Kosygin's obsession with China.

Meanwhile, there had been other developments.

Three months earlier, in a moment of indiscretion in a drawing room of the governor's mansion in Nashville, Tennessee, before 125 educators, government officials, and newsmen, President Johnson had said:

> I wouldn't want to be quoted on this—but we've spent $35 or $40 billion on the space program. And if nothing else had come out of it except the knowledge we've gained from space photography, it would be worth ten times what the whole program has cost.
>
> Because, tonight, we know how many missiles the enemy has. And, it turns out, our guesses were way off. We were doing things we didn't need to do. We were building things we didn't need to build. We were harboring fears we didn't need to harbor.

In 1962, after Fidel Castro had refused to permit ground inspection in Cuba to determine that all Soviet missiles had been withdrawn, President Kennedy had foreshadowed this moment when he said, "The camera, I think, is actually going to be our best inspector." So it has become.

Supplemented by electronic snooping devices, the satellite

cameras used for surveillance by both the Americans and the Russians have radically altered the range and nature of information available on nuclear energy activities. The huge increase of American missiles in the early 1960's had been the result of misinformation on what the Russians were up to. When the buildup began, the United States' spy-in-the-sky program had been relatively primitive. But by the time of Johnson's remarks, technical innovations, such as cloud cover sensors to prevent wasting film, had overcome most of the deficiencies. By the mid-1960's, McNamara was publicly reporting with confidence exact numbers of Soviet missiles.

The American spy-in-the-sky program was openly talked about by the Pentagon when it began, but by 1964 even the code names had been labeled top secret. Nonetheless, the public caught dramatic glimpses of the effectiveness of satellite photography for the first time during the 1965 8-day flight of Gemini-5. Pictures of the earth from space left little doubt of the camera's capability. Officials who know say that in pictures taken from about 100 miles up, experts can distinguish with precision missile and ABM sites, submarine construction pens, vehicles, individuals, and even smaller objects of military interest. The remarkable clarity is due, in part, to stereo photography, in which double cameras provide a third dimension for the photo interpreter. The program, still surrounded by secrecy, is believed to be two-part: area surveillance satellites that orbit for three to four weeks and close-look satellites that stay up about five days to rephotograph objects of interest in the area pictures. The film capsules, ejected from the satellites, descend by parachute and are recovered by American aircraft in the Hawaiian area.*

In an article in *Aviation Week and Space Technology* on September 15, 1969, Philip J. Klass reported that the U.S. area

---

* The story of SAMOS, the first spy-in-the-sky satellite was told in an article by Howard Simons and Chalmers M. Roberts in the *Washington Post* on December 8, 1963. It was later reprinted in *The New Front Page*, by John Hohenberg, Columbia University Press, 1966.

surveillance satellites orbit for three to four weeks and the close-look satellites orbit for no more than five days before the film is recovered. He estimated by extrapolation from known data that "since early 1966, the U.S. has orbited 8–9 of the smaller photo-reconnaissance satellites per year, with virtually no overlap between successive spacecraft" and that during this period there had been "an area-surveillance type spacecraft in orbit during approximately half of the days in the year." The Soviet Union, he estimated, "has achieved comparable days-in-orbit coverage since 1966–67 by launching more than 20 of its eight-day satellites per year."

The rival Soviet spy-in-the-sky program is conducted with Cosmos satellites, which provide, among other material, such intelligence information as the precise location of American missiles, which is vital for targeting. Soviet confidence in their system can be judged from the fact that in November, 1963, during discussions on the treaty to assure the peaceful uses of outer space, the Russians dropped their insistence on a ban on observation satellites. At that point, the Russians had launched only ten or eleven Cosmos satellites. (By December 31, 1969, they had launched 145 photographic satellites; the best unofficial estimate of comparable American launchings as of the same date is 182.)

Despite astonishingly accurate surveillance from the skies, the camera can disclose only facts or clues to facts. It cannot probe the minds of men nor disclose what is on the drawing boards. The Johnson Administration knew what was being deployed and, in part, what was being developed in the Soviet Union, but it remained uncertain about how far the missile and ABM programs would go. Thus, the Administration sought, despite the information available, to protect the United States against the unknown intentions of the Kremlin by continuing its own weapons development and beginning an ABM program.

Although Johnson apparently had decided to go ahead with some sort of an ABM system by mid-1967, the decision was not announced until September 18 in a speech McNamara delivered

before the United Press International Editors and Publishers Conference in San Francisco. On that date, to the surprise of most Americans, McNamara accepted, if he did not heartily endorse, the idea of a "thin" or minimal ABM designed to protect against Chinese missiles, which was enough to satisfy Johnson's need for an ABM to protect himself politically from Republican critics as well as from the hawks in his own Democratic Party.

McNamara's speech was replete with warnings against the uselessness of a "heavy" ABM system to protect against Soviet missiles. The Russians "would clearly be strongly motivated to so increase their offensive capability as to cancel out our defensive advantage" from such a system, he argued. The United States and the Soviet Union would end, after spending billions, "relatively at the same point of balance on the security scale that we are now." McNamara spoke of the missile talks then still impending, saying that if they should fail, both nations "would be forced to continue on a foolish and feckless course." He added, "There is a kind of mad momentum intrinsic to the development of all new nuclear weaponry."

He went on to state the dilemma of the day: "The plain fact of the matter is that we are now facing a situation analogous to the one we faced in 1961 . . . we are uncertain of the Soviets' intentions." His remark was testimony to the fear of the unknown in the action-reaction cycle and to the limitations of even such fine intelligence devices as reconnaissance satellites.

Still, there was no word from Moscow about starting the talks.

McNamara stated that as of October 1, 1967, the Soviet Union had increased its ICBM launchers to 720 from only 340 a year earlier. They had also tested a fractional orbital weapon, dubbed FOBS.* Offsetting these offensive advances was the fact that

---

* On November 2, 1967, McNamara announced that the Soviet Union might have operational in 1968 a "fractional orbital bombardment system (FOBS)." Whereas ICBM's are launched on a ballistic trajectory going as high as 800 miles, FOBS is a satellite launched on a low orbital trajectory that rises 100 miles above the earth. Initially, the advantage of FOBS was its ability to avoid the American warning system by approaching the United

the majority of the American intelligence community, as Mc-Namara stated on January 22, 1968, had concluded that the Tallinn Line was not an ABM system.

The evidence is uncertain, but some experts guess that the announcement of the anti-Chinese "thin" ABM system, the Sentinel, was used in Kremlin debates as the rationale for stepping up deployment of the Soviet SS-9 missile program. This program apparently was designed to penetrate a "thick," or anti-Soviet, ABM system which, it may have been concluded in the Kremlin, the Americans would eventually construct despite McNamara's words. The SS-9 is a massive Soviet ICBM estimated by the United States to pack in a single warhead a nuclear punch of between 12 and 25 megatons in explosive power. The Russians, having developed rockets of great thrust, which had put them first in the space race for so long, were able to mount huge warheads. (Earlier American concentration on miniaturization techniques, packing a lot into a small space, had meant less megatonnage per missile, but more missiles.)

By the end of 1967, the United States still had a large lead in the number of missiles, but total Soviet megatonnage was estimated as already on a par or perhaps ahead of that of the United States. While McNamara kept arguing that mere megatonnage was meaningless, that it amounted to overkill, others demanded both more American missiles and an anti-Soviet ABM system, as well.

Not until June 27, 1968, did the Soviet Union, through Gromyko, announce that it was "ready for an exchange of opinion" on "mutual restriction and subsequent reduction of strategic

---

States from the south, a possibility since countered by the installation of additional warning devices.

McNamara said that the United States had studied, but rejected, development of an American FOBS. He indicated that such a weapon was less accurate than an ICBM. The Russians have continued to conduct FOBS tests, and American experts consider it a potential weapon against U.S. strategic bomber bases. Since FOBS presumably would be directed to its target before completion of an orbit, it is not considered to be in violation of the ban on weapons in orbit provided by the outer space treaty.

vehicles for the delivery of nuclear weapons—offensive and defensive—including anti-missile." Gromyko, speaking to the Supreme Soviet at the time, indicated, however, that the decision in principle for at least "an exchange of opinion" with the United States had been won over considerable opposition. He then said, "To the good-for-nothing theoreticians who try to tell us . . . that disarmament is an illusion, we reply: by taking such a stand you fall into step with the most dyed-in-the-wool imperialist reaction, weaken the front of struggle against it." Gromyko did not identify the nationality of the "theoreticians" but it is a Soviet technique to surface internal differences by such obtuse phraseology. This theme was to recur in another Gromyko speech on July 10, 1969, probably indicating that the opponents of talks still had not given in to the mid-1968 Kremlin decision.

Four days after Gromyko's 1968 speech, while presiding at the White House ceremonial signing of the nonproliferation treaty, Johnson announced agreement with Moscow "to enter in the nearest future into discussions on the limitation and reduction of both offensive strategic nuclear weapons delivery systems and systems of defense against ballistic missiles."

But the "nearest future" was not to be. Johnson pressed the Russians for a summit meeting with Kosygin to launch the SALT talks with fanfare. The final affirmative answer came on August 19, but was negated by the Soviet invasion of Czechoslovakia the next day.

Two other factors by now also had entered the picture.

The first was that both the Russians and the Americans were beginning to test their multiple-warhead weapons, although in 1968 the Russians slowed down what Defense Secretary Clark M. Clifford, McNamara's successor, called "the only positively identified Soviet ABM complex, that at Moscow."

The other factor was the American Presidential campaign. On October 24, Candidate Nixon charged the Democrats with "creating a security gap for America." He said that American superiority in ICBM's had "become only marginal" and that "the trend is

that even this slight edge will soon be gone." In place of the Democrats' "peculiar, unprecedented doctrine called 'parity,'" Nixon promised "to restore our objective of clear-cut military superiority" in the "aggregate" rather than "competition weapon by weapon." After the Russian invasion of Czechoslovakia, he called for Senate delay in consenting to the nuclear nonproliferation treaty, with the result that it was not voted upon until after he became President.

Nevertheless, the Johnson Administration worked out a series of proposals for the SALT talks and urged Moscow to set a date, but without result. After Nixon's election and before his inauguration, ACDA chief Foster, at Johnson's request, tried but failed to convince the President-elect to support beginning the talks immediately. Nixon responded that Johnson remained President until January 20, and that he, Nixon, would assume no responsibility for whatever Johnson might do about the talks before then. Word of this response apparently reached Moscow and no doubt accounts for the Russian decision to delay until Nixon assumed the Presidency.

Five days before leaving office, Clifford challenged Nixon's campaign remarks about the disappearing American missile superiority. He projected that by the end of 1969, the Russians would have deployed over 1,000 ICBM's in protective silos, compared to the American force of 1,054.* At the end of Khrushchev's

---

* ICBM's are buried, in concrete silos, widely spaced from one another, to protect them against damage from a nuclear explosion within a certain distance. The harder the silo, that is, the more strengthened by concrete construction or by emplacement in rock areas rather than in earth, the better the protection. Against such defensive measures, the offense tries to increase the accuracy of its ICBM's to negate the protective action. Offensive measures, as of early 1970 at least, appear to be more effective than defensive measures. In a paper entitled "Advanced Strategic Missiles, A Short Guide," published by the Institute for Strategic Studies in London, Ian Smart wrote, "A 1 MT [megaton] nuclear explosion on a surface of ordinary soil will pile up debris over an area which extends about a quarter of a mile from the point of the explosion. Any missile silo within that circle will almost certainly be unable to eject its missile once the debris has been deposited." The Soviet SS-9 is expected to have quarter-mile accuracy.

regime, the Soviet Union had possessed about 200 ICBM launchers, only part of them in hardened silos. The Brezhnev-Kosygin regime had obviously closed the gap.

But numbers and megatonnage are not the only measures of capability. While the Russians were "moving vigorously to catch up with the United States at least in numbers of strategic missiles —both land-based and sea-based," said Clifford, "it also is apparent that they are still well behind us in advanced missile technology —accuracy, MIRV's and penetration aids." Accordingly, he added:

> It is reasonable to conclude that even if the Soviets attempt to match us in numbers of strategic missiles we shall continue to have, as far into the future as we can now discern, a very substantial qualitative lead and a distinct superiority in the numbers of deliverable weapons and the over-all combat effectiveness of our strategic delivery forces.

On January 20, 1969, Richard Milhous Nixon became President. That same day in Moscow, a Soviet spokesman said of the missile talks that "when the Nixon Administration is ready to sit down at the negotiating table, we are ready to do so, too."

He added that an agreement "is quite feasible though not easy."

V. Moving to the Table

> After a period of confrontation, we are entering an era of negotiation. Let all nations know that during this Administration our lines of communication will be open. . . . I know that peace does not come through wishing for it—that there is no substitute for days and even years of patient and prolonged diplomacy.
>
> *President* RICHARD M. NIXON
> *January 20, 1969*

In 1958, when Dwight D. Eisenhower was in the White House and Richard Nixon was his Vice-President, Eisenhower wrote in a letter to the Kremlin leaders that the two superpowers must deal with each other or "end up in the ludicrous posture of our just glaring silently at each other across the table."

How the superpowers deal with each other over arms control matters, however, cannot escape being affected by their political relationships. The story of the rival schemes for general and complete disarmament (G and C in the experts' lingo) illuminates that fact.

In September, 1960, after the Eisenhower-Khrushchev relationship had reached a total impasse in the wake of the U-2 affair and the aborted Paris summit conference, the Soviet leader came to the United Nations in New York, where he attempted to create a new ruling "troika" of Communist, capitalist, and neutralist

heads for the world organization, indulged in picturesque fit of shoe-banging, and put forward a Soviet plan for total disarmament. American officials discounted the plan as a grandiose propaganda move. Eisenhower would have nothing to do with it. But President Kennedy, in August, 1962, while discussing with his U.N. envoy, Adlai Stevenson, the American position within the General Assembly for the coming year, accepted the importance, for propaganda purposes, of matching the Soviet proposal. Stevenson argued for, and Kennedy agreed to, the introduction of a G and C disarmament plan that would permit the United States to propose specific steps toward a general goal—a technique that Kennedy preferred. The Kennedy decision grew out of months of Soviet-American discussions, which had produced what was called an agreed set of principles, although the agreement was more semantic than real.

The American plan, like the Soviet proposal, provided for various stages of disarmament and covered nuclear and conventional weapons as well as military manpower. Not surprisingly, each scheme sought to protect national areas of strength to the last possible moment in an over-all disarmament plan.

After Khrushchev's overthrow in October, 1964, Russian interest in G and C plans quickly declined, and Moscow, like Washington, concentrated on specific issues in arms control. General and complete disarmament quite obviously represented far too big a bite for either nation, and it still does.

Through concentration on specifics, agreement had been reached, or nearly reached, on a number of issues when Richard Nixon came to the Presidency. Those achievements, and the negotiating experiences behind them, plus rapidly accelerating weapons development, made it imperative that the new President pick up where his predecessor had left off in the effort to curb the arms race.

In view of the progress made toward talks during the Johnson era and the Soviet statement of interest on Inauguration Day, Nixon faced the problem of devising a negotiating position and

arranging for the talks. There were two key elements in the Nixon approach: the talks had to be fitted into a larger scheme of foreign policy, and the bargaining position had to be Nixon's own and not the legacy of the Johnson Administration. Thus, delay was inevitable.

At his first press conference, on January 27, 1969, Nixon said that he favored strategic arms talks but that "it is a question of not only when but the context of those talks." He said he took a position between those who would "go forward with such talks clearly apart from any progress in political settlement" and those who felt that "until we make progress on political settlements it would not be wise to go forward on any reduction of our strategic arms, even by agreement with the other side."

Therefore, said the President, it was his belief that "what we must do is to steer a course between those two extremes." He defined his course:

> What I want to do is to see to it that we have strategic arms talks in a way and at a time that will promote, if possible, progress on outstanding political problems at the same time—for example, on the problem of the Mid-East and on other outstanding problems in which the United States and the Soviet Union, acting together, can serve the cause of peace.

He clearly had the Vietnam War in mind, though he did not mention it.

This Nixon thesis came to be known as "linkage," although the word was assiduously avoided on the public record. The Russian reaction, quite expectedly, was negative, and there has been no evidence that the thesis has affected Moscow's position on either Vietnam or the Middle East.

At the same press conference, the President also altered his terminology in regard to the position from which he would bargain. When a reporter reminded Nixon of his campaign demands for nuclear "superiority" over the Soviet Union, the President replied, "I think the semantics may offer an inappropriate

approach to the problem." He said he would settle for "sufficiency," a term used earlier by his national security adviser, Henry A. Kissinger. He added, "I think 'sufficiency' is a better term, actually, than either 'superiority' or 'parity.' " Five months later, a reporter asked Deputy Defense Secretary David Packard what the term "sufficiency" meant. "It means," replied Packard, "that it's a good word to use in a speech. Beyond that it doesn't mean a God-damned thing." In public relations terms, Packard may have been correct, but in terms of international relations, he was totally wrong.

The men in the Kremlin, especially since the advent of the nuclear age, have long sought American acknowledgment of Soviet parity with the United States, both parity in general, as befits a great power, and parity in nuclear arms—not only for psychological reasons but because of the importance of creating what Thomas W. Wolfe, in *Soviet Power and Europe: 1965–69*, called

> a climate of acknowledged parity favorable to the pursuit of many of [the Soviet Union's] more important foreign policy objectives. Besides permitting the Soviet Union to deal politically with the United States as a strategic equal, a parity situation could be expected to undermine the remaining European faith in America's pledges to defend Europe even at the risk of nuclear war [and to limit American willingness] to intervene militarily against Third World "national liberation" movements without the backup of a superior strategic posture to deter Soviet counter-moves.

That Nixon was indeed prepared to accept a posture of parity, whatever nomenclature might be used, was evident from his remark to the NATO ministers during his visit to Brussels on April 10, 1969: "The West does not today have the massive nuclear predominance that it once had, and any sort of broad-based arms agreement with the Soviets would codify the present balance."

As the Nixon era took shape, those most skeptical about coming to terms with Moscow on arms limitation began to suggest that

the Russians were seeking more than parity in the nuclear field. The Communist doctrinal commitment, according to Wolfe, long has been to "the goal of quantitative and qualitative superiority, a goal often pushed into the background by stubborn realities but never foresworn." In Washington, there was talk by Secretary of Defense Melvin R. Laird of the Soviet SS-9 missile as a "first strike" weapon, a line of reasoning reminiscent of the Eisenhower period when there was fear of a "nuclear Pearl Harbor."

Each new Administration, especially if the President is of a different political party than his predecessor, launches what it calls a complete review of policy. Shortly after taking office, Nixon asked for an appraisal of the SALT proposals inherited from the Johnson Administration. When the review was complete, Nixon's program was said to be not very different from Johnson's. However, as the arms race continued on into 1970, the Nixon Administration had to make alterations in its program to take into account technological changes and to ensure a variety of options at the bargaining table.

In his first months in office, the President had to cope with more immediate issues than launching the strategic arms limitation talks. There was the Vietnam War, the Middle East crisis, a trip to Western Europe to reassure the Allies, and domestic issues of all kinds. Not until June 11 was the arms review complete enough for the Administration to suggest a July 31 date for the start of talks. By then, the Kremlin was apparently having serious second thoughts.

One of the issues Nixon faced was what to do about the Sentinel anti-ballistic-missile defense system proposed by Johnson and McNamara. On March 14, the President announced that he had trimmed down the program and renamed it Safeguard and that it would go forward as "a measured construction on an active defense of our retaliatory forces." Furthermore, he stated, "we believe the Soviet Union is continuing their ABM development." They were most likely "making substantially better second-generation ABM components" and "continuing the deployment of

very large missiles with warheads capable of destroying our hardened Minuteman forces" (a reference to the Soviet SS-9 missiles). They had "been substantially increasing the size of their submarine-launched ballistic missile force" and also were developing their fractional orbital missile.

The Nixon decision was to provide "for local defense of selected Minuteman missile sites and an area defense designed to protect our bomber bases and our command and control authorities" as well as to "provide a defense of the continental United States against an accidental attack" and "substantial protection against the kind of attack which the Chinese Communists may be capable of launching throughout the 1970's."

The decision set off a great debate in the U.S. Senate and across the nation, culminating on August 6 in Senate approval of the Safeguard system by the margin of a single vote. A 50-50 tie on the most crucial of two roll-call votes failed to add to the bill an amendment that would have held up deployment of the system. (Amendments require a majority to carry.)

There were three main components to Nixon's decision to transform the Sentinel program into the Safeguard program and to the subsequent congressional and public debate: (1) the technical feasibility of the ABM system, (2) the additional money involved over a period of years in a military budget already under wide attack for consuming too much of the nation's resources, and (3) the effect a decision to deploy an ABM system might have on the expected arms talks with the Soviet Union.

The details of the technical feasibility argument were complex and much disputed, the central point being, then as now, that in the field of nuclear weaponry offensive capabilities have far outstripped defensive measures. Technical problems involved in the complex ABM system cited in the 1969 discussions still plague the program. Cost figures for the system, like those for so many other major weapons developments, both nuclear and nonnuclear, are apparently impossible to determine with any exactitude. These two factors have led many to believe that billions would be com-

mitted for a system of doubtful technical validity at the very moment that the national will seems to call for a reshaping of the country's priorities to give more emphasis to solving domestic problems.

The dominant issue, however, both within the Administration and in the congressional and public debate, was the potential effect of launching the Safeguard system at a moment when it appeared the United States and the Soviet Union, having reached a point of rough parity in nuclear weaponry, were about to meet to discuss how to curb the spiraling arms race. The compelling argument, both to the President and the Congress, was that approval of the beginning of the Safeguard system would add to the bargaining weight of the American position at the SALT talks. Those who took this view, including Nixon, accepted the necessity of trying for an agreement to curb the arms race, but they felt that the chances of success were probably not very great. Even if they were to succeed, it would take months, or more likely years, to reach any accord. In short, it would be too risky to put aside the ABM plans. If Johnson had not proposed the Sentinel system, if it had been Nixon who first had to decide whether to launch an American ABM system, the answer might possibly have been different. But Sentinel existed when Nixon came to office and thus already had a life of its own, which the new President and the Congress found it difficult to deny.

Nixon's decision, contained in his March 14, 1969, announcement of the Safeguard system, centered on two points: protection of America's land-based ICBM's against a direct attack by the Soviet Union and defense of the American people against a possible Chinese nuclear attack within the next decade. The first concern rested on a suspicion, later to grow into a widespread belief throughout the Administration, that the only conceivable reason the Soviet Union was building a large number of SS-9 missiles was to create a force that could destroy the land-based American missiles, including the 1,000 Minuteman missiles. Those most alarmed, taking what is known in military jargon as the

"worst case" view, foresaw a potential Soviet first strike against the United States. Others, who took a more comprehensive view of Soviet-American relations, suspected that the Kremlin leaders hoped to create a situation in which the threat of a strike that could destroy all American land-based missiles would severely, if not fatally, limit the bargaining power of the American President. As to the potential Chinese threat, Nixon took the position in private conversation that he simply could not permit the possibility that his successor, a decade later, would have no instrument of protection against nuclear blackmail by Peking, a theme he was to enlarge upon in 1970.

The action-reaction phenomenon was evident again, and caution won the day in both the Administration and in Congress. To hold back on the ABM system, especially after Johnson had endorsed it, was considered too much of a risk. The only concession Nixon made to the opposition was to limit the extent of the ABM system and to promise to review, and possibly modify, his decision "as the threat changes, either through negotiations or through unilateral actions by the Soviet Union or Communist China." He insisted that the Safeguard program was not provocative, that the modifications in the Sentinel plans eliminated any reason for the Soviet Union to see it as "the prelude to an offensive strategy threatening the Soviet deterrent," and that the program provided "an incentive for a responsible Soviet weapons policy and for the avoidance of spiraling U.S. and Soviet strategic arms budgets."

As long as both the United States and the Soviet Union have nuclear weapons that each knows the other can deliver, the balance of terror is preserved by mutual deterrence. The introduction of rival ABM systems, however, if they were able to prevent the delivery of most if not all offensive missiles, would upset that balance to the degree that the defenses of one nation or the other would be superior in effectiveness. The initiation of the Soviet ABM system had produced cries of alarm in the United States; Moscow was moving to upset the balance. The beginnings of the

American ABM system must surely have produced a mirror-image reaction in the Kremlin. An effective ABM defense for one side alone would, given the offensive weapons already in place, produce the conditions in which a first strike would be a thinkable risk in military terms. Hence, Nixon argued, by limiting the Sentinel system, which, despite denials, some felt was a prelude to a "thick" system to provide complete protection for the American population, he was not moving to "an offensive strategy threatening the Soviet deterrent."

The Senate debate centered on the ABM, its technical feasibility, its cost, and whether it would upset the balance of terror on the eve of the arms talks. By the time the Senate voted, however, opponents of the Safeguard system had come to realize the importance of the other new scientific development, the multiple-headed, independently targetable warheads known as MIRV's. The congressional debate brought to light much new information on the MIRV, vital data for both American and Soviet consideration at the SALT talks.

MIRV was conceived in response to fears that a Soviet ABM system could provide a defense that American weapons with but a single warhead might not be able to penetrate. The strongest public proponent of MIRV development (and, indeed, of a whole spectrum of continuing efforts to assure American superiority) was Dr. John S. Foster, Jr., the Pentagon's research and engineering chief and former head of the University of California's Lawrence Radiation Laboratory at Livermore. Foster, referring to the Russians, declared that his aims were "to make sure that whatever they do of the possible things that we imagine they might do, we will be prepared."

While the Senate argued over the ABM issue and tried to determine the significance of MIRV, Foster and the Pentagon fought to continue and complete MIRV testing. When senators began to call for a MIRV test ban as a first order of business at the coming arms talks, Foster argued that "an effective limitation on Soviet ABM's should be a precondition to a ban on further

MIRV testing." He also cast doubt, in testimony before a House Foreign Affairs subcommittee on August 5, 1969, according to the public portion of the record, on the ability of the United States to police a MIRV test ban. To Foster, the American MIRV was designed as a second strike weapon—for a retaliatory blow only—to deter a Soviet first strike and therefore "must be considered as a stabilizing influence" in the arms race. The Soviet Union was soon made aware by the American debate that a MIRV test ban might be the initial U.S. proposal at the talks. Furthermore, it may have been that many of the arguments in favor of the ban were found convenient by those in the Soviet Union who opposed a strategic missile agreement with the United States. That there continued to be such opponents could be deduced from Gromyko's July 10, 1969, speech, which undoubtedly reflected the will of the Kremlin majority. The arms race, he said, had long ago become a folly. Much else of what he said was reminiscent of reasoning in the United States:

There are problems connected with disarmament that require urgent solution. Among these problems, one of the most important is the problem of the so-called strategic arms. The point of the matter is primarily whether the big powers ought to come to an agreement to arrest the race of creating increasingly destructive means of attack and counterattack, or whether each of them is to try to break out ahead in one sphere or another to obtain military advantage against his rivals, which will force the latter to mobilize even greater national resources for the arms race; and thus ad infinitum.

There is another side of the matter, too, that also cannot be ignored by a state's long-term policy. It is linked to a considerable extent with the fact that the systems of the control and direction of arms are becoming increasingly autonomous, if one can put it this way, from the people who create them. Human capacity to hear and see are incapable of reacting to modern speeds. The human brain is no longer capable of assessing at sufficient speed the results of the multitude of instruments. The decisions adopted by man depend in the last analysis upon the conclusions provided by computers. The government[s] must do everything possible to be able

to determine the development of events and not to find themselves in the role of captives of the events.

Once again Gromyko said the Soviet Union was ready for "an exchange of views" on arms limitations. But it was more than three months before talks began.

Meanwhile, scientific development raced on in both countries. By mid-1969, the United States had made nine flight tests of Poseidon submarine-borne missiles with MIRV warheads and nine tests of Minuteman III. The test program was scheduled to be completed in May, 1970, with first deployment following closely thereafter. The Soviet MRV and MIRV programs were thought in Washington to be somewhat less advanced. John S. Foster, Jr., said on August 5, 1969, that in his judgment the Soviet "triplet," (three bombs in a single warhead) "probably is a MIRV" designed to attack hard targets, namely American Minuteman missile sites. Furthermore, Foster assumed that the Russians "under normal circumstances would be ready to deploy the SS-9 triplet some time in the latter half" of 1970, a date not far beyond the completion date of the American schedule. Thus, by the fall of 1969, it appeared that the MIRV genie was out of the bottle. (Some officials said the genie had escaped as far back as 1962, when the Polaris A-3 missile, with a multiple but not independently targetable warhead, was first placed in service aboard an American submarine.)

Whether the American estimate of the Soviet MIRV development was overstated or understated, the gap itself may have played a part in the long Soviet delay in agreeing to start talks. Perhaps the Kremlin feared that it might be embarrassed by an American proposal at the talks for a quick freeze on further MIRV tests.

The action-reaction phenomenon once again was evident in MIRV development. Had the two superpowers met in the fall of 1968, at the time MIRV tests for Poseidon and Minuteman III missiles were about to get under way, they might have been able

"Shall We All Agree That There's No Hurry?"

—Copyright 1969 by Herblock in *The Washington Post*

to agree on a mutual freeze and thus have prevented escalation of the nuclear arms race to a new, more dangerous, and more expensive level. Whether the same results would have been obtained if the Nixon Administration had been willing to start talks just after the new President took office is debatable, but perhaps not impossible. But clearly, by the time the talks did begin, the problem had become far more complex.

The Nixon Administration did act quickly on one arms control issue. Shortly after taking office, the President gave the go-ahead to Senate consideration of the nuclear nonproliferation treaty, and consent was voted, 83 to 15, on March 13, 1969. However, Moscow withheld ratification, apparently waiting for the West Germans to sign, and the United States also delayed formal ratification in hopes of concluding the process on the same day as the Soviet Union.

The West German election in October, 1969, and the subsequent choice of Willy Brandt, head of the Social Democratic Party, as chancellor, finally broke the nonproliferation treaty logjam. Brandt, as foreign minister in the previous coalition government of Kurt Georg Kiesinger, had long advocated West German signature, but in vain. Once in office, Brandt signed the treaty in Bonn on November 28, and by prior agreement the United States and the Soviet Union completed their own ratification processes, leaving only the final act of depositing their ratifications.*

---

* In general, multilateral international agreements provide that one or more governments involved, usually major powers, will act as the depository (or depositories) of the document. In a physical sense, someone has to hold the document; in a diplomatic sense, there must be some specified place to which nations can direct messages affecting such an agreement, for example, either to join an existing treaty or to serve notice the document is no longer considered binding. In the United States (where the physical depository is a State Department vault), the common belief is that the Senate ratifies a treaty, but this is not technically correct. The Constitution provides that the Senate shall give its "consent" by a two-thirds vote of those present. The President then signs the instrument of consent and, finally, deposits the ratification document. Only when that last step has been taken is the treaty binding on the United States, assuming that by then it has had the number

Brandt, however, issued a statement saying that the German signature on the document was based on several understandings, among them that the U.N. resolution calling on its members for action in case of either a nuclear threat or an actual attack applied without restriction to West Germany, even though that country is not a U.N. member. Furthermore, West Germany pointed out that the treaty provided an eighteen-month period for melding the IAEA-Euratom inspection provisions. Until that step had been completed, West Germany would not ratify the treaty.

Nonetheless, the West German signature, plus Brandt's new and more friendly policy toward the Soviet Union and Eastern Europe, had increased the treaty's prospects. Japan, for example, signed in February, 1970, lest it lose the opportunity afforded signatory nations to play a role in formulating the inspection provisions.

On March 5, 1970, when the required forty nonnuclear nations had completed ratification, including deposit of their ratifications in Moscow, London, or Washington, the United States and the Soviet Union made their deposits, and the treaty at last came into force. Still, it lacked adherence from such important nuclear-potential nations as Australia, Israel, Japan, India, and Pakistan.

Nixon's general review of American post-Vietnam policy in Asia produced a new doctrine in the broad area of nuclear protection for nonnuclear nations. The new doctrine was disclosed by the President on July 25, 1969, during a stop at Guam en route to Asia. He said then that in the future Asian nations would be expected to take primary responsibility for their own military defense with a single stated exception: the threat of a major power involving nuclear weapons. An anonymous White House spokesman (identified as Henry A. Kissinger) later added that

---

of final approvals by other nations required to bring it into force. The final two steps—signing and depositing the document—are usually *pro forma* but they can be used, as in the case of the nonproliferation treaty, for purposes of delay.

the Administration would have to take into account the nature of the threat to any nation, so that a threat with nuclear weapons would have to be treated with a special gravity, whether or not a formal American commitment to such a nation existed.

Nixon's remarks at Guam could not be directly quoted, but he later put the most important phrases on public record. In his 1970 report to Congress on "United States Foreign Policy for the 1970's," he formulated the doctrine this way: "We shall provide a shield if a nuclear power threatens the freedom of a nation allied with us, or of a nation whose survival we consider vital to our security and the security of the region as a whole."

But these generalities, which left the initiative in the hands of the United States, were no more satisfactory to the nuclear-potential nations that had not acceded to the nonproliferation treaty than had been the joint Soviet-American pledges at the United Nations.

Technical arguments, the issue of on-site inspection, and the continuing arms race itself have thus far prevented agreement on extending the 1963 nuclear test ban treaty so as to include underground explosions. Since that treaty took effect, the U.S. Atomic Energy Commission has announced a total of 173 weapons-related American underground tests through December 31, 1969. The AEC also announced that its detection network had disclosed, in the same period, three Soviet underground tests and thirty-four seismic signals, which presumably represented tests. However, not all tests of either nation are announced by the AEC. To do so would disclose the degree of sophistication of the American detection system. (In the same period, the AEC reported two British underground tests, thirteen French atmospheric tests, and one Chinese underground and nine Chinese atmospheric tests.)

Once above-ground testing had been banned, American and Soviet scientists developed techniques to try out devices both more powerful and, as in the case of ABM and MIRV testing, more sophisticated than had previously been carried out underground. Thus the test ban, while protecting the world's popula-

tion from most of the contamination resulting from atmospheric testing, did not, as some of its proponents had hoped, inhibit the arms race itself. In a few of these underground tests, in both the Soviet Union and the United States, some radioactive debris escaped into the atmosphere and drifted into Canada from the United States and into China and Japan from the Soviet Union. Both Moscow and Washington, although they exchanged formal notes for the record, avoided charges of violation of the test ban treaty and proclaimed that the venting (as it was called) was unintentional and harmless to humans.

Detection devices to monitor underground tests have improved over the years, but not to the point that the United States was prepared to accept the Soviet proposal for an underground ban without on-site inspection. Third countries, notably Sweden, have tried to develop compromise techniques, but to no avail. Sweden proposed a challenge-and-response system under which the nation suspecting a violation would challenge the other to disprove it, perhaps by on-site inspection, and be permitted to withdraw from the treaty if it found the response unsatisfactory. Another proposal was to ban the larger underground tests and limit tests to a specific level as measured on the internationally accepted seismic scale.

After leaving his post as head of the U.S. Arms Control and Disarmament Agency, William C. Foster declared, "The time has come for a hard look at the necessity for on-site inspections." In a speech on October 8, 1969, he argued for a comprehensive test ban (CTB):

> It is hard to believe that the security risk posed by the relatively few tests the Soviets might be able to carry out without being detected by national means would exceed the security risk of unlimited numbers of Soviet weapons tests that are permitted in the absence of a CTB. Of course, it can be pointed out that without a CTB the U.S. also could continue testing and thereby counter-balance the Soviet tests. But would this really counterbalance the security risk or would it merely add fuel to the nuclear arms race?

Foster, with the luxury of having shed public responsibility, gave voice to the internal arguments in which he had so long been involved when he said that "the crux of the problem is how much assurance is adequate, and this is a political rather than a technical decision." So far, the rule of thumb has prevailed: where there is technical doubt, political decisions tend to be on the conservative side.

In October, 1969, the United States and the Soviet Union reached an additional agreement on a pre-emptive step to avoid enlarging the locale of the arms race by ensuring that the world's seabeds be reserved for peaceful purposes only. The effort to reach this agreement, initiated in 1967, had followed the pattern of the successful effort to ban nuclear weapons from outer space.

Although both Washington and Moscow readily agreed to the principle of the treaty, each sought to protect its own interests in the final document. The Soviet Union called for complete demilitarization, a ban inclusive enough to preclude not only nuclear weapons emplaced on seabeds but also defensive mines and various submarine detection devices that the United States already had emplaced to track the expanding Soviet underwater fleet. The United States proposal was limited to a ban on nuclear weapons and other weapons of mass destruction (specifically, chemical and biological weapons). In mid-August, 1969, the Russians offered to accept the American version of the treaty if the United States would accept the Soviet proposal that the ban become effective at the 12-mile offshore limit rather than at the 3-mile limit Washington had proposed.

By fall, an agreement satisfactory to Washington and Moscow had been reached, but other nations had become disturbed about their rights under the rather generalized inspection provisions and about the effects of the offshore limitation on certain coastal areas. The inspection agreement in the draft treaty permitted any nation to check for itself the international waters covered, a task so difficult that probably only the United States and the Soviet Union could or would undertake it. The U.N. General Assembly

expressed these feelings on December 12, 1969, when it asked the two drafting powers to clear up the uncertainties when they next met at the Geneva Disarmament Conference in 1970. While Washington waited for Soviet word on when and where to start the SALT talks, the Sino-Soviet conflict appeared to be approaching the point of warfare.

A word should be said here about China, which has become increasingly important in the nuclear calculations of both the United States and the Soviet Union. The Chinese nuclear weapons and missile tests, monitored by American observation satellites and other means, have shown a high degree of technical sophistication. Although, by 1969, the program lagged behind American estimates, John S. Foster, Jr., Pentagon research chief, said on February 24, 1970, that a Chinese test of an ICBM could be expected within the year.

Exactly what the Russians knew or thought about the Chinese program is unknown, but Red Army marshals have clearly grown increasingly worried about China's nuclear growth, especially in light of the intensifying Sino-Soviet political controversies and the recent military clashes along the two countries' long common borders. Some analysts have even suggested that the Soviet ABM system was designed in part to protect against Chinese missiles. This view was acknowledged indirectly by the Nixon Administration when Henry A. Kissinger, in an interview in *Look* magazine on August 12, 1969, stated, "I doubt if the Soviet Union will give up the Moscow (ABM) system, and I doubt I would urge them to."

Although the record shows that the Chinese Communists have acted in a generally prudent manner militarily since coming to power, their excessively bellicose language has engendered fears. It is not easy to dismiss totally, for example, the widely printed Chinese polemic of 1960 in which Peking professed no fear of nuclear war with the United States and declared that the inevitable Communist victory "would create very swiftly a civilization thousands of times higher than the capitalist system and a

truly beautiful system for [the Communists] themselves." Mao Tse-tung and his followers, verbally at least, have consistently rejected Khrushchev's warning that, although the United States may be a paper tiger, as Peking has claimed, "the paper tiger has nuclear teeth."

In September, 1969, when relations between the Soviet Union and China had reached a new high point of tension, the accident of death brought Kosygin to Hanoi for the funeral of Ho Chi Minh, the leader of North Vietnam. The Soviet leader then made a quick trip to Peking, where he met with Chinese Premier Chou En-lai. After the meeting, it was announced that the two nations would meet to talk over their border quarrel on October 20, 1969.

To Washington's surprise, on the day the Sino-Soviet talks began, Soviet Ambassador Dobrynin met President Nixon secretly at the White House. A few days later, on October 25, a joint announcement was made of the date—November 17—and the place—Helsinki, Finland—for preliminary discussions of negotiations on curbing the strategic arms race.

The coincidence of dates for the beginning of the Moscow-Peking talks and the Dobrynin call on Nixon added to the American conviction that one of the reasons for the Kremlin's delay in agreeing to the SALT talks had been to avoid jeopardizing the chances of resolving the quarrel with China. The Soviet leaders long had been aware of Peking's charges that Moscow and Washington were acting in collusion against China. The Soviet leaders had also been wary of signs that the Nixon Administration was beginning to relax American hostility toward the Peking regime. The Chinese, in turn, played upon Soviet worries by agreeing in December, 1969, to resume the Chinese-American diplomatic dialogue that Peking had broken off two years earlier. It was evident, as the 1970's began, that the triangular Washington-Moscow-Peking relationship would be critical in world affairs in general and in relation to arms control measures in particular.

On the day of the Washington-Moscow announcement of the

SALT talks, Secretary of State William P. Rogers sought to bury the Nixon "linkage" thesis—anathema to Moscow—by telling a press conference that the SALT talks "are not conditional in any sense of the word. We haven't laid down any conditions for those talks." But the Administration hedged when Nixon's press secretary, commenting on the Rogers statement the following day, stated that "these talks cannot take place in a vacuum. The President's feeling is that there is a certain relation between SALT and outstanding political problems." Moscow expressed annoyance but nothing more.

At his press conference, Rogers also did what so many secretaries of state before him had done when American-Soviet talks were announced: he warned against "euphoria" and predicted long and difficult discussions. He also noted that the Moscow-Washington announcement had referred to negotiations "on curbing the strategic arms race," not on disarming the two superpowers. Rogers pointed out that Peking's nuclear program had not progressed far enough to require China to join the talks. If the two superpowers could reach agreement, he added, "We can deal with China's problem later on."

Announcement of the date for the SALT talks brought renewed congressional and public pressure on Nixon to propose at Helsinki a mutual freeze on MIRV testing while the discussions were under way, in hopes that such a step would lead to a permanent ban, perhaps in connection with a ban or limitation on rival ABM systems. But the President, on the eve of the talks, ruled out any such proposal. Indeed, the United States secretly tipped off the Soviet Union that there would be no American proposals, and Washington expressed the hope that there would be none from Moscow either. This turned out to be the case. Nixon wanted instead an exchange of views in order to define the scope of the more substantive talks to follow the preliminaries at Helsinki. In Washington, caution was the order of the day, and the same appeared to be true in Moscow.

To head the American delegation, Nixon named Gerard C.

Smith, whom he had also selected to succeed William C. Foster as head of the Arms Control and Disarmament Agency. Smith had been a State Department official in the Eisenhower years and a leading advocate of the ill-fated multilateral nuclear force. He now found himself in the position of his predecessors, pushing for Presidential approval of risk-taking, in contrast to those who advocated a cautious approach to arms control. The four other American delegation members were Paul H. Nitze, who had served as Deputy Secretary of Defense in the last years of the Johnson Administration; Llewellyn E. Thompson, the retired Ambassador to the Soviet Union, who had tried to get the SALT talks under way for Johnson; Harold Brown, formerly head of the Lawrence Radiation Laboratory, chief of Pentagon research, and Secretary of the Air Force, and at present President of the California Institute of Technology; and Major General Royal B. Allison, representing the Joint Chiefs of Staff, who, during the previous year, had immersed himself in the nuclear arms control problem.

The Soviet delegation was comparable. It was headed by Deputy Foreign Minister Vladimir S. Semyonov, the top Moscow expert on Germany. He was picked in place of the top Soviet arms control expert, V. V. Kutzenov, who was then leading the Soviet delegation at the Peking talks. Sitting on Semyonov's right at the Helsinki table was Colonel General Nikolai V. Ogarkov, First Deputy Chief of the General Staff (the Soviet equivalent of the American Joint Chiefs). On Semyonov's left was Dr. Alexander N. Shchukin, a scientific academician. In all, the Soviet group of 6 delegates and 18 advisers included 5 generals, an admiral, and 2 colonels. The American group of 5 delegates and 19 advisers had only 1 general and 3 field-grade officers. Each group included many who had lived in the other group's country and spoke its language; many had long been associated with arms control.

At the single public session in Helsinki, both sides spoke of hopes for "mutually acceptable" limitations on the arms race. In

a message to the conference, Nixon repeated his concept of "sufficiency," declaring that he did not "underestimate the suspicion and distrust that must be dispelled if you are to succeed in your assignment." He alluded to his linkage theory by saying that he was "conscious of the historical fact that wars and crises between nations can arise not simply from the existence of arms but from clashing interests or the ambitious pursuit of unilateral interests. That is why we seek progress toward the solution of the dangerous political issues of our day."

The latter statement indicated, once again, how intertwined in the President's thinking about arms control were Soviet-American relationships affecting the Middle East, Vietnam, and the East-West problem in Europe.

The atmosphere at international conferences, especially at strictly Soviet-American meetings, usually provides a clue to what is occurring behind closed doors. During the five weeks of the Helsinki meeting, there were constant reports by both sides of "business-like" sessions without polemics, interspersed with social events at which smiles and clinking champagne glasses were the order of the day. The end result, publicly, was a December 22, 1969, communiqué. This was the key paragraph:

> The preliminary exchange of views which took place concerning the limitations of strategic arms was useful to both sides. As a result of that exchange, each side is able better to understand the views of the other with respect to the problems under consideration. An understanding was reached on the general range of questions which will be the subject of further U.S.-Soviet exchanges.

The two nations agreed to resume negotiations on April 16, 1970, in Vienna and to return at an unspecified date to Helsinki. The Vienna talks, as was the case at Helsinki, were to alternate between the Soviet and American embassies, thus providing a degree of secrecy satisfactory to both countries.

It appeared that at Helsinki the two sides accepted the idea of mutual deterrence—hopefully at the existing rough parity of nu-

clear arms. Each sought to learn how the other approached the problem and how various weapons systems, including ABM's and MIRV's, were viewed within the context of the deterrence concept. The exchanges—usually in the form of working papers read by one side to the other at the conference table and expanded on in private social conversations—were both preliminary and philosophical rather than detailed. This was made evident by the post-Helsinki feeling expressed privately by American and Soviet officials that the Vienna round of talks would have to get down to specific proposals by each side if there were to be any agreement in 1970.

On the American side, the NATO allies, as Nixon had pledged, were told what had transpired at Helsinki. Still, as 1970 began, many of these nations, with the exception of Great Britain and perhaps France, had not, in Washington's view, realized the significance of a potential agreement based on a rough Soviet-American parity in place of the long-held American nuclear superiority. Whether this realization would lead to a feeling among Western European countries that the United States— because of the increased danger to itself—would be less willing to come to their aid in the future than it had in the past remained to be seen.

One of the uncertainties at Helsinki concerned Soviet intentions in building so many massive SS-9 ICBM's. By February 20, 1970, according to Secretary of Defense Melvin R. Laird, the Soviet Union had deployed or had under construction over 275 SS-9's. Other officials estimated that, at the current rate of deployment, the figure would approach 400 by the fall of 1970.

An official American projection issued on February 18, 1970, estimated that by the end of the year the Soviet Union would have 1,290 ICBM's, compared to 1,054 for the United States, and 300 submarine-launch ballistic missiles, compared to 656 for the United States. The President expressed concern about the multiple warhead program for the SS-9 and about the Soviet Union's "apparent interest" in improving ICBM accuracy.

In megatonnage, or what is sometimes called "throw weight" (what one side can hurl at the other), the Soviet Union was considerably ahead in terms of land-based missiles.

Moscow's potential for adding MIRV warheads to its SS-9's and for creating a force of mobile, land-based missiles ("easily camouflaged" and "hardly detected by [American] air and space reconnaissance," as the commander of the Soviet Strategic Rocket Forces had boasted in early 1968) added to worries in Washington on the eve of the Vienna meeting.

Exactly what developments produced counterpart worries in Moscow can only be surmised; certainly the far larger American nuclear submarine fleet and the apparently greater American progress in MIRV testing were among such worries. One about which there was no doubt was the development of the American Safeguard ABM system.

On January 30, 1970, President Nixon announced at a press conference that he had decided, after a review, to proceed with the Safeguard system. The first phase, begun after congressional approval in mid-1969, was deployment of the ABM system to protect two complexes of Minuteman missiles, one at Malmstrom Air Force Base in Montana, and the other at Grand Forks Air Force Base in North Dakota. The President indicated at his press conference, that the first phase was to be enlarged and completed, and the second phase was to be initiated, but he did not disclose any details.

On February 24, Laird announced the new program. He called for congressional authorization of an additional Safeguard site at Whiteman Air Force Base in Missouri and of advance preparation work on five more sites, but without a commitment for deployment. The five new sites were to be located in the northeast, the northwest, the Washington, D.C., area, the Michigan-Ohio area, and at Warren Air Force Base in Wyoming. Laird called this "modified phase II" Safeguard program a minimum effort and added that he believed it to be the only viable course, "given

President Nixon's determination to postpone additional actions on U.S. offensive systems this year in order to advance prospects for success at SALT."

Nixon, in January, repeated the two major reasons he had given the previous March for fashioning the Safeguard system: protection of the American ICBM force from Soviet attack and defense of the general population against the possibility of a Chinese attack a decade hence. In speaking of China, Nixon said that, within ten years, "It will be very important for the United States to have some kind of defense so that nuclear blackmail could not be used against the United States" (or its Pacific allies). He appeared to be thinking of the effect his Guam doctrine— the pulling back of conventional American military power— would have on the balance of power in Asia. Thus he argued that the Safeguard system would give the United States "a credible foreign policy in the Pacific it otherwise would not have."

The Nixon decision, with the second round of the SALT talks impending, set off a new round of congressional and public debate on the Safeguard system, the MIRV program, and their relationship to a possible strategic arms limitation agreement with the Soviet Union.

The problems ahead in arms control were highlighted on February 18 in the President's report to Congress on United States foreign policy for the 1970's. He informed Congress and the nation, "We are now entering an era in which the sophistication and destructiveness of weapons present more formidable and complex issues affecting our strategic posture." He found a serious threat to the retaliatory capability of the United States in the growing forces of Soviet missiles, land- and sea-based, with greater accuracy and with multiple warheads. He suggested three categories of proposals for the SALT talks that would enable the United States to respond to a broad range of Soviet proposals: a limitation on the numbers of missiles, limitations on the capabilities of missiles, and a reduction in offensive forces.

The dilemma Nixon faced in his efforts to design strategic forces for the 1970's was described in these words:

> I recognize that decisions on shaping our strategic posture are perhaps the most complex and fateful we face. The answers to these questions will largely determine whether we will be forced into increased deployments to offset the Soviet threat to the sufficiency of our deterrent, or whether we and the Soviet Union can together move from an era of confrontation to one of negotiation, whether jointly we can pursue responsible, non-provocative strategic arms policies based on sufficiency as a mutually shared goal or whether there will be another round of the arms race.

Two days later, Defense Secretary Laird told Congress that the Soviet Union was continuing rapid deployment of major strategic offensive weapons systems at a rate that could, by the mid-1970's, "place us in a second-rate strategic position with regard to the future security of the free world." Laird announced a military budget for fiscal 1971 that was designed to preserve a range of options for the development of new systems—land-based and, perhaps, mobile missiles, a new submarine missile system, a new manned bomber—all of which, he indicated, would be necessary unless there was progress at the SALT talks. In announcing his budget, Laird once again expressed the gnawing American fear:

> Because the Soviet Union is a closed society, they can conduct their military research and development programs behind a thick veil of secrecy, making it very difficult for us to assess their progress in a timely manner. . . . We simply do not have enough knowledge to assess the threat properly. The only prudent course is to advance our knowledge at a reasonable pace in every area of significance to our future military strength.

As the April 16 date for reconvening the SALT talks in Vienna approached, the bold and the fearful in Washington, in and out of the Administration, began to put pressure on the President. Some wanted him to make only cautious proposals at the talks;

others wanted him to suggest a moratorium on MIRV and ABM deployment, as well as a freeze of ICBM's at the current level. From Moscow came charges that many in the United States, and especially Laird, did not seem to want to curb the arms race at all. It was the familiar mood music that always precedes a serious Soviet-American conference.

The technical problems inherent in any agreement would be intricate. But the essential fact is that the decision leading to agreement would be political. Once again, an American President faced the splendid isolation of the White House at a fateful moment in history. And far away, in Moscow, where there were no prying newsmen or obstreperous legislators to reveal the internal arguments in the Kremlin, the Soviet leaders faced the same critical moment.

Thus, the decade of the 1970's began in hope and fear, in action and reaction. What had been true for a quarter of a century was still true. If a nuclear holocaust was to be avoided, each side was compelled by the stark facts of the nuclear age to talk with the other side; yet each was consumed with doubts about the other's intentions, doubts that induced extreme caution in both Washington and Moscow. But the fundamental truth remained. As President Johnson had put it, on August 26, 1966, "Uneasy is the peace that wears a nuclear crown."

The Baruch Plan

Statement by Bernard M. Baruch, United States Representative to the United Nations Atomic Energy Commission, June 14, 1946

MY FELLOW MEMBERS OF THE UNITED NATIONS ATOMIC ENERGY COMMISSION, AND MY FELLOW CITIZENS OF THE WORLD:

We are here to make a choice between the quick and the dead. That is our business.

Behind the black portent of the new atomic age lies a hope which, seized upon with faith, can work our salvation. If we fail, then we have damned every man to be the slave of Fear. Let us not deceive ourselves: We must elect World Peace or World Destruction.

Science has torn from nature a secret so vast in its potentialities that our minds cower from the terror it creates. Yet terror is not enough to inhibit the use of the atomic bomb. The terror created by weapons has never stopped man from employing them. For each new weapon a defense has been produced, in time. But now we face a condition in which adequate defense does not exist.

Science, which gave us this dread power, shows that it *can* be made a giant help to humanity, but science does *not* show us how to prevent its baleful use. So we have been appointed to obviate that peril by finding a meeting of the minds and the hearts of our people. Only in the will of mankind lies the answer.

It is to express this will and make it effective that we have been assembled. We must provide the mechanism to assure that atomic energy is used for peaceful purposes and preclude its use in war. To that end, we must provide immediate, swift, and sure punishment of those who violate the agreements that are reached by the nations.

Penalization is essential if peace is to be more than a feverish interlude between wars. And, too, the United Nations can prescribe individual responsibility and punishment on the principles applied at Nürnberg by the Union of Soviet Socialist Republics, the United Kingdom, France, and the United States—a formula certain to benefit the world's future.

In this crisis, we represent not only our governments but, in a larger way, we represent the peoples of the world. We must remember that the peoples do not belong to the governments but that the governments belong to the peoples. We must answer their demands; we must answer the world's longing for peace and security.

In that desire the United States shares ardently and hopefully. The search of science for the absolute weapon has reached fruition in this country. But she stands ready to proscribe and destroy this instrument—to lift its use from death to life—if the world will join in a pact to that end.

In our success lies the promise of a new life, freed from the heart-stopping fears that now beset the world. The beginning of victory for the great ideals for which millions have bled and died lies in building a workable plan. Now we approach fulfilment of the aspirations of mankind. At the end of the road lies the fairer, better, surer life we crave and mean to have.

Only by a lasting peace are liberties and democracies strengthened and deepened. War is their enemy. And it will not do to believe that any of us can escape war's devastation. Victor, vanquished, and neutrals alike are affected physically, economically, and morally.

Against the degradation of war we can erect a safeguard. That is the guerdon for which we reach. Within the scope of the formula we outline here there will be found, to those who seek it, the essential elements of our purpose. Others will see only emptiness. Each of us carries his own mirror in which is reflected hope—or determined desperation—courage or cowardice.

There is a famine throughout the world today. It starves men's bodies. But there is a greater famine—the hunger of men's spirit. That starvation can be cured by the conquest of fear, and the substitution of hope, from which springs faith—faith in each other, faith that we want to work together toward salvation, and determination that those who threaten the peace and safety shall be punished.

The peoples of these democracies gathered here have a particular concern with our answer, for their peoples hate war. They will have a heavy exaction to make of those who fail to provide an escape. They are not afraid of an internationalism that protects; they are unwilling to be fobbed off by mouthings about narrow sovereignty, which is today's phrase for yesterday's isolation.

The basis of a sound foreign policy, in this new age, for all the nations here gathered, is that anything that happens, no matter where or how, which menaces the peace of the world, or the economic stability, concerns each and all of us.

That, roughly, may be said to be the central theme of the United Nations. It is with that thought we begin consideration of the most important subject that can engage mankind—life itself.

Let there be no quibbling about the duty and the responsibility of this group and of the governments we represent. I was moved, in the afternoon of my life, to add my effort to gain the world's quest, by the broad mandate under which we were created. The resolution of the General Assembly, passed January 24, 1946 in London, reads:

"Section V. Terms of Reference of the Commission

"The Commission shall proceed with the utmost despatch and enquire into all phases of the problems, and make such recommendations from time to time with respect to them as it finds possible. In particular the Commission shall make specific proposals:

"(*a*) For extending between all nations the exchange of basic scientific information for peaceful ends;

"(*b*) For control of atomic energy to the extent necessary to ensure its use only for peaceful purposes;

"(*c*) For the elimination from national armaments of atomic weapons and of all other major weapons adaptable to mass destruction;

"(*d*) For effective safeguards by way of inspection and other means to protect complying States against the hazards of violations and evasions.

"The work of the Commission should proceed by separate stages, the successful completion of each of which will develop the necessary confidence of the world before the next stage is undertaken. . . ."

Our mandate rests, in text and in spirit, upon the outcome of the Conference in Moscow of Messrs. Molotov of the Union of Soviet Socialist Republics, Bevin of the United Kingdom, and Byrnes of the United States of America. The three Foreign Ministers on December 27, 1945 proposed the establishment of this body.

Their action was animated by a preceding conference in Washington on November 15, 1945, when the President of the United States, associated with Mr. Attlee, Prime Minister of the United Kingdom, and Mr. Mackenzie King, Prime Minister of Canada, stated that international control of the whole field of atomic energy was immediately essential. They proposed the formation of this body. In examining that source, the Agreed Declaration, it will be found that the fathers of the concept recognized the final means of world salvation—the abolition of war. Solemnly they wrote:

"We are aware that the only complete protection for the civilized world from the destructive use of scientific knowledge lies in the prevention of war. No system of safeguards that can be devised will of itself provide an effective guarantee against production of atomic weapons by a nation bent on aggression. Nor can we ignore the possibility of the development of other weapons, or of new methods of warfare, which may constitute as great a threat to civilization as the military use of atomic energy."

Through the historical approach I have outlined, we find ourselves here to test if man can produce, through his will and faith, the miracle of peace, just as he has, through science and skill, the miracle of the atom.

The United States proposes the creation of an International Atomic Development Authority, to which should be entrusted all phases of the development and use of atomic energy, starting with the raw material and including—

1. Managerial control or ownership of all atomic-energy activities potentially dangerous to world security.

2. Power to control, inspect, and license all other atomic activities.

3. The duty of fostering the beneficial uses of atomic energy.

4. Research and development responsibilities of an affirmative character intended to put the Authority in the forefront of atomic knowledge and thus to enable it to comprehend, and therefore to detect, misuse of atomic energy. To be effective, the Authority must itself

be the world's leader in the field of atomic knowledge and development and thus supplement its legal authority with the great power inherent in possession of leadership in knowledge.

I offer this as a basis for beginning our discussion.

But I think the peoples we serve would not believe—and without faith nothing counts—that a treaty, merely outlawing possession or use of the atomic bomb, constitutes effective fulfilment of the instructions to this Commission. Previous failures have been recorded in trying the method of simple renunciation, unsupported by effective guaranties of security and armament limitation. No one would have faith in that approach alone.

Now, if ever, is the time to act for the common good. Public opinion supports a world movement toward security. If I read the signs aright, the peoples want a program not composed merely of pious thoughts but of enforceable sanctions—an international law with teeth in it.

We of this nation, desirous of helping to bring peace to the world and realizing the heavy obligations upon us arising from our possession of the means of producing the bomb and from the fact that it is part of our armament, are prepared to make our full contribution toward effective control of atomic energy.

When an adequate system for control of atomic energy, including the renunciation of the bomb as a weapon, has been agreed upon and put into effective operation and condign punishments set up for violations of the rules of control which are to be stigmatized as international crimes, we propose that—

1. Manufacture of atomic bombs shall stop;

2. Existing bombs shall be disposed of pursuant to the terms of the treaty; and

3. The Authority shall be in possession of full information as to the know-how for the production of atomic energy.

Let me repeat, so as to avoid misunderstanding: My country is ready to make its full contribution toward the end we seek, subject of course to our constitutional processes and to an adequate system of control becoming fully effective, as we finally work it out.

Now as to violations: In the agreement, penalties of as serious a nature as the nations may wish and as immediate and certain in their execution as possible should be fixed for—

1. Illegal possession or use of an atomic bomb;
2. Illegal possession, or separation, of atomic material suitable for use in an atomic bomb;
3. Seizure of any plant or other property belonging to or licensed by the Authority;
4. Wilful interference with the activities of the Authority;
5. Creation or operation of dangerous projects in a manner contrary to, or in the absence of, a license granted by the international control body.

It would be a deception, to which I am unwilling to lend myself, were I not to say to you and to our peoples that the matter of punishment lies at the very heart of our present security system. It might as well be admitted, here and now, that the subject goes straight to the veto power contained in the Charter of the United Nations so far as it relates to the field of atomic energy. The Charter permits penalization only by concurrence of each of the five great powers—the Union of Soviet Socialist Republics, the United Kingdom, China, France, and the United States.

I want to make very plain that I am concerned here with the veto power only as it affects this particular problem. There must be no veto to protect those who violate their solemn agreements not to develop or use atomic energy for destructive purposes.

The bomb does not wait upon debate. To delay may be to die. The time between violation and preventive action or punishment would be all too short for extended discussion as to the course to be followed.

As matters now stand several years may be necessary for another country to produce a bomb, *de novo*. However, once the basic information is generally known, and the Authority has established producing plants for peaceful purposes in the several countries, an illegal seizure of such a plant might permit a malevolent nation to produce a bomb in 12 months, and if preceded by secret preparation and necessary facilities perhaps even in a much shorter time. The time required—the advance warning given of the possible use of a bomb—can only be generally estimated but obviously will depend upon many factors, including the success with which the Authority has been able to introduce elements of safety in the design of its plants and the degree to which illegal and secret preparation for the military use of

system of control is the setting forth, in comprehensive terms, of the functions, responsibilities, powers, and limitations of the Authority. Once a charter for the Authority has been adopted, the Authority and the system of control for which it will be responsible will require time to become fully organized and effective. The plan of control will, therefore, have to come into effect in successive stages. These should be specifically fixed in the charter or means should be otherwise set forth in the charter for transitions from one stage to another, as contemplated in the resolution of the United Nations Assembly which created this Commission.

13. *Disclosures.* In the deliberations of the United Nations Commission on Atomic Energy, the United States is prepared to make available the information essential to a reasonable understanding of the proposals which it advocates. Further disclosures must be dependent, in the interests of all, upon the effective ratification of the treaty. When the Authority is actually created, the United States will join the other nations in making available the further information essential to that organization for the performance of its functions. As the successive stages of international control are reached, the United States will be prepared to yield, to the extent required by each stage, national control of activities in this field to the Authority.

14. *International Control.* There will be questions about the extent of control to be allowed to national bodies, when the Authority is established. Purely national authorities for control and development of atomic energy should to the extent necessary for the effective operation of the Authority be subordinate to it. This is neither an endorsement nor a disapproval of the creation of national authorities. The Commission should evolve a clear demarcation of the scope of duties and responsibilities of such national authorities.

And now I end. I have submitted an outline for present discussion. Our consideration will be broadened by the criticism of the United States proposals and by the plans of the other nations, which, it is to be hoped, will be submitted at their early convenience. I and my associates of the United States Delegation will make available to each member of this body books and pamphlets, including the Acheson-Lilienthal report, recently made by the United States Department of State, and the McMahon Committee Monograph No. 1 entitled "Essential Information on Atomic Energy" relating to the McMahon

reactors, the use of such tracers, and to some extent the production of power should be open to nations and their citizens under reasonable licensing arrangements from the Authority. Denatured materials, whose use we know also requires suitable safeguards, should be furnished for such purposes by the Authority under lease or other arrangement. Denaturing seems to have been overestimated by the public as a safety measure.

7. *Definition of Dangerous and Non-Dangerous Activities.* Although a reasonable dividing line can be drawn between dangerous and non-dangerous activities, it is not hard and fast. Provision should, therefore, be made to assure constant reexamination of the questions and to permit revision of the dividing line as changing conditions and new discoveries may require.

8. *Operations of Dangerous Activities.* Any plant dealing with uranium or thorium after it once reaches the potential of dangerous use must be not only subject to the most rigorous and competent inspection by the Authority, but its actual operation shall be under the management, supervision, and control of the Authority.

9. *Inspection.* By assigning intrinsically dangerous activities exclusively to the Authority, the difficulties of inspection are reduced. If the Authority is the only agency which may lawfully conduct dangerous activities, then visible operation by others than the Authority will constitute an unambiguous danger signal. Inspection will also occur in connection with the licensing functions of the Authority.

10. *Freedom of Access.* Adequate ingress and egress for all qualified representatives of the Authority must be assured. Many of the inspection activities of the Authority should grow out of, and be incidental to, its other functions. Important measures of inspection will be associated with the tight control of raw materials, for this is a keystone of the plan. The continuing activities of prospecting, survey, and research in relation to raw materials will be designed not only to serve the affirmative development functions of the Authority but also to assure that no surreptitious operations are conducted in the raw-materials field by nations or their citizens.

11. *Personnel.* The personnel of the Authority should be recruited on a basis of proven competence but also so far as possible on an international basis.

12. *Progress by Stages.* A primary step in the creation of the

ownership, dominion, licenses, operation, inspection, research, and management by competent personnel. After this is provided for, there should be as little interference as may be with the economic plans and the present private, corporate, and state relationships in the several countries involved.

2. *Raw Materials.* The Authority should have as one of its earliest purposes to obtain and maintain complete and accurate information on world supplies of uranium and thorium and to bring them under its dominion. The precise pattern of control for various types of deposits of such materials will have to depend upon the geological, mining, refining, and economic facts involved in different situations.

The Authority should conduct continuous surveys so that it will have the most complete knowledge of the world geology of uranium and thorium. Only after all current information on world sources of uranium and thorium is known to us all can equitable plans be made for their production, refining, and distribution.

3. *Primary Production Plants.* The Authority should exercise complete managerial control of the production of fissionable materials. This means that it should control and operate all plants producing fissionable materials in dangerous quantities and must own and control the product of these plants.

4. *Atomic Explosives.* The Authority should be given sole and exclusive right to conduct research in the field of atomic explosives. Research activities in the field of atomic explosives are essential in order that the Authority may keep in the forefront of knowledge in the field of atomic energy and fulfil the objective of preventing illicit manufacture of bombs. Only by maintaining its position as the best-informed agency will the Authority be able to determine the line between intrinsically dangerous and non-dangerous activities.

5. *Strategic Distribution of Activities and Materials.* The activities entrusted exclusively to the Authority because they are intrinsically dangerous to security should be distributed throughout the world. Similarly, stockpiles of raw materials and fissionable materials should not be centralized.

6. *Non-Dangerous Activities.* A function of the Authority should be promotion of the peaceful benefits of atomic energy.

Atomic research (except in explosives), the use of research reactors, the production of radioactive traces by means of non-dangerous

atomic energy will have been eliminated. Presumably no nation would think of starting a war with only one bomb. This shows how imperative speed is in detecting and penalizing violations.

The process of prevention and penalization—a problem of profound statecraft—is, as I read it, implicit in the Moscow statement, signed by the Union of Soviet Socialist Republics, the United States, and the United Kingdom a few months ago.

But before a country is ready to relinquish any winning weapons it must have more than words to reassure it. It must have a guarantee of safety, not only against the offenders in the atomic area but against the illegal users of other weapons—bacteriological, biological, gas— perhaps—why not? against war itself.

In the elimination of war lies our solution, for only then will nations cease to compete with one another in the production and use of dread "secret" weapons which are evaluated solely by their capacity to kill. This devilish program takes us back not merely to the Dark Ages but from cosmos to chaos. If we succeed in finding a suitable way to control atomic weapons, it is reasonable to hope that we may also preclude the use of other weapons adaptable to mass destruction. When a man learns to say "A" he can, if he chooses, learn the rest of the alphabet too.

Let this be anchored in our minds:

Peace is never long preserved by weight of metal or by an armament race. Peace can be made tranquil and secure only by understanding and agreement fortified by sanctions. We must embrace international cooperation or international disintegration.

Science has taught us how to put the atom to work. But to make it work for good instead of for evil lies in the domain dealing with the principles of human duty. We are now facing a problem more of ethics than of physics.

The solution will require apparent sacrifice in pride and in position, but better pain as the price of peace than death as the price of war.

I now submit the following measures as representing the fundamental features of a plan which would give effect to certain of the conclusions which I have epitomized.

1. *General.* The Authority should set up a thorough plan for control of the field of atomic energy, through various forms of

bill recently passed by the United States Senate, which may prove of value in assessing the situation.

All of us are consecrated to making an end of gloom and hopelessness. It will not be an easy job. The way is long and thorny, but supremely worth traveling. All of us want to stand erect, with our faces to the sun, instead of being forced to burrow into the earth, like rats.

The pattern of salvation must be worked out by all for all.

The light at the end of the tunnel is dim, but our path seems to grow brighter as we actually begin our journey. We cannot yet light the way to the end. However, we hope the suggestions of my Government will be illuminating.

Let us keep in mind the exhortation of Abraham Lincoln, whose words, uttered at a moment of shattering national peril, form a complete text for our deliberation. I quote, paraphrasing slightly:

"We cannot escape history. We of this meeting will be remembered in spite of ourselves. No personal significance or insignificance can spare one or another of us. The fiery trial through which we are passing will light us down in honor or dishonor to the latest generation.

"We say we are for Peace. The world will not forget that we say this. We know how to save Peace. The world knows that we do. We, even we here, hold the power and have the responsibility.

"We shall nobly save, or meanly lose, the last, best hope of earth. The way is plain, peaceful, generous, just—a way which, if followed, the world will forever applaud."

My thanks for your attention.

Aerial Inspection Proposals Submitted by the Western Powers and the Soviet Union

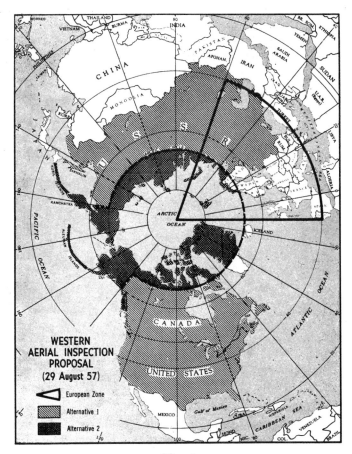

WESTERN
AERIAL INSPECTION
PROPOSAL
(29 August 57)

▷ European Zone

▨ Alternative 1

■ Alternative 2

MAP 1

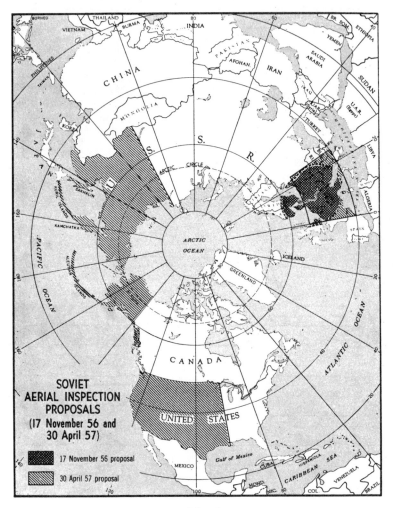

SOVIET AERIAL INSPECTION PROPOSALS
(17 November 56 and 30 April 57)

17 November 56 proposal

30 April 57 proposal

Map 2

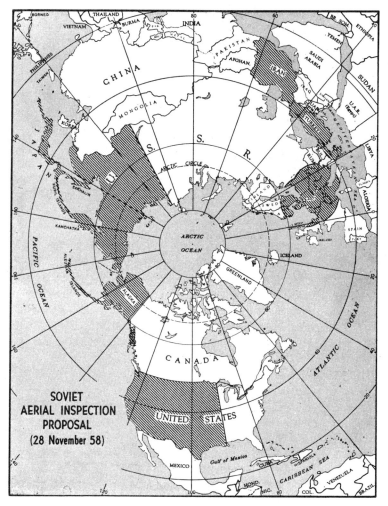

SOVIET
AERIAL INSPECTION
PROPOSAL
(28 November 58)

Map 3

Treaty Banning Nuclear Weapon Tests in the Atmosphere, in Outer Space, and Under Water

The Governments of the United States of America, the United Kingdom of Great Britain and Northern Ireland, and the Union of Soviet Socialist Republics, hereinafter referred to as the "Original Parties",

Proclaiming as their principal aim the speediest possible achievement of an agreement on general and complete disarmament under strict international control in accordance with the objectives of the United Nations which would put an end to the armaments race and eliminate the incentive to the production and testing of all kinds of weapons, including nuclear weapons,

Seeking to achieve the discontinuance of all test explosions of nuclear weapons for all time, determined to continue negotiations to this end, and desiring to put an end to the contamination of man's environment by radioactive substances,

Have agreed as follows:

Article I

1. Each of the Parties to this Treaty undertakes to prohibit, to prevent, and not to carry out any nuclear weapon test explosion, or

any other nuclear explosion, at any place under its jurisdiction or control:

(a) in the atmosphere; beyond its limits, including outer space; or underwater, including territorial waters or high seas; or

(b) in any other environment if such explosion causes radioactive debris to be present outside the territorial limits of the State under whose jurisdiction or control such explosion is conducted. It is understood in this connection that the provisions of this subparagraph are without prejudice to the conclusion of a treaty resulting in the permanent banning of all nuclear test explosions, including all such explosions underground, the conclusion of which, as the Parties have stated in the Preamble to this Treaty, they seek to achieve.

2. Each of the Parties to this Treaty undertakes furthermore to refrain from causing, encouraging, or in any way participating in, the carrying out of any nuclear weapon test explosion, or any other nuclear explosion, anywhere which would take place in any of the environments described, or have the effect referred to, in paragraph 1 of this Article.

Article II

1. Any Party may propose amendments to this Treaty. The text of any proposed amendment shall be submitted to the Depositary Governments which shall circulate it to all Parties of this Treaty. Thereafter, if requested to do so by one-third or more of the Parties, the Depositary Governments shall convene a conference, to which they shall invite all the Parties, to consider such amendment.

2. Any amendment to this Treaty must be approved by a majority of the votes of all the Parties to this Treaty, including the votes of all of the Original Parties. The amendment shall enter into force for all Parties upon the deposit of instruments of ratification by a majority of all the Parties, including the instruments of ratification of all of the Original Parties.

Article III

1. This Treaty shall be open to all States for signature. Any State which does not sign this Treaty before its entry into force in accordance with paragraph 3 of this Article may accede to it at any time.

2. This Treaty shall be subject to ratification by signatory States. Instruments of ratification and instruments of accession shall be deposited with the Governments of the Original Parties—the United States of America, the United Kingdom of Great Britain and Northern Ireland, and the Union of Soviet Socialist Republics—which are hereby designated the Depositary Governments.

3. This Treaty shall enter into force after its ratification by all the Original Parties and the deposit of their instruments of ratification.

4. For States whose instruments of ratification or accession are deposited subsequent to the entry into force of this Treaty, it shall enter into force on the date of the deposit of their instruments of ratification or accession.

5. The Depositary Governments shall promptly inform all signatory and acceding States of the date of each signature, the date of deposit of each instrument of ratification of and accession to this Treaty, the date of its entry into force, and the date of receipt of any requests for conferences or other notices.

6. This Treaty shall be registered by the Depositary Governments pursuant to Article 102 of the Charter of the United Nations.

Article IV

This Treaty shall be of unlimited duration.

Each Party shall in exercising its national sovereignty have the right to withdraw from the Treaty if it decides that extraordinary events, related to the subject matter of this Treaty, have jeopardized the supreme interests of its country. It shall give notice of such withdrawal to all other Parties to the Treaty three months in advance.

Article V

This Treaty, of which the English and Russian texts are equally authentic, shall de deposited in the archives of the Depositary Governments. Duly certified copies of this Treaty shall be transmitted by the Depositary Governments to the Governments of the signatory and acceding States.

IN WITNESS WHEREOF the undersigned, duly authorized, have signed this Treaty.

DONE in triplicate at the city of Moscow the fifth day of August, one thousand nine hundred and sixty-three.

For the Government of the United States of America	For the Government of the United Kingdom of Great Britain and Northern Ireland	For the Government of the Union of Soviet Socialist Republics

Treaty on the Nonproliferation of Nuclear Weapons July 1, 1968

The States concluding this Treaty, hereinafter referred to as the "Parties to the Treaty,"

Considering the devastation that would be visited upon all mankind by a nuclear war and the consequent need to make every effort to avert the danger of such a war and to take measures to safeguard the security of peoples,

Believing that the proliferation of nuclear weapons would seriously enhance the danger of nuclear war,

In conformity with resolutions of the United Nations General Assembly calling for the conclusion of an agreement on the prevention of wider dissemination of nuclear weapons,

Undertaking to cooperate in facilitating the application of International Atomic Energy safeguards on peaceful nuclear activities.

Expressing their support for research, development and other efforts to further the application, within the framework of the International Atomic Energy Agency safeguards system, of the principle of safeguarding effectively the flow of source and special fissionable materials by use of instruments and other techniques at certain strategic points,

Affirming the principle that the benefits of peaceful applications of nuclear technology, including any technological by-products which may be derived by nuclear-weapon States from the development of

nuclear explosive devices, should be available for peaceful purposes to all Parties to the Treaty, whether nuclear-weapon or non-nuclear-weapon States,

Convinced that, in furtherance of this principle, all Parties to the Treaty are entitled to participate in the fullest possible exchange of scientific information for, and to contribute alone or in cooperation with other States to, the further development of the applications of atomic energy for peaceful purposes,

Declaring their intention to achieve at the earliest possible date the cessation of the nuclear arms race and to undertake effective measures in the direction of nuclear disarmament,

Urging the cooperation of all States in the attainment of this objective,

Recalling the determination expressed by the Parties to the 1963 Treaty banning nuclear weapon tests in the atmosphere, in outer space and under water in its Preamble to seek to achieve the discontinuance of all test explosions of nuclear weapons for all time and to continue negotiations to this end,

Desiring to further the easing of international tension and the strengthening of trust between States in order to facilitate the cessation of the manufacture of nuclear weapons, the liquidation of all their existing stockpiles, and the elimination from national arsenals of nuclear weapons and the means of their delivery pursuant to a treaty on general and complete disarmament under strict and effective international control,

Recalling that, in accordance with the Charter of the United Nations, States must refrain in their international relations from the threat or use of force against the territorial integrity or political independence of any State, or in any other manner inconsistent with the Purposes of the United Nations, and that the establishment and maintenance of international peace and security are to be promoted with the least diversion for armaments of the world's human and economic resources,

Have agreed as follows:

Article I

Each nuclear-weapon State Party to the Treaty undertakes not to transfer to any recipient whatsoever nuclear weapons or other nuclear

explosive devices or control over such weapons or explosive devices directly, or indirectly; and not in any way to assist, encourage, or induce any non-nuclear-weapon State to manufacture or otherwise acquire nuclear weapons or other nuclear explosive devices, or control over such weapons or explosive devices.

Article II

Each non-nuclear-weapon State Party to the Treaty undertakes not to receive the transfer from any transferor whatsoever of nuclear weapons or other nuclear explosive devices or of control over such weapons or explosive devices directly, or indirectly; not to manufacture or otherwise acquire nuclear weapons or other nuclear explosive devices; and not to seek or receive any assistance in the manufacture of nuclear weapons or other nuclear explosive devices.

Article III

1. Each non-nuclear-weapon State Party to the Treaty undertakes to accept safeguards, as set forth in an agreement to be negotiated and concluded with the International Atomic Energy Agency in accordance with the Statute of the International Atomic Energy Agency and the Agency's safeguards system, for the exclusive purpose of verification of the fulfillment of its obligations assumed under this Treaty with a view to preventing diversion of nuclear energy from peaceful uses to nuclear weapons or other nuclear explosive devices. Procedures for the safeguards required by this article shall be followed with respect to source or special fissionable material whether it is being produced, processed or used in any principal nuclear facility or is outside any such facility. The safeguards required by this article shall be applied on all source or special fissionable material in all peaceful nuclear activities within the territory of such State, under its jurisdiction, or carried out under its control anywhere.

2. Each State Party to the Treaty undertakes not to provide: (a) source or special fissionable material, or (b) equipment or material especially designed or prepared for the processing, use or production of special fissionable material, to any non-nuclear-weapon State for peaceful purposes, unless the source or special fissionable material shall be subject to the safeguards required by this article.

3. The safeguards required by this article shall be implemented in a manner designed to comply with article IV of this Treaty, and to avoid hampering the economic or technological development of the Parties or international cooperation in the field of peaceful nuclear activities, including the international exchange of nuclear material and equipment for the processing, use or production of nuclear material for peaceful purposes in accordance with the provisions of this article and the principle of safeguarding set forth in the Preamble of the Treaty.

4. Non-nuclear-weapon States Party to the Treaty shall conclude agreements with the International Atomic Energy Agency to meet the requirements of this article either individually or together with other States in accordance with the Statute of the International Atomic Energy Agency. Negotiation of such agreements shall commence within 180 days from the original entry into force of this Treaty. For States depositing their instruments of ratification or accession after the 180-day period, negotiation of such agreements shall commence not later than the date of such deposit. Such agreements shall enter into force not later than eighteen months after the date of initiation of negotiations.

Article IV

1. Nothing in this Treaty shall be interpreted as affecting the inalienable right of all the Parties to the Treaty to develop research, production and use of nuclear energy for peaceful purposes without discrimination and in conformity with articles I and II of this Treaty.

2. All the Parties to the Treaty undertake to facilitate, and have the right to participate in, the fullest possible exchange of equipment, materials, and scientific and technological information for the peaceful uses of nuclear energy. Parties to the Treaty in a position to do so shall also cooperate in contributing alone or together with other States or international organizations to the further development of the applications of nuclear energy for peaceful purposes, especially in the territories of non-nuclear-weapon States Party to the Treaty, with due consideration for the needs of the developing areas of the world.

Article V

Each Party to the Treaty undertakes to take appropriate measures to ensure that, in accordance with this Treaty, under appropriate international observation and through appropriate international procedures, potential benefits from any peaceful applications of nuclear explosions will be made available to non-nuclear-weapon States Party to the Treaty on a non-discriminatory basis and that the charge to such Parties for the explosive devices used will be as low as possible and exclude any charge for research and development. Non-nuclear-weapon States Party to the Treaty shall be able to obtain such benefits, pursuant to a special international agreement or agreements, through an appropriate international body with adequate representation of non-nuclear-weapon States. Negotiations on this subject shall commence as soon as possible after the Treaty enters into force. Non-nuclear-weapon States Party to the Treaty so desiring may also obtain such benefits pursuant to bilaterial agreements.

Article VI

Each of the Parties to the Treaty undertakes to pursue negotiations in good faith on effective measures relating to cessation of the nuclear arms race at an early date and to nuclear disarmament, and on a treaty on general and complete disarmament under strict and effective international control.

Article VII

Nothing in this Treaty affects the right of any group of States to conclude regional treaties in order to assure the total absence of nuclear weapons in their respective territories.

Article VIII

1. Any Party to the Treaty may propose amendments to this Treaty. The text of any proposed amendment shall be submitted to the Depositary Governments which shall circulate it to all Parties to the Treaty. Thereupon, if requested to do so by one-third or more of the Parties to the Treaty, the Depositary Governments shall convene

a conference, to which they shall invite all the Parties to the Treaty, to consider such an amendment.

2. Any amendment to this Treaty must be approved by a majority of the votes of all the Parties to the Treaty, including the votes of all nuclear-weapon States Party to the Treaty and all other Parties which, on the date the amendment is circulated, are members of the Board of Governors of the International Atomic Energy Agency. The amendment shall enter into force for each Party that deposits its instrument of ratification of the amendment upon the deposit of such instruments of ratification by a majority of all the Parties, including the instruments of ratification of all nuclear-weapon States Party to the Treaty and all other Parties which, on the date the amendment is circulated, are members of the Board of Governors of the International Atomic Energy Agency. Thereafter, it shall enter into force for any other Party upon the deposit of its instrument of ratification of the amendment.

3. Five years after the entry into force of this Treaty, a conference of Parties to the Treaty shall be held in Geneva, Switzerland, in order to review the operation of this Treaty with a view to assuring that the purposes of the Preamble and the provisions of the Treaty are being realized. At intervals of five years thereafter, a majority of the Parties to the Treaty may obtain, by submitting a proposal to this effect to the Depositary Governments, the convening of further conferences with the same objective of reviewing the operation of the Treaty.

Article IX

1. This Treaty shall be open to all States for signature. Any State which does not sign the Treaty before its entry into force in accordance with paragraph 3 of this article may accede to it at any time.

2. This Treaty shall be subject to ratification by signatory States. Instruments of ratification and instruments of accession shall be deposited with the Governments of the United States of America, the United Kingdom of Great Britain and Northern Ireland and the Union of Soviet Socialist Republics, which are hereby designated the Depository Governments.

3. This Treaty shall enter into force after its ratification by the States, the Governments of which are designated Depositaries of the

Treaty, and forty other States signatory to this Treaty and the deposits of their instruments of ratification. For the purposes of this Treaty, a nuclear-weapon State is one which has manufactured and exploded a nuclear weapon or other nuclear explosive device prior to January 1, 1967.

4. For States whose instruments of ratification or accession are deposited subsequent to the entry into force of this Treaty, it shall enter into force on the date of the deposit of their instruments of ratification or accession.

5. The Depositary Governments shall promptly inform all signatory and acceding States of the date of each signature, the date of deposit of each instrument of ratification or of accession, the date of the entry into force of this Treaty, and the date of receipt of any requests for convening a conference or other notices.

6. This Treaty shall be registered by the Depositary Governments pursuant to article 102 of the Charter of the United Nations.

Article X

1. Each Party shall in exercising its national sovereignty have the right to withdraw from the Treaty if it decides that extraordinary events, related to the subject matter of this Treaty, have jeopardized the supreme interests of its country. It shall give notice of such withdrawal to all other Parties to the Treaty and to the United Nations Security Council three months in advance. Such notice shall include a statement of the extraordinary events it regards as having jeopardized its supreme interests.

2. Twenty-five years after the entry into force of the Treaty, a conference shall be convened to decide whether the Treaty shall continue in force indefinitely, or shall be extended for an additional fixed period or periods. This decision shall be taken by a majority of the Parties to the Treaty.

Article XI

This Treaty, the English, Russian, French, Spanish and Chinese texts of which are equally authentic, shall be deposited in the archives of the Depositary Governments. Duly certified copies of this Treaty

shall be transmitted by the Depositary Governments to the Governments of the signatory and acceding States.

IN WITNESS WHEREOF the undersigned, duly authorized, have signed this Treaty.

Done in triplicate, at the cities of Washington, London and Moscow, this first day of July one thousand nine hundred sixty-eight.

United Nations Security Council Resolution 255, Adopted by the Security Council at Its 1433d Meeting on 19 June 1968

The Security Council,

Noting with appreciation the desire of a large number of States to subscribe to the Treaty on the Non-Proliferation of Nuclear Weapons, and thereby to undertake not to receive the transfer from any transferor whatsoever of nuclear weapons or other nuclear explosive devices or of control over such weapons or explosive devices directly, or indirectly; not to manufacture or otherwise acquire nuclear weapons or other nuclear explosive devices; and not to seek or receive any assistance in the manufacture of nuclear weapons or other nuclear explosive devices,

Taking into consideration the concern of certain of these States that, in conjunction with their adherence to the Treaty on the Non-Proliferation of Nuclear Weapons, appropriate measures be undertaken to safeguard their security,

Bearing in mind that any aggression accompanied by the use of nuclear weapons would endanger the peace and security of all States,

1. Recognizes that aggression with nuclear weapons or the threat of such aggression against a non-nuclear-weapon State would create a situation in which the Security Council, and above all its nuclear-weapon State, permanent members, would have to act immediately in accordance with their obligations under the United Nations Charter;

2. Welcomes the intention expressed by certain States that they will provide or support immediate assistance, in accordance with the Charter, to any non-nuclear-weapon State Party to the Treaty on the Non-Proliferation of Nuclear Weapons that is a victim of an act or an object of a threat of aggression in which nuclear weapons are used;

3. Reaffirms in particular the inherent right, recognized under Article 51 of the Charter, of individual and collective self-defense if an armed attack occurs against a Member of the United Nations, until the Security Council has taken measures necessary to maintain international peace and security.

Declaration of the Government of the United States of America Made in the United Nations Security Council in Explanation of Its Vote for Security Council Resolution 255

The Government of the United States notes with appreciation the desire expressed by a large number of States to subscribe to the treaty on the non-proliferation of nuclear weapons.

We welcome the willingness of these States to undertake not to receive the transfer from any transferor whatsoever of nuclear weapons or other nuclear explosive devices or of control over such weapons or explosive devices directly, or indirectly; not to manufacture or otherwise acquire nuclear weapons or other nuclear explosive devices; and not to seek or receive any assistance in the manufacture of nuclear weapons or other nuclear explosive devices.

The United States also notes the concern of certain of these States that, in conjunction with their adherence to the treaty on the non-proliferation of nuclear weapons, appropriate measures be undertaken to safeguard their security. Any aggression accompanied by the use of nuclear weapons would endanger the peace and security of all States.

Bearing these considerations in mind, the United States declares the following:

Aggression with nuclear weapons, or the threat of such aggression, against a non-nuclear-weapon State would create a qualitatively new situation in which the nuclear-weapon States which are permanent members of the United Nations Security Council would have to act immediately through the Security Council to take the measures necessary to counter such aggression or to remove the threat of aggression in accordance with the United Nations Charter, which calls for taking "* * * effective collective measures for the prevention and removal of

threats to the peace, and for the suppression of acts of aggression or other breaches of the peace * * *". Therefore, any State which commits aggression accompanied by the use of nuclear weapons or which threatens such aggression must be aware that its actions are to be countered effectively by measures to be taken in accordance with the United Nations Charter to suppress the aggression or remove the threat of aggression.

The United States affirms its intention, as a permanent member of the United Nations Security Council, to seek immediate Council action to provide assistance, in accordance with the Charter, to any non-nuclear-weapon State party to the treaty on the non-proliferation of nuclear weapons that is a victim of an act of aggression or an object of a threat of aggression in which nuclear weapons are used.

The United States reaffirms in particular the inherent right, recognized under Article 51 of the Charter, of individual and collective self-defense if an armed attack, including a nuclear attack, occurs against a Member of the United Nations, until the Security Council has taken measures necessary to maintain international peace and security.

The United States vote for the resolution before us and this statement of the way in which the United States intends to act in accordance with the Charter of the United Nations are based upon the fact that the resolution is supported by other permanent members of the Security Council which are nuclear-weapon States and are also proposing to sign the treaty on the non-proliferation of nuclear weapons, and that these States have made similar statements as to the way in which they intend to act in accordance with the Charter.

Bibliography

Books and articles on various aspects of the nuclear years, relatively scarce in the early period, have multiplied in geometric proportions in the past decade. There is now a wealth of detailed material available —most written by Americans, a considerable amount by other non-Communist authors, but still very little by Soviet writers.

Two continuing sources contain essential information: the annual reports of the U.S. Arms Control and Disarmament Agency and the agency's series entitled Documents on Disarmament. The former covers the work of the agency since its founding; the latter contains basic material about arms control efforts since 1945. Both are available from the Government Printing Office, Washington, D.C. Additional primary sources are the publications of the Institute for Strategic Studies, a private, London-based organization. They include the annual Military Balance and Strategic Survey and the Adelphi Papers, reprints of important articles from Eastern and Western sources on issues in the arms field. A most useful Adelphi Paper is No. 63, "Advanced Strategic Missiles: A Short Guide," by Ian Smart (December, 1969). Also important are the annual defense posture statements that were prepared during the years when Robert S. McNamara was U.S. Secretary of Defense. They are invaluable sources of facts and figures about weapons systems and of the diplomatic context surrounding weapons development.

ACHESON, DEAN. *Present at the Creation.* New York: W. W. Norton, 1969. The former Secretary of State's detailed memoirs.

BADER, WILLIAM B. *The United States and the Spread of Nuclear Weapons.* New York: Pegasus, 1968.

BARUCH, BERNARD M. *My Own Story.* New York: Holt, Rinehart and Winston, 1957.

BEAL, JOHN ROBINSON. *John Foster Dulles: 1888–1959.* New York: Harper & Bros., 1959. A highly favorable account of a powerful Secretary of State.

BECHHOEFER, BERNHARD G. *Postwar Negotiations for Arms Control.* Washington, D.C.: The Brookings Institution, 1961. The definitive account of what occurred from the genesis of the Baruch Plan through 1960.

BYRNES, JAMES F. *Speaking Frankly.* New York: Harper & Bros., 1947. Includes the former Secretary of State's version of his differences with President Truman.

CHASE, HAROLD W., and LERMAN, ALLEN H., eds. *Kennedy and the Press.* New York: Thomas Y. Crowell, 1965. An annotated collection of the President's press conferences.

CHAYES, ABRAM, and WIESNER, JEROME B., eds. *ABM.* New York: Harper & Row, 1969. A melange of authors explain why they believe the ABM is not needed.

CLEMENS, WALTER C., JR., *The Arms Race and Sino-Soviet Relations.* Stanford, Calif.: The Hoover Institution, 1968. A well-documented, conservative view.

DALLIN, ALEXANDER, et al. *The Soviet Union and Disarmament.* New York: Praeger, 1964. A discussion of Soviet rationale and behavior to which Larson, cited below, is the sequel.

DJILAS, MILOVAN. *Conversations with Stalin.* New York: Harcourt, Brace & World, 1962. A rare glimpse into Stalin's postwar thinking.

EISENHOWER, DWIGHT D. *White House Years.* 2 vols. Garden City, N.Y.: Doubleday, 1963–65.

FLEMING, DENNA F. *The Cold War and Its Origins, 1917–60.* 2 vols. Garden City, N.Y.: Doubleday, 1961. An early version of revisionist history in which most of the blame is attached to the United States.

FONTAINE, ANDRÉ. *History of the Cold War.* 2 vols. New York: Pantheon, 1968–69. The account of an eminent French journalist from a perspective outside the capitals of the two major antagonists.

GARTHOFF, RAYMOND L. *Soviet Military Policy.* New York: Praeger, 1966. One of many useful works by a leading analyst who is also a practitioner for the U.S. Government.

GRODZINS, MORTON, and RABINOWITCH, EUGENE, eds. *The Atomic Age.* New York: Basic Books, 1963. A collection of articles from the *Bulletin of Atomic Scientists*, 1945 to 1962.

HALLE, LOUIS J. *The Cold War as History.* New York: Harper & Row, 1967. A lucid explanation in which the Marshall Plan's role is emphasized.

HILSMAN, ROGER. *To Move a Nation.* Garden City, N.Y.: Doubleday, 1967. A spirited and partisan view of the politics of foreign policy in the Kennedy era.

HORELICK, ARNOLD L., and RUSH, MYRON. *Strategic Power and Soviet Foreign Policy*. Chicago: University of Chicago Press, 1966. A well-documented RAND study.

KISSINGER, HENRY A. *Nuclear Weapons and Foreign Policy*. New York: Harper & Bros., 1957.

LAMONT, LANSING. *Day of Trinity*. New York: Atheneum, 1965. How it all began at Alamogordo, in fascinating detail.

LARSON, THOMAS B. *Disarmament and Soviet Policy, 1964–68*. Englewood Cliffs, N.J.: Prentice-Hall, 1960. Highly useful sequel to Dallin, cited above.

LILIENTHAL, DAVID E. *The Atomic Energy Years, 1945–50*. Vol. 2 of The Journals of David E. Lilienthal. New York: Harper & Row, 1964. Contemporary memoranda on the Truman era.

MACMILLAN, HAROLD. *Tides of Fortune, 1945–55*. New York: Harper & Row, 1969. A less-than-satisfactory British account of a turbulent decade.

SCHLESINGER, ARTHUR M., JR. *A Thousand Days: John F. Kennedy in the White House*. Boston: Houghton Mifflin, 1965.

SCHUBERT, JACK, and LAPP, RALPH E. *Radiation: What It Is and How It Affects You*. New York: The Viking Press, 1957.

SIDEY, HUGH. *John F. Kennedy, President*. New York: Atheneum, 1963. Best of the journalists' histories of the Kennedy era.

SNOW, EDGAR. *The Other Side of the River*. New York: Random House, 1961. Contemporary China as seen by one of those rare people with access to Mao Tse-tung.

SOKOLOVSKII, V., ed. *Soviet Military Strategy*. Englewood Cliffs, N.J.: Prentice-Hall, 1963. A RAND translation of an important Soviet work. Annotated.

SORENSEN, THEODORE H. *Kennedy*. New York: Harper & Row, 1965.

STERN, PHILIP M. (with the collaboration of HAROLD P. GREEN). *The Oppenheimer Case: Security on Trial*. New York: Harper & Row, 1969. An absorbing and definitive account of a celebrated case.

TATU, MICHEL. *Power in the Kremlin: From Khrushchev to Kosygin*. New York: The Viking Press, 1969. A detailed examination by a long-time Moscow correspondent of *Le Monde*.

TRUMAN, HARRY S. *Memoirs*. 2 vols. Garden City, N.Y.: Doubleday, 1955–56.

ULAM, ADAM B. *Expansion and Coexistence: The History of Soviet Foreign Policy, 1917–67*. New York: Praeger, 1968. Probably the best in its field.

VANDENBERG, ARTHUR H., JR., ed. *The Private Papers of Senator Vandenberg.* Boston: Houghton Mifflin, 1952.

WISE, DAVID, and ROSS, THOMAS B. *The Invisible Government.* New York: Random House, 1964. The CIA stripped naked, as nearly as any outsider can do it.

WOLFE, THOMAS W. *Soviet Power and Europe.* 2 vols. Santa Monica, Calif.: The RAND Corporation, 1968–69. Sweeping views and excellent insight. Well documented.

Index

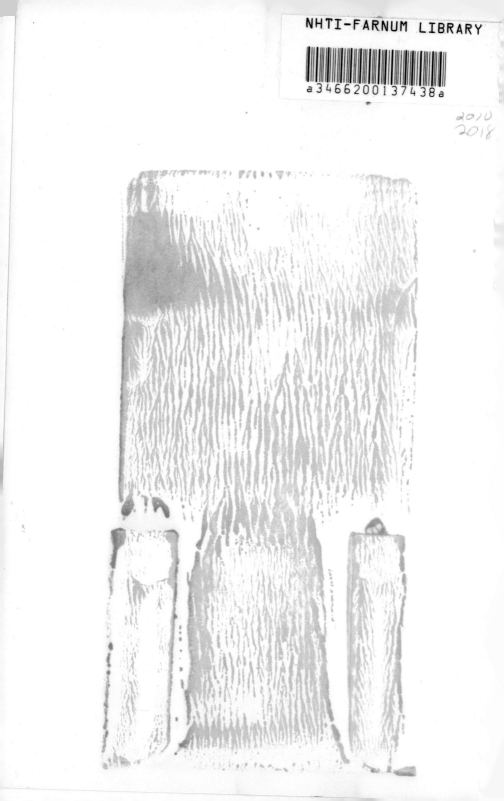

THE USES
OF DIVISION

UNITY AND DISHARMONY
IN LITERATURE

By

John Bayley

THE VIKING PRESS

NEW YORK

Copyright © John Bayley 1976

All rights reserved

Published in 1976 by The Viking Press
625 Madison Avenue, New York, N.Y. 10022

LIBRARY OF CONGRESS CATALOGING IN PUBLICATION DATA
Bayley, John, 1925–
The uses of division.
1. Literature, Modern—History and criticism.
I. Title.
PN701.B3   809   76–12355
ISBN 0–670–74216–3

Printed in the United States of America

Farrar, Straus & Giroux, Inc.: From *High Windows*, Copyright © 1974 by Philip Larkin, From works by John Berryman: from *His Toy, His Dream, His Rest*, *The Dream Songs*, Copyright © 1959, 1962, 1963, 1964, 1965, 1966, 1967, 1968, 1969 by John Berryman, *Homage to Mistress Bradstreet*, Copyright © 1956 by John Berryman, and *Love and Fame*, Copyright © 1970 by John Berryman.

Philip Larkin and Faber & Faber Ltd.: From *The Whitsun Weddings and High Windows*.

The Macmillan Publishing Co., Inc.: From "The Road at My Door" from *Collected Poems* of W.B. Yeats, Copyright © 1928 by Macmillan Publishing Co., Inc., renewed 1956 by Georgie Yeats.

The Marvell Press: From *The Less Deceived* by Philip Larkin.

In the second section of the book part of the chapter on Keats is based on a lecture, 'Keats and Reality,' originally delivered to the British Academy in the series of Chatterton Lectures on an English Poet. The first chapter on Shakespeare incorporates material from a lecture on *Troilus and Cressida* given at the Shakespeare Festival at Stratford, Ontario. Some of the exposition in Chapter I is expanded from an article commissioned by the *Times Literary Supplement* on contemporary ideas about 'Character.'

I should like to take the opportunity of thanking students, both graduate and undergraduate, who have taken part in tutorials and seminars where questions about the novel came up; and particularly Miss Joanne Williams for her interest and support during several terms of such discussions.

CONTENTS

Uses in the Novel

Uses in Poetry

Uses in Shakespeare

8

Uses in the Novel

CHAPTER I

1. Novelist and Critic

Criticism is mainly a matter of transferring a set of ideas from life to literature, and the critic may not himself be conscious just how few these are. The chapters which follow are an attempt to make one kind of use of this limitation. Authors a critic has been especially familiar with over a number of years may have led him to adopt certain principles of understanding, standards and controls which make more clear aspects of their genius or areas of their work, and which in turn help him to judge other kinds and degrees of achievement. The clue that has come up constantly during my study and enjoyment of the writers who figure in this book is that of the involuntary divisions, amounting to a total disunity, which seems to characterize the reality of their art, and to make them what they are.

This is an obvious point, which is none the less often ignored. The usual critical instinct is to show that the work under discussion is as coherent, as aware, as totally organized, as the critic desires his own representation of it to be. It often seems to be the critic's business to prove that the artist was himself a supreme critic. Sometimes, it is true, he may be. Proust is the remarkable instance of a great artist who is also and simultaneously a great critic, explaining as he goes along not only how it became possible for him to write his novel, but what is the point and justification for art in such an enterprise. None the less, and however much his example may have been followed since, Proust is far from typical of the novelist's process. Recognition and elucidation of the organizing and unifying power of the creative and critical intelligence may not get us very far with Dickens or Jane Austen, nor yet with Keats and Shakespeare.

Of course the creative process always begins in division, in ideas and inklings tumbling over each other in the darkness, in Dryden's phrase; but this necessary commencement is not

the point. We take for granted that the work of art represents
a solution, a confluence and a harmony—getting the statue
clean away from the marble, as D. H. Lawrence called it—and
again the obvious truth in such metaphor is not what is here
in question: what matters, rather, is the extent to which disunity
and division may themselves have become aspects—indispensable and irremovable ones—of the artistic whole. This seemed
to me the case with the authors I had felt drawn to write about,
and the phenomenon began to interest me retrospectively. It
seemed worth going into, in search of unexpected kinds and
standards of judgments, rather than to develop anything much
in the way of a critical 'theory'.

The point would be how such a literature works on us, and
how we work upon it, finding what accident rather than intention
put there, and perceiving ourselves how contradictions enlarge
and emancipate the world of experience it offers. The art which
is in any sense explicit, moving us to accept or reject it, to
first one and then the other, or to a modified assent to some
things 'in it', and not others—such an art is not found in the
felicities of a genius inherently baffled and divided. Proust comes
in handy again; for many of his readers, particularly in England
or America, surely feel that the immense pretension of his work,
its massive Bergsonian enterprise of turning life and time into
art, is, quite simply, not what makes it compulsively readable
and ensures its lasting fascination. The *madeleine*, that all too
notorious biscuit dipped in tea, in fact does no more than make
an already familiar point about the way memory works. And,
as Roger Shattuck points out in his book on Proust, one corner-
stone of the work rests on even humbler foundations, the analysis
that follows Montaigne in finding that consciousness is dissati-
fied with whatever it possesses, and is fascinated only by what
it cannot have.

This would not matter if Proust were not himself so closely
identified with his grand concept of the work, if we could feel—
as with so many other authors—that the real interest was not
only undeclared by narrator and method but unperceived by them.
But the enormous exercise of the will towards self-realization
which he has put forth has left Proust, as it left Stendhal,
strangely uninteresting in himself. Self-realization has destroyed
his own potential: his views have become as dull as his letters.
What remains is the authenticity of his world, his eye for trait

and his ear for dialogue, above all his humour, or more accurately his power to make things funny. These reveal a world absorbing in range and detail, but also curiously elementary, flat and two-dimensional as a lesson in *exposition*. There is nothing unsettled or left over to give the whole job a saving instability, to invite by reticence or by irresolution participation by us in the processes of genius. It may be that ultimately, with Proust, we feel we are not in the world of a great transforming spirit of the imagination, like those as diverse as Tolstoy or Hardy or Racine, but with what amounts to a brilliant *translator* (a word that keeps occurring in the final section of the great work) or memoirist, Saint-Simon of the self, whose powers were made for this job alone and not for any complex and irresolute interplay between spirit and the world.

We can take the matter a stage further back. Proust's narrator, like Madame Bovary, finds that the grass is only green elsewhere; that even a bowl of sugar in a grand house, as Emma finds at her single ball, is transformed by this *erreur d'âme* into a different and exotic substance. How much of the novel's—all novels'—material stems from this discovery and from the dissatisfactions that produce it . . . Proust's solid literary backing came from Balzac; and Balzac too is all surface, the most extroverted of all novelists and the novel's greatest *propriétaire*. Like Proust he is not increased by division, as the contrast with Dickens reveals. Where Dickens is the novel's least unified and unitary figure, Balzac, his peer in size and fecundity, is all expansive exposition and logic, innocent of the tension and the reticence which inspires Dickens's imaginative process. As with Proust, the man and his work are at one in Balzac in a very straightforward sense. The worldly and adroit Dickens of business and worldly dealings is not the Dickens of the novels; his *Household Words* prospered, while Balzac's Parisian journal lost money spectacularly. And this shows that Dickens's creations come from a deep level of his unconscious while Balzac's are an aspect of his daily life—he turned his hopes and disasters into fiction as he lived through them, becoming in turn Birotteau, Goriot and Vautrin, Grandet, Gobseck and Nucingen. The poet Yeats adored the novelist Balzac, but nothing could be less Balzacian than Yeats's edict that 'the intellect of man is forced to choose/ Perfection of the life or of the work'. Balzac was a bankrupt inventing bankrupts, an obsessed man dreaming up obsessions: he compelled life to behave to him in the style in which he imagined his own creations.

Yeats's fondness for Balzac is an example of how the artist is rarely given to the common reader's enjoyment of the complication and imbalance so often constituted in a completed work of art. Artists prefer, it may be, an openness which they can themselves transform. In this they are most unlike critics. Where Dickens, in the context of a critical discussion, reveals depths both of conscious sophistication and unconscious meaning, Balzac's obviousness is increased by his very energy and flamboyance; he has no buried riches for the critic to dig up, little for him to offer to engage the renewed interest of the student. In *S/Z*, a structuralist analysis of Balzac's story *Sarrasine*, Roland Barthes comes to some distinctly unsurprising conclusions, notably that Balzac's plot and style is based more on literary cliché than on life. A seemingly arcane method is used to establish what most readers who open a novel take for granted.

But of course the point of Barthes's study is the method itself, intended to excite and intrigue the student, to distract him from the dullness of a 'classic'. Unlike the students, the literary profiteers need no such artificial lure. Henry James loved Balzac, and made use of him, deepening and equivocating his demonstrations of power and the will so that they acquire the uncertainty of inner drama. He does it in *The Aspern Papers*, that most Balzacian of tales, in which the hero has been metamorphosed from capitalist adventurer into the no less unscrupulous would-be possessor of a literary treasure trove, and then begins to aquire a conscience about his situation, an awareness transformed into narrative by way of James's own majestically equivocal consciousness.

Proust, as is natural in the French novel tradition, makes a straightforward use of Balzac, transforming the great capitalist fantasy of possession into the social fantasy of snobbery. He adds no real 'inside', for he has none; only the external theorization which gives to the quest a symmetry and meaning. Such intellectual buttressing is not uncommon in imaginative works whose ambition is to be exhaustive; Joyce's *Ulysses* has it, and so has *The Faerie Queene*, both in a much simpler and impersonal form, which allows an 'inside' to grow independently in it. An imposed form protects the creator in the fruitful dispersion and distraction of his powers. We can do without the Ulysses myth, though Joyce could not, and we can do without Bergson and the *madeleine*, although Proust required them. But his need was fatally more integral, and more personal. Whereas Joyce's structure liberated what may seem to us his real powers, his incongruous and contingent understanding of himself and human life, Proust's keeps him a prisoner within it. He cannot get out, and it seems there is nowhere for him to get out to. The organization he has created is either a substitute for the more volatile and disparate 'meanings' of the work, or it discloses that these have no existence for Proust, that all he has achieved is suitably *asservi*.

*   *   *

To possess an 'inside' a work of literature must display as a part of its achievement some kind of reticence, and the tensions of reticence; and these are a sure indication of powers unresolved below the surface, unresolved in what they suggest to us and the impression they make, but effective and triumphant at the level of artistic exposition. Shakespeare is of course the supreme example. A sure balance, an adroitness in withdrawal and effacement that seems like second nature (as from all that we know of him it was) allies with his genius in presenting an art in which query and contradiction, possibility and puzzlement, are everywhere underneath drama but nowhere embarrass or thwart it at the level of speech. When T. S. Eliot spoke of *Hamlet* as 'most certainly an artistic failure' he showed a singular disregard for this obvious truth. The success is in presenting a play which retains its mystery in idea while wholly and prodigally spending its material in action. *Hamlet* is, so to speak, superficial at the highest level. That Shakespeare did not 'know' *Hamlet* is certain; but that he grasped what was involved must be equally the case, and the turmoil of what was involved, which the artist does not have to get straight or make up his mind about, settles out at the point of maximum effect.

The effect on an audience of *The Beggar's Opera*, or of Wilde's only masterpiece, *The Importance of Being Earnest*, is not in this context much dissimilar. With an ease which seems hardly conscious of the scope of its own insolence Wilde produced not a mystery or an allegory, but a world in which dialogue

and action have alike the bewitching certainty of dramatic effect
and the lost undertones of social and self-query. The ruthlessness
of men and women in the roles which each has forced on or
extorted from the other; the absolute need for society, its
fashions and its disciplines, and the equal need to escape from
it into its anti-world, whose *louche* conventions are both different
and the same: these are just two of the implications that move
beneath the action; and the fact that Wilde himself was only
confusedly aware of what was involved in the bravura of his
own creation is shown by the fact that after his prison sentence
he thought he could still move in two worlds, go 'bunburying'
one day and enchant on the next the rich and powerful in their
own milieu.

This appeal to Wilde's one masterpiece may seem fanciful,
but it demonstrates, more graphically and more obviously than
the invocation of Shakespeare, how compatible the most immaculate display of art can be with a rich confusion of underlying
impulse and motive. And to anyone who has discovered how
to make use of such art, rather than be used, *The Importance of
Being Earnest* can hardly fail to be ultimately a more rewarding
work than the intellectually organized dramatic texts of Wilde's
contemporary, Ibsen. In most of his plays Ibsen simply takes
over the audience, a patronage more memorable and more
powerful than Shaw's, but still a patronage; and that is not
how the divided art that has produced the greatest comedy
tensions—the only real theatrical experience—works. Organization men may be as confused deep down as other artists, but
their confusions are not congenial—not even accessible—to the
spectator or reader in terms of the total comprehended artistic
effect.

To return to the distinction between the art of Proust, and
that of Joyce, Milton, or Spenser. All are God-like in the
authority of their conceptions, but those conceptions, as time
passes, are seen to constitute an increasingly small part of the
artistic whole; and it is here that Proust may go down while the
others continue to rise. The artist must set out to be a god of some
sort and impose the authority and organization of his art upon
the world. If he abjures, if he deliberately abdicates, as many if
not most contemporary novelists have done, he will forfeit
everything, both the force of his conception and the freedom
of his involuntariness. But it is for the reader to refuse to adore

or even to accept divinity, while noting and profiting from the incongruous medley of achievements and illuminations which subsume and accompany the divine claim. We hate the palpable design upon us, as Keats said, though the design may be necessary to the artist in order that what was not designed may come into being.

It was a very large part, if indeed it was not the whole part, of Sterne's design in *Tristram Shandy* to make a satire on Locke and on the 'wires and pulleys' theory of consciousness which dominated his school of thinking in the eighteenth century; but the outcome was very different, just how different has been well expressed by A. D. Nuttall at the end of his study of *Tristram Shandy*, in his book on philosophy and the literary imagination, *The Common Sky*. He points out that Sterne's attack is not in itself either cogent or methodical.

> The incisive criticisms are all mere sparks, which drift from us and are lost in darkness. They are never marshalled; their collective force is never assessed. To be sure, if they had been, *Tristram Shandy* would not be the literary masterpiece it is. . . . It remains, not the destroyer of the fashionable world-picture, but, with its chaotic determinism, its biological psychology and its microscopic observation, its one adequate literary monument.

Sterne, in fact, found himself saying and giving what was in him, rather than demolishing Locke; the design for demolition merged into a new kind of creation which by setting the fashionable notions of consciousness in a comic world did the job very much better. Sterne turned our quotidian consciousness into a new vision of art and hence of itself; and this he did in a way in which Proust—for all his grandiose purpose and method— was not able to achieve. The design for Proust's vision still remains outside the apparent inclusiveness of his art, while Sterne's in *Tristram Shandy* has been metamorphosed into the novel itself.

2. *The Authentic and the Sincere*

When we say that consciousness in *Tristram Shandy* has accidentally become a work of art, or presents itself in the form

of a work of art, we are also on the way to identifying fiction
with kinds of consciousness, and *vice versa*. And that is indeed
the way it has turned out, for the modern reflective consciousness cannot in some sense but see itself as taking part in a novel,
the novel being the standard literary reflection of the individual
in our age. When we speak of 'character' we really mean something that exists only in literature though it is usefully and
almost unconsciously extrapolated back from literature into life.
Simone Weil deplored the fact that contemporary consciousness
sees its image in this form, but it is difficult to see how things
could be otherwise. It is for this reason that so many novelists
feel the compulsion to be contemporary, to hunt about for the
kind of people and the kind of situation which hits off the modern
moment; and though these efforts to be explicit are rarely
successful—for what is typical of an age can only seem so by
hindsight—they do reveal the extent to which both the novelist
and his public are determined to identify themselves with fiction
as a mirror—almost as a trustee—of consciousness.

So much so that the novel finds its most hallowed source of
satire in biting the hand that feeds it, mocking the mental
habits it has itself brought into being. The kind of treatment
Jane Austen gives her heroine in *Northanger Abbey* was already
traditional. Out of the mockery can come new insight—we
should not forget the unobtrusive sharpness with which Jane
Austen distinguishes between Catherine's novel-natured awareness and her natural good feeling—and by disowning itself the
novel can achieve new scenarios to personify awareness. The
process can become sterile, especially in fiction today, no longer
compelled to certain equivocations by social custom, or protected by it from seeing nothing but its own self in the mirror.
In *My Life as a Man* Philip Roth has a hero whose sexual
behaviour is always inventing a scene in conformity with the
fictional consciousness which has invaded every elemental
desire. The novel has become lost in its own preoccupations, so
that the last stronghold of instinct, sexual behaviour in bed,
becomes a minefield of queries, duties and commandments
implanted by 'serious literary studies'. 'Where Emma Bovary
had read too many romances of her period, it would seem that I
had read too much of the criticism of mine.'

The novel that once showed the open map of love, creating
a consciousness for the country, ends up here in the closed

road of sex, fortunately still able to mock itself. But the loneliness of the American literary consciousness that makes it, in novel after novel, the sole index of reality, does not normally find the escape-route of self-mocking comedy. Hemingway's bondage in his later work to his own fictional image of consciousness is perpetuated unremittingly in novelists like Joyce Carol Oates, who take over by pretension the average American awareness and give it the literary status of private nightmare.

The process can be seen as beginning in the early nineteenth century, when the solitary consciousness—the associate and in some sense the begetter of Romanticism—was categorized by Hegel as emerging from collective identity and seeing itself in a solitary state—which the novel speedily turned into a kind of collective and literary solitude. Every reader of a novel is alone in his experience, however populous the world he is asked to inhabit; compared with other kinds of art it is—and indeed should be—the reader's experience that he is the only person to have been there, and for the first time.

Hegel's solitary spirit, cut off by the logic of historical progress from old tribal identities, could find some sort of substitute for them in and as fiction, which, as we see from the success of Byron's poems, did not need in early days to have the form of the novel. One of the most influential texts of this kind was Goethe's *The Sorrows of Werther*, which Lionel Trilling, in his book *Sincerity and Authenticity*, has taken as a prototype sketch of the 'authentic spirit', unconditioned by the old ties of social morality and obligation, but 'moving to its next stage of development'. *Werther* is a tragic tale, because the hero is divided between desire for the social good of his time—marriage, reputation, domestic felicity—and an obscure awareness, ultimately fatal, that these things are not for him. His love for Charlotte really was 'as words could never utter': Thackeray's derisive doggerel makes defensive fun of a power that was disconcerting—because it totally divided his nature. Albert, to whom Charlotte is betrothed, is the honest social consciousness which for Werther, who is spirit seeking its freedom, is an impossibility. Werther wants to be like that, but 'moving on to the next stage of development' forbids it: the dilemma is precisely in the terms in which Hegel was to define tragedy. Werther's world disintegrates: death is the only way out.

Goethe, we can be sure, did not in any sense 'select' the

figure of Werther as being a portent of the age, and the fantastic success of the book, the impression it made on clever and stupid alike, does not mean that the abstract significance which a sensitive historian of ideas like Lionel Trilling reads back into it was at all clearly understood at the time. Goethe was probably less conscious of what he was about than Sterne in *Tristram Shandy*, but in both cases the novel took over, demonstrating thus early on its powers of holding ideas and assertions of the individual consciousness—the author's consciousness—in solution; its capacity to achieve the stasis of art while remaining caught and held in all its various contingencies, and divided against itself. The historian of ideas can render a novel transparent for us, as it were, in the prism of history; and our objection to many a would-be meaningful contemporary novel is that the writer has tried to do the job and render the transparency himself. The novel must remain both solid and opaque, and D. H. Lawrence claimed that it 'is the highest form of human expression so far attained . . . because it is so incapable of the absolute'. It solves no problems; it does not even formulate them.

Lionel Trilling sees it as an important moment in the development of the form when the ideal of *sincerity* gives way to the ideal of *authenticity*; that is, when the conventional values of man being 'true' to himself in society give way to the wholly wayward and unpredictable values of consciousness on its own, Hegel's 'spirit in self-estrangement'. It is arguable, although Trilling does not say so, that authenticity could consist in one assertion: 'I am the hero of a novel and therefore authentic' for, as I remarked earlier, the modern consciousness finds itself through the fiction and is to that extent identical with it. A clear case in a specialized branch of the modern novel—the detective story—would be Raymond Chandler's hero, Philip Marlowe. Marlowe is 'authentic', in Trilling's and the Hegelian sense, not because of the rather unconvincing moral claims made on his behalf, but because he is himself his own story, narrator, and actor. Whether we accept it or not, Marlowe's authenticity is wholly a matter of his book, and, if we wish, we can acquire that authenticity from him at second-hand, as contemporaries acquired that of Werther or of Byron's heroes, with the difference that this Marlovian authenticity is far more solitary and *sui generis*.

But it seems more likely that the consciousness which has both found and fed on the novel as its chosen literary form does not, in fact, proceed from 'sincerity' to 'authenticity' but plays one off against the other, making use of both. The novelist himself may be both the tool and the beneficiary of the process. One of Trilling's examples is Diderot's curious work *Le Neveu de Rameau*, which so many critics of the human psyche and its development have taken as a key text. Written about 1770, in the same decade as *Werther*, the book records from Diderot's standpoint, as *honnête homme* committed to the social ideal of sincerity, the extraordinary and clowning self-display of the composer Rameau's nephew, a pure *authentique* in whom utter shamelessness and anarchy of impulse appears as the index of integrity. The nephew certainly strikes us as a highly modern kind of portent, and not long after his arrival he was seized on gleefully by Hegel as an example of the concept of emergent and anarchic *geist*. Diderot, in a sense his 'creator', for the real nephew only comes to us through his authorial medium, is both wholly fascinated by this phenomenon and deeply disapproving, and this division, or rather equilibrium, was to become—we could say—the most powerful weapon in the novelist's armoury. Only think of Quilp, in Dickens's *The Old Curiosity Shop*, who receives the whole charge of the 'authentic' that lurked in Dickens, while at the same time the social and moral forces in the story are devoted to his destruction. *Wuthering Heights* achieves at a much intenser imaginative level the same equilibrium between Heathcliff and the Lintons, and the two houses which embody their relation and its antagonisms. By the time of D. H. Lawrence's novel, the *geist* of Rameau's nephew is in complete control, its derisiveness merging into new prophecy which is none the less remote from any social ideal.

Tom Jones is an eighteenth-century hero of the 'sincere', and the fact that he is a scapegrace and far from perfect does not make him in the least 'authentic'—it merely gives greater flexibility, humanity and good sense to the social ideal. Thackeray, like Fielding, is a novelist unconcerned with the 'authentic', and unendowed, despite his position in the nineteenth century, with any underground sympathy for it: his amused contempt for Werther may have something uneasy about it but not the uneasiness which comes from covert understanding. Becky Sharp is the example of how Thackeray resolutely situates character inside the old-fashioned social conditioning. When she says she could have been a good woman if she had five thousand a year, the 'sincere' might almost be said to utter, in terms of fiction, its last gasp. If it is true, if Thackeray or Becky herself mean it, then Becky becomes—and fortunately for the novel at a late stage of it—a person of no inner potential. If it is not true, then Becky still does not become in any sense an *authentique*, because the remark shows her perfectly able and willing to live in society on its own terms, paying the normal debt that vice owes to virtue, which is simply the reversed coin of 'sincerity'. Becky is in fact wholly a socially conditioned person, a proper denizen of Vanity Fair, and as a heroine that is her true justification. There is nothing divided in Thackeray's creative regard for her, nor, so far as we can see, in Thackeray himself.

In Jane Austen there is. As she shows us in *Northanger Abbey*, and more interestingly in *Sense and Sensibility*, she could divine that the sub-Werther cult threatened the authority of the novel about society as it did honest society itself, and for the same reasons. But her genius was itself an enemy within the gates; it could be, and was, anarchic; it sniffed the solitude of the future; it understood deep down the alienation of *geist*. These may seem wild words, but the fact is that our continued and indeed increasing fascination with her world is based on an apprehension of what might loosely be called the revolutionary in her, the tension between the growing claims of the individual and those of society. The weight of her art hangs, literally, in the balance. It understands—to adapt a remark of Q. D. Leavis about Sir Thomas Bertram, which I shall have occasion to quote again—that any purely social ideal is invaluable, but that it is also insufferable; and that though the novel may reconcile the two, nothing else can.

There is thus something in her art which makes the novel of honest society, both before and after her, look distinctly anachronistic. For in so far as it accepted society, and saw its dramatis personae as living in and for it, the novel of the nineteenth century was already tainted with retrospection, in terms of Hegelian authenticity all but out of date. The great idea of the novel for Balzac or George Eliot, which investigated and analysed the *comédie humaine*, took its majestic flight like Athene's bird, when darkness was already falling. The metaphor is Hegel's: he had said that the owl of wisdom was only seen by twilight, and this certainly applies to the novel about society and social custom: its authors could understand and contain within their art what was vanishing or had already vanished.

The device of the historical novel is in one sense a means of investigating and celebrating the social arrangements and attitudes, not of some bygone era but of an ethos that can be apprehended because it is disappearing; *Vanity Fair* and *Middlemarch* are notably retrospective, and the moral musing of the authors, their patriarchal authority over scene and characters, would hardly be possible if this were not so. Zola's science of social description is tacitly based on the same formula: that the novelist can stand outside the social scene and observe it sympathetically and dispassionately, from a unified and rational standpoint. The sympathy is vital, for it is a mark of non-involvement; the novelist is not himself bedevilled, torn between conflicting desires and emotions. The immense success of Scott is in part due to the felt absence of such things; all is love, understanding, and appreciation, of the good and the bad alike in their social context, for history was to Scott the 'honest' social world on a larger scale. It is no wonder that his detractors compared Zola to Scott, even labelling him 'romantic' by that association. ('It is at Médan [Zola's home]', said Anatole France, 'that the last of the Romantics is in hiding'.)

This is the real reason why Scott has no heroes and heroines. To be alive such persons must be authentic portents of their time, as Werther, Adolphe, Heathcliff, and even Emma Woodhouse are, and not fitting picturesquely into their social niche or category, as do even such memorable portraits as that of Balfour of Burley in *Old Mortality*. In this sense even George Eliot's Lydgate is also such a social portrait rather than an authentic hero; he, like Romola and Tito Melema in their Florentine historical context, is seen in terms of the old values of social sincerity, selfishness and unselfishness, character related to utility and moral function. Balzac, by contrast, has heroes of real and authentic ominousness, like Vautrin, who, though he is given a deliberate social 'meaning' in terms of the age (he was modelled in part on Vidocq, the Paris police chief), carries the full charge of Balzac's own anarchic and Rameauesque personality. Though Balzac has none of the reticence of the divided author and is never, like Diderot, at the same time personally fascinated and socially disapproving, he is himself simply a robust version of anarchic *geist*, of which his great heroes and heroines are reflections.

It remained for Proust to summate the retrospective social novel and to add to it, what neither Zola nor George Eliot from their standpoint of detachment had been able to do, the scientific investigation and discovery of the self as a social phenomenon. Proust is nothing if not a social scientist (his father and brother were doctors) but he perceived that the fully conscious and unified self could not look on at, and understand, the world it lived in, without relegating the world to precisely that safe social and moral enclave which gives to so much great nineteenth-century fiction the air of being written after the event. The rediscovery of time for Proust is, so to speak, a device for bringing right up to date, to the dynamic moment, the social world which other novelists had only been able to control, analyse and understand from a distance in time and space. By making it the means of discovering and justifying himself—himself as a unique Hegelian portent in art—he bestows on society the full relevance and immediacy of the authentic. Or that is what would appear to be his aim. In practice, as I have already suggested, the drive towards stability and structure in Proust is too overwhelming; no chance of life remains for those accidents and divisions which keep the novel non-absolute; life abounds and flourishes in the parts but not in the projection of the whole.

The kind of accident which keeps the balance of art, and thus achieves the true aesthetic totality of which the novel is capable, might be seen by contrast on a big scale in *War and Peace* and on a smaller one in *Mansfield Park*. In his analysis of the way in which sincerity is superseded by authenticity, Lionel Trilling takes *Mansfield Park* as a case of a brilliant defence in art of the old social ideal—he calls it 'pedagogical'—and with an effect as arresting as it is unexpected he offers us the names of Jane Austen and Robespierre as twin incorruptibles. Both, he feels, were honestly intolerant defenders of strict social ideals doomed by the inexorable dialectic of changing fashion— incongruent champions of virtues destined alike to succumb to the anarchic geist of Napoleonism and Byronism. In terms of history this is brilliantly relevant: archaism and revolution can indeed wear the same guise and acquire disfavour for the same reasons, as those two emphatically presented honest souls,

Fanny and Edmund, have done with Jane Austen's readers for so long. Fanny indeed would appear to personify the ideal of sincerity, being true to her upbringing in refusing to take part in the theatricals where freer spirits can show off the authentic and independent modern spirit, and few readers are sorry when Edmund's persuasion betrays her. But that is just the point: not only is her capitulation probably the right and unselfish social course—a point that is properly left unclear in the novel—but it brings her into the area of the artist's equivocation. Jane Austen is not a revolutionary in the fanatical or evangelical sense which Trilling's comparison implies, but in the sense entailed by the divisive artistic genius.

We can see the same power at work at the end of *War and Peace*, celebrating a mode of life which commands our total and fascinated response, even though—or perhaps because—it depends largely on the support of the dull, the hypocritical or the foolish. Jane Austen may have believed in her ideal of society, which *Mansfield Park* represents, as devoutly as Robespierre in the festival of Reason and the reign of terror, but that does not make her a prig or a monster. Pedagogue she may be in her plan for *Mansfield Park*, but at the great climax when Sir Thomas returns to find the play in progress she is the vessel both of serene authority and of joyous anarchy: in the exercise of her art she is both Rameau and Diderot, honest soul and wilful *geist*.

3. *'Art Speech'*

Here is the most important clue we could have to the divisions that make for fictional genius. Jane Austen had no intention of using what Samuel Butler called 'a set of proposals for radical subversion', and yet her novels undoubtedly subvert; not in the sense in which Butler set out to do the job, but in terms of a complete dimension of fiction whose depth and scope the reader grows gradually to perceive. I shall return later to the ways in which acceptance and rejection, loyalty and subversion, work in the family setting of her art, but I want first to go into the question of whether and in what ways the general principle applies to more recent novels and novelists, who are very different both from her and from each other.

Jane Austen's novels make demands on the reader without his knowing it, and without themselves seeming to know it either. So dense and complex an art today would draw far more attention to itself, and be far more deliberately exigent. Ivy Compton-Burnett is a case, and her subversiveness is not only far more explicit than Jane Austen's but more impassive. In *Dolores*, her first attempt at fiction, she tackled the matter head on, under the direct inspiration of Samuel Butler. Confession and subversion were one and the same, and the result is a boring —or to the intrigued a 'revealing'—book, which could influence and enlighten those in the same boat, but which has nothing to say to the real novel reader. Ivy Compton-Burnett realized this, and in a fourteen-year gestation period produced a method which she never afterwards changed, to convey what one of her characters called the fact that 'A family is itself. And of course there are things hidden in it. They could hardly be exposed'.

That is indeed the problem. Exposure involves statement, which the novel has learnt almost too self-consciously to shun. Probably Jane Austen did not know she should shun it. With her affection for and apprenticeship to Richardson's *Sir Charles Grandison*, and its shared cult of the moral feelings, she was eager to enter into the brisk intellectual and cultural warfare of her time, to strike blows for principle, and to investigate such important contemporary issues as romantic feeling or the duties of ordination. But her art insensibly learnt to exploit more and more subtly the twin roles of guardian and subverter which are deliberately programmed into the formalism of the Compton-Burnett technique. It would not have occurred to her to distinguish between making and saying, as the modern novel does, and D. H. Lawrence's term—'art speech'—would have meant nothing to her; for this, and many other equivalents in the twentieth-century novelist's terminology, in fact disclose an obsession with compounding the statement and utterance which make the novel the standard mouthpiece of a new message. It is indeed a singular fact, which needs more emphasis than it has received, that in proportion as the novel becomes a mouthpiece it develops defensive new techniques of 'art-speech' and fictional presentation. Its whole aesthetic, which has become very elaborate, is founded on this fact.

*   *   *

I propose to consider briefly three 'mouthpieces'—Lawrence, Forster, and Kipling—whose particular interest, in terms of my argument, is that they are more confused even than the indirections of their dogma allow. All are much concerned with the use of art to make fiction say what they want to say. We may feel with them all that, though art is being manipulated in order that it should speak on their behalf, this process contrasts with what is more radically and involuntarily divided in their personalities and in the works, and what these reveal is at this date as interesting to the critic, or more interesting, than their 'views'. D. H. Lawrence and E. M. Forster are, of course, more obviously intelligent than Kipling: though it might be truer to say that Kipling, like some of Tolstoy's characters, does not condescend to intelligence—he is too absorbed in the ethos of the society he describes. The effect for us is a variation on the kind of art of which Shakespeare is the grand exemplar, where the exercise of intelligence appears as a privilege tacitly surrendered by the author to the reader. Kipling allows his own intelligence to be concealed by the values of the society he is concerned to identify with and to publicize.

What seems worth concentrating on, in this study, are the various ways in which three such direct and forceful personalities emancipate their art from themselves. The process can seem inadvertent: alternatively it can appear highly self-conscious and sometimes self-defeating. Forster's whole style, for instance, is involved in patterns and curlicues of self-depreciation—the very syntax proclaims through its subdued comic mastery: 'Don't take me too seriously, old fellow'. This is of course a way of saying: you would be ill-advised not to take me very seriously indeed. Certainly Forster's mastery of social comedy owes much to Jane Austen, but we have only to compare the opening of *Howards End* ('One may as well begin with Helen's letter to her sister . . .') with that of *Pride and Prejudice* to see that where Jane Austen uses epigram as a tradition of her form, Forster, by inverting it, backs into a disclaimer of any such depersonalizing consequence.

This whimsical reluctance to make his bow as a novelist in the conventional way in practice puts Forster ever at our elbow. It is of course quite absent in Lawrence. Lawrence may hector and declaim if he feels like it, or he may not; but in either case the effect is completely natural; nothing could be less evidently strategic than his style. Yet Lawrence is as concerned as Forster—indeed more so—with his own kind of insistence on the independence of the novel, as a work of art, from the personality and views of its author. He has the greatest distrust for 'all novelists with an idea of themselves'. In two contexts at least Forster too muses on the lack of control the novelist has, and what he says seems as true as it is perceptive. In a piece called 'Inspiration' he suggests that the mind of the author 'as it were turns turtle, sometimes with rapidity, and a hidden part of it comes to the surface and controls the pen. On returning to his normal state he looks over what he has written. It surprises him. He couldn't do it again. He can't explain to the reader how it was done.' And in *Aspects of the Novel* he suggests how this process can result in the emancipation and freedom of the work.

> Expansion. That is the idea the novelist must cling to. Not completion. Not rounding off but opening out. When the symphony is over we feel that the notes and tunes composing it have been liberated, they have found in the rhythm of the whole their individual freedom. Cannot the novel be like that?

Certainly that is what both novelists *want* the novel to be like. Lawrence makes the point much more forcefully in his essay *The Novel*, published in *Phoenix*, where great emphasis is laid on the novel as 'the highest form of human expression so far attained', for the reason that it is 'so incapable of the absolute'. 'They can't fool the novel', he asserts of all those novelists 'with an idea of themselves', because it 'gives them away'. 'Let me hear what the novel says', he demands at the climax—'as for the novelist, he is usually a dribbling liar.'

These all seem unexceptionable sentiments, adding up to the ideal recipe for what Pushkin, in a memorable phrase at the end of *Eugene Onegin*, described as 'a free novel'. And it is true that *The Rainbow* and *Women in Love*, as much as *Howards End* and *A Passage to India*, do on the face of it conform to the idea they suggest of imaginative fiction's independence and instability. Expansion takes place; nothing is decided; nothing can be. No character—not even Birkin in *Women in Love*—is allowed to have things all his own way or to engross, either tacitly or openly, the *life* of the work, in the important sense which that word takes on in the worlds of both novelists.

Birkin may be the major vessel and representative of life, as in their different ways are Mrs Wilcox and Margaret Schlegel, Leonard Bast and Aziz, but we are not to feel that the novelist's thumb (to use another Lawrentian metaphor) is in the balance to make them unassailable.

The balance is kept, yes, but what is keeping it? Is there too strong an awareness on the part of the novelist—as their comments might indicate—of the fact that it *must* and *ought* to be preserved, so that freedom becomes not an involuntary attribute of the way the form has worked out, but a calculated requirement which the novelist hopes for from experience, and has in a sense bargained for? A long way from Pushkin's 'free novel'? The novel that expands away from its author . . . the novel that can't be fooled . . . might not these things ultimately seem a form of iron control by other means?

In a sense the problem is almost a tautological one. A writer who says, as Lawrence does, that 'metaphysic must always subserve the artistic purpose beyond the writer's conscious aim', is hardly able to claim that anything has happened beyond his consciousness, because it seems as if he knew it was going to. If he knew, how was it unconscious? Lawrence worked intensively and successively on *The Rainbow* and *Women in Love*, producing several distinct versions; and in his illuminating essay 'The Exploratory Imagination of D. H. Lawrence', Mark Kinkead-Weekes argues that the rewritings show Lawrence doing what he claimed. But they might also be seen in another way: as the accomplishment of a final solution, the working out of which in terms of Lawrence's metaphysical system is one and the same with the realization of a work of art. Such a suggestion of fiat and finality, of 'I have spoken', could be seen as being implicit in the image Lawrence uses. 'You know the perfect statue is in the marble . . . but the thing is getting it out clean.' To lay stress on the meanings such a metaphor suggests is perhaps hardly fair, but there is none the less a sense of finality in this. The novel may stand complete and separate from its creator, but it is hardly envisaged here as provisional and 'non-absolute', not completing itself but still expanding.

And indeed it is doubtful whether the novel which the 'authentic' consciousness produces could ever really be seen as properly inhabiting the area in which fiction has acquired the sobriety and neutrality of an independent life, for such a consciousness is bound to be organized on a war footing against whatever 'honest' society it finds itself in. The hidden part of the mind which comes to the top and controls the pen may not be the daily state of the consciousness but it is all the more for that a dominant agency. To be surprised by the effects produced, as Forster tells us that he was by those of *The Longest Journey* ('. . . the only one of my books that has come upon me without my knowledge'), does not in the case of these two novelists mean that the book has ended up outside himself: rather the opposite. In its quest for the world, the spirit in estrangement makes the world out of itself; the authentic consciousness cannot but be doctrinaire. In terms of art it cannot remain in the provisional, the non-absolute, because its real aim is self-definition and self-justification, and to use the novel for this purpose must be an act of finality.

The argument, often applied in the case of Lawrence, that the novelist's art neutralizes and even to some extent ridicules the dogmas of the prophet, is thus really a contradiction in terms. In this context at least the Lawrence world is an Hegelian 'organic whole'; the criticisms and objections that his art makes, from the inside, are like the criticisms voiced in *Pravda* or at workers' meetings: they do not disturb party unity, the fact that—in Birkin's words—'everything hangs together', and they are not intended to. As Forster himself pointed out about Lawrence: 'you cannot say, "let us drop his theories and enjoy his art", because the two are one'; 'if he did not preach and prophesy he could not see and feel'—and Forster must have known about this from the inside.

It is true that Lawrence himself seems to have misunderstood Forster and mistaken the role of the Wilcoxes in *Howards End* —he complains in a letter that these 'business people' are glorified, and that such people are 'no good'—but he was too close to the novel at the time to see, as we surely can from a more distant perspective, that the Wilcoxes are not a true alternative centre produced by division and inner uncertainty, but a carefully controlled aspect of the ideological structure. Forster gives the Wilcoxes their due in the same way that Lawrence demythologizes Birkin and puts real barbs in the ridicule and the good sense which Ursula and others direct against him. Forster himself reports that Lawrence thought

Leonard Bast the best thing in *Howards End*, though he may seem to us by ordinary fictional standards one of the weakest, and this is significant, because it shows that Lawrence divined the extreme importance of Bast to Forster in terms of the novel's imaginative and projective sympathy.* The mind that created Leonard Bast has 'turned turtle'; but the effect is to call in question the authority of the social comedy which the novel presents. How far is it compromised by the demands of hidden fantasy?

In his succinct study of Lawrence, Frank Kermode is at some pains to show how Lawrence 'cuts the metaphysic down to novelistic size . . . by obscuring doctrine with narrative symbolisms capable in their nature of more general and more doubtful interpretation'. But though it may give a certain aesthetic pleasure to the critic to observe how this is done, it is hard to imagine any reader getting the message wrong, or failing to be pushed in the right direction by the sheer imaginative pressure. 'How we should read *Great Expectations*' is the title of an illuminating essay by Q. D. Leavis, which I shall have occasion to return to later on, but it is hard to imagine any need for an essay entitled 'How we should read *Women in Love*'.

In one important sense, to be discussed in a moment, this is not true of Forster, but in general we can also be very clear where we are with him, knowing that his tolerance, like his verbal impishness and frivolity, is a matter of technique, and that his air of self-deprecation and puzzlement masks an implacable authority. Deprecation does, it is true, have a role in compounding the lack in Forster of Lawrence's superb and unfailing imaginative conviction: the occasional gesture of throwing up the hands is carefully desynchronized from moments of real weakness but it answers the general purpose. When Margaret muses, what do we feel?

> Starting from Howards End, she attempted to realise England. She failed—visions do not come when we try, though they may come through trying. But an unexpected love of the island awoke in her, connecting on this side with the joys of the flesh, on that with the inconceivable.

---

* See Angus Wilson, 'A Conversation with E. M. Forster'. *Encounter*, November 1957.

This is not really Margaret reflecting on the theme of the novel, and failing to do so in much more than a gushingly inadequate way. It is Forster himself presenting the theme, and taking a perfectly justifiable refuge in the inadequacy of his heroine. Behind her he makes a *moue* at the difficulty of his task. When Ursula, in *Women in Love*, attacks Birkin or Loerke, Lawrence of course supplies her with the right ammunition to do a deadly job; and this, like Forster's use of Margaret, is an effective device. But *Women in Love* is of course far more intensely imagined and moves on a higher plane of realization. Like all the other characters, Ursula is totally alive in her own being, her own desires and actions; whereas Margaret is not only used by Forster to deprecate his own already 'crablike sideways movement' towards the ambitious effect. Inadequacy of another kind makes him unable to realize her existence, which means she can be fitted the more easily into the purely *voulu* pattern of love and marriage to Wilcox.

Howards End is not a *new* novel like *Women in Love*, but is artfully constructed out of three or four more or less traditional narrative methods, Austenian comedy predominating. 'Only connect'—yes; but in practice the modes of this novel cannot expect to be very well articulated, let alone fused. That they are not gives the book its peculiarly Forsterian character, its quiddity and charm. But it means, too, that even Mrs Wilcox, on whom should rest so important a role in the general 'hanging together 'of the novel, has no substance at all compared with the strange brooding presence of Mrs Crich, mother of Gerald in *Women in Love*. Lawrence's knowledge and confidence is such that in a few phrases the inwardness of the Crich *ménage* is with us. He does not have to spell it out (although with Gerald he goes on to do so). There is no doubt that *Women in Love* could be called Shakespearean in this vital sense—between its scenes, or 'leaps' as Kermode well names them, the life of the dramatis personae is always fully assumed and accounted for—and Leavis's term 'dramatic poem' defines this aspect of the novel's form.

But that form too can fail, in so far as it takes on a resemblance to a Lawrence *nouvelle*, and in general to the form of the modern short story as practised by Katherine Mansfield, his contemporary, whom Lawrence despised. The weakness here is the simulated provisional ending, which leaves matters to appearance interrogative but in practice all too unified. This may seem an unfair judgment, for since the authentic consciousness can by definition have no real doubts about itself, the ways in which it simulates the checks and balances of art must inevitably have something factitious about them. At the end of the novel Birkin wants something else, that 'eternal union with a man' which the dead Gerald might have given him, and which Ursula cannot. She calls the idea perverse, 'false, impossible', and he answers 'I don't believe that'. Nor do we, because the whole novel has already spelled out for us the situation, and the consciousness identified with it.

That is why the art of Lawrence, in the sense in which it is praised by Kinkead-Weekes and Kermode, is really a superficial affair. Suppose Lawrence had completed and retained the ending he began, in which Gudrun writes a letter describing the child she has had by Gerald. Suppose, even, he had left in the first discursive and overtly homosexual prologue—could it be said that our *knowledge* of the work would be in any sense changed? The alterations that give the book its present form are not more much than cosmetic. In fact, in one way the earlier version seems to have been truer to the bedrock reality of Lawrence's grasp on people, for it not only makes no secret of Birkin's attraction to Gerald, but describes a much more convincing relation between Birkin and Hermione than the strangely implausible liaison which in the final text is alluded to with a rather hangdog but self-satisfied air. *

It is indeed arguable that the matter in the book which seems to objectify Birkin and cut him down to size—culminating in the extraordinary brilliance of the Café Pompadour scene when Birkin's letter is read out amidst ridicule and rescued by Gudrun—have in practice the opposite effect: like the humiliations of Dostoevsky's 'Underground Man' they exist to apotheosize the authentic consciousness that dominates the book.

And such a consciousness cannot, in terms of art, be ended (Dostoevsky does not attempt to do so but ends with the triumphant jeer that there is more, much more, where that came from). The contrived objectivity of the *nouvelle*-type

---

* Though the couple are based on the Morrells from Garsington, Alexander Roddice is Hermione's brother, not husband, in the novel.

ending—successful in terms of that form in *The Fox* and *The Captain's Doll*—is gratingly incompatible with the unique form of the consciousness-dominated novel which Lawrence brings off in *Women in Love*. Consciousness devours that form too completely for it to sustain either a beginning—which it does not pretend to have—or an ending. For such an intense consciousness the ending is nowhere and anywhere, perhaps in the intense dream-like absurdity of their continental journey, and Ursula thinking of Birkin—'Oh, if he were the world as well, if only the world were he! If only he could call a world into being, that should be their own world!'

Both Lawrence and Forster, the one in *Women in Love* and the other in *Howards End*, reach the end of the road as regards themselves. There they are. But for Forster the crabwise and cautious process of self-revelation involved itself in a theoretical programme—the claims of the public as against the private life, of power against sensibility—which fails to make any headway against the fantasia of consciousness in the book, the fantasy of 'realising England', which is the self, from *Howards End*. No wonder the end of that novel is of a badness which bears no comparison to the only faintly unspontaneous open ending of *Women in Love*. The odour of split symbols, carefully poured out as a libation to the infant sensibilities springing up in England, is almost nauseous; it is the smell not of the confusion that brings life to art but of the carefulness and concealment that pretends to such confusion.

In *Howards End* Forster tries to make use of an apparently impressive theme to enlarge himself, but the theme walks away. In his study of Forster, Lionel Trilling tried bravely to stop it and bring it back by claiming that it made the novel a masterpiece which 'develops to the full the themes and attitudes of the early books' and justifies them by 'connecting them with a more mature sense of responsibility'. Forster himself attempted a new novel, *Arctic Summer*, in which the theme of serving the world and being the self was to be further developed, but this was aborted and it is not difficult to see why. If we recall how much he learnt from Jane Austen, and how effortlessly naturalistic are the conflicts and moral oppositions she sets up, he must have known how unreal his own were. The crucial failure is that the novel can never admit what the novelist knows: that he depends totally on his intellectual and social bourgeois status, while his romantic and sexual dreams and yearnings are of the lower class. The two cannot be brought together in the chosen fictional form, and the substituted conflict of Wilcoxes and Schlegels is mere shadow-boxing. But what the form does reveal is Forster's own dilemma.

The fact is that with these novels Lawrence and Forster completed themselves, and there was nowhere else for them to go. Lawrence's 'record of the profoundest experiences of the self', as he described it in an unused foreword for the American edition of *Women in Love*, achieves apocalyptic size because that self is so significant a portent for the *dies irae* of the times. Forster's was a more personal affair, which could more readily be set aside for the experiences which were to produce *A Passage to India*, and when that was completed Forster, as he himself tells us, found there was 'no more to say'. Lawrence had plenty more to say, and in the different world of *Kangaroo*, and the superb introduction he wrote for Magnus's Foreign Legion book, the self ceases to be apocalyptic and becomes a person, humorous, hard-bitten, shrewd, not the least requiring the art-like objectification that *Women in Love* created for it. The great drama of the self is over, but whatever the compensations the reader is bound to feel a little let down, some sense of anticlimax. For there *are* things in the complex dramatic style of *Women in Love* which bear out Lawrence's words about trusting the tale, not the teller: beyond the devices to glorify Birkin by sacrificing him to the others there is a kind of real unconsciousness, the totally self-forgetful vulnerability of a great genius in language, the involuntariness of being such as we have in the novels of Hardy (which Lawrence had been making a study of) and which may strike us more and more, as we read Lawrence, as a kind of ultimate 'home' in him. (Forster remarks that Hardy is 'home' in a sense that Meredith never is.)

What I have in mind, and myself grow more attached to with each reading, is the unconscious humour of the glowing texture, in accounts of food, clothes, gesture and speech; and the way in which these things emerge in contrast to the *chétif* and malign accuracy of self-glorifying intention. Here is a random example of the way that intention works:

This strange sense of fatality in Gerald, as if he were limited to one form of existence, one knowledge, one activity, a sort of fatal halfness, which to himself seemed wholeness, always overcame Birkin after their moments of passionate approach, and filled him with a sort of contempt, or boredom. It was the insistence on the limitation which so bored Birkin in Gerald.

This kind of thing becomes dead and predictable in repetition, as do the dialogues of apocalypse, doom, and hatred of the decaying age, even the set-piece symbols of them, like the drowning, the tormented horse at the level-crossing and the end of Gerald in the snow. What increases in vitality and life is something more involuntary, coming out—again as in Hardy —in unstudied language that does not force a meaning, and whose rightness, like his, has a certain family oddity, almost quaintness. Thus Ursula and Birkin at the Saracen's Head have a venison pasty—'of all things'—and the prim little phrase recurs when Gudrun at the Pompadour 'wanted an iced cocktail, of all things'. Gudrun observes excitedly that it is 'impossible really to let go in England, of that I am assured'. Hermione, we learn early on, 'had various intimacies of mind and soul with various men of capacity'; and 'Gudrun had already come to know a good many people of repute and standing'. The candour which comes over word and syntax often brings the action incongruously close to the medium in which such later novels as *Kangaroo* and *The Plumed Serpent* have frankly come to rest; and this effect beneath the dramatic tensions of *Women in Love* embarrasses their mode of operation with a difference disconcerting because unallowed-for by the author. Here is the real 'non-absolute' it may be, yet here it is something that Lawrence can neither turn into the 'art speech' of the novel nor produce with that openly conversational, take-it-or-leave-it, air that is the natural medium of the travel novels, and even more of the Magnus piece. There Lawrence analyses with shrewd hard humour and good sense the ambivalence of his own feelings ('I detest terrible things, and the people to whom they happen', he observes of Magnus, who had attracted him precisely by the promise of being one of those people).

The habits of women observed (in fact Frieda and her sister) the clothes, the stockings and the food—especially the food— liberate the text of *Women in Love* by laughing at its dramatic intentness. Cheerfulness breaks in, rather than what Lawrence called 'full, bitter conscious realization'. Such realization is of course compatible with any amount of social satire, because in that context the author is so evidently armed at all points. Compare those kinds of phrases, by no means trivial in impression, which settle round the girls, with the use made of Gudrun in the following comedy exchange with Hermione and Sir Joshua Mattheson, who are taken from Ottoline Morrell and Bertrand Russell.

> Hermione waited for the dust to settle, and then she said, untouched:
> 'Yes, it is the greatest thing in life—to *know*. It is really to be happy, to be *free*'.
> 'Knowledge is, of course, liberty', said Mattheson.
> 'In compressed tabloids', said Birkin, looking at the dry, stiff little body of the Baronet. Immediately Gudrun saw the famous sociologist as a flat bottle, containing tabloids of compressed liberty. That pleased her. Sir Joshua was labelled and placed for ever in her mind.

This is cunning, in a fairly obvious sense, because Lawrence is getting his own back while disassociating himself from the self-limiting reaction of a Gudrun who is here only a pawn in his game. In the same scene he defends and glorifies himself, as Birkin, much more directly; but in fact the whole drama licences and stylizes the creating self to the point where it becomes possessed of everything around it. The comic freedom of *Women in Love*, so different from its art, may indeed— in Lawrence's own words—give the author 'a kick in the behind' and 'leave us to learn', but only does so by drawing undue attention to the limitations of the main method. Like Gudrun's little carvings which 'have a sort of funniness that is quite unconscious and subtle', the unconscious in the book shows up its concentrated ferocities of consciousness, and the subordination of its drama to the author, who cannot but be obtrusively omniscient, even when—and perhaps especially when—he is seeking to negate it through symbol into what Lawrence calls 'the lapse of consciousness'.

Consciousness has not produced the emancipation which both its method and its message invoke. One reason is the unification of art and its meaning, the fiction and the interpretation, which is portended in both novels and which has become the norm; so much so that Richard Poirier can offer without irony a definition of the 'modern' in fiction as 'the novel which includes the interpretation that will be made of it'. This concept wipes out at a blow the old spacious idea of the novel as going somewhere, usually in a fairly modest and conventional sense, and arriving —if it is a masterpiece—at quite other goals in the hearts and minds of posterity.

Another reason for the loss of freedom—if we feel it to be that—in the modern novel is its abandonment of restraints, of such conventional demands as continuity and progress, or even of a satisfying conclusion, which is often the same as a 'happy ending'. The expression of the authentic consciousness is increasingly accepted as a substitute for these things. Many novels, it is true—*Madame Bovary* for example—tell an objective tale as well as *being* Madame Bovary, but this extrapolation of consciousness does not deceive the author and is not intended to deceive his readers. Deep down we know, and are meant to know, that Emma Bovary is a kind of deliberately demeaned parody of Flaubert's own consciousness of things. The much more elaborate formalization and distancing of their awareness practised by later novelists, down to the *nouveau roman* and beyond, tell the same tale: manipulations designed to eliminate mind and its logic or to compound any possible authorial approach, end up by enclosing the reader the more completely in the directing consciousness.

Consciousness deals with space, the known dimensions of itself, and cannot easily fall in with the unknown eventualities of time. Birkin, Ursula and Gerald do not really live in time, which is no doubt why Lawrence abandoned the incongruous coda at the end of *Women in Love* which told how Gudrun had borne Gerald's child (and also why he fails to produce any real sense of progress in *The Lost Girl*, and why he abandoned *Mr Noone*, an apparent re-exploration of the straightforward sequential novel). This is of real importance, because it does seem as if only the temporal aspect of a fiction—at one time literalized in the process of coming out in parts—can produce characters who seem independent of their creator; who start off without knowing their destination and seem to look back on him almost as one of themselves. Such a novel is going somewhere but does not know its journey: its end is not in its beginning, as are those of the Forster and Lawrence novels. For Flaubert, too, the end was in the beginning, which was why—in terms of the novel—he had no alternative to *'Emma Bovary—c'est moi'*. Jane Austen, on the other hand, acknowledging outside herself what was feasible for the novel's form, set Emma Woodhouse going in order to find out what such a person might do; and the novel that learnt from Emma's case can instruct our own.

The novel that 'hangs together' in a single unity of consciousness cannot offer privacy or discontinuity, which, as Jane Austen shows, are the privileges of division between society and self. Neither Jane Austen nor Tolstoy attempts to absorb into themselves characters who are not naturally a part of themselves; the different person is left on his own, as—say—Mary Crawford in *Mansfield Park* is by Jane Austen, or Dolokhov in *War and Peace* by Tolstoy. Lawrence, on the other hand, is determined to appropriate Gerald and Hermione: partly because their difference exasperates him into denying it, and attacking the invulnerability which is its outward sign ('No one could put her down, no one could make mock of her'), but chiefly because his genius requires total possession in order to *be* genius. His possession of children, like the young Billy and Dora Brangwen ('Dora, peeping from the floss of her fair hair, hung back like some tiny dryad, that has no soul') is for this reason almost magical in its lack of effort. The children, *soulless*, are an integral part of Lawrence's vision, like the green beetles, animals and plants. But in the truly divided author like Tolstoy, so much exists that is not, so to speak, an aspect of Tolstoyness. Even if his consciousness resents the phenomenon of beings outside itself —which in one sense it came increasingly to do—his power as a novelist seems actually to have welcomed such intractability.

And to have emphasized its puzzlement. The sobriety of Tolstoy issues from these separations, where Lawrence's self-fulfilment comes from singleness. This is why the ending of *Women in Love* can only affect hesitation, and is really as willed a conclusion as the grandiose metaphor used to round off *The Rainbow*. By contrast, the strange mixture of tranquillity and disquiet at the end of *War and Peace* is produced by the still increasing aliveness of its characters, whose unforeseen queries and new purposes appear to disturb and divide the intentions of the author, even as these were bringing the immense tale to its proper close in achievement and satisfaction.

* * *

I am not trying to use the distinction involved here for a belittling attack on Lawrence, but in an attempt to show how radical is the difference between what I would call the novel of unity and the novel of division. Lawrence in fact often insists that the second kind is really the first, as we can see from his comments on both Tolstoy's and Hardy's novels. For although the novel may be 'incapable of the absolute', Lawrence naturally insists on his own absolute version of how we should read *Anna Karenina*. 'The novel itself gives Vronsky a kick in the behind, and knocks old Leo's teeth out and leaves us to learn'. It is of course the function of a great divided novel to suggest different things to different people; but here Lawrence is taking over the novel behind its author's back, as it were, and endowing it with the single-minded and single-vision assertiveness of his own novels. The novelist may not have known what he was about, he suggests, but the novel did, a reversal of roles positively comical in its implications, because a divided novelist can hardly produce a wholly dogmatic novel. Lawrence goes on to make the point that Tolstoy, 'being a great creative artist, was true to his characters. But being a man with a philosophy he wasn't true to his own *character*'. This is indeed the crux: for by not being 'true' to his own character does not Tolstoy involuntarily allow his creations full room to possess and deploy theirs?

Tolstoy for Lawrence is 'a self-conscious *I am*', with too much personality to have a true character. And character, says Lawrence, 'is the flame of a man, which burns brighter or dimmer . . . yet remaining one single separate flame flickering in a strange world'. This is indeed the image for the novel as Lawrence creates it—'quick . . . interrelated in all its parts, vitally, organically'. And this indeed is unity: such a flame, burning in total integrity as itself, is the principle of creation for Lawrence. The 'self-conscious *I am*' which he saw in Tolstoy is, however, paradoxically more capable of conferring a similar kind of separateness and independence on its creations.

When he rails at 'Old Leo's' dishonesty and disingenuousness Lawrence does not tell us whether Tolstoy produced his characters in spite of his failings or because of them. He insists on his own no-nonsense view of *Anna Karenina*, heedless of the fact that the novel shows us all the different ways in which the fate of their situation is pulling the characters. 'When you look at it, all the trouble comes from Vronsky's and Anna's fear of *society'*. How contemptible of Vronsky to collapse—'merely because people at the opera turn backs on him! As if people's backs weren't preferable to their faces anyway!' For Lawrence of course they were; he was determined that for himself and Frieda they should be, but Tolstoy and his novel were of a different opinion, several different opinions. The novel shows that 'the trouble' and indeed the tragedy of Anna and Vronsky is that they cannot do without society, though they supposed they could, and the implications of this are endless and timeless. The claims of society, and Vronsky and Anna's need for it, are as vital to *Anna Karenina* as they are valueless to Lawrence. He makes use of the novel, but he does not really read it at all.

The same cannot be said for his reading of Hardy. It is clear that Lawrence understood very well the social and intellectual queries and complications in that fascinating and much underrated novel *The Hand of Ethelberta*. Its heroine is a type he could use: her situation between different worlds of class is one he was often to explore; and his comments on Tess, on Jude and Sue Bridehead are as illuminating about Hardy as they are about his own imaginative preoccupations. He perceives the depth and the reticence in Hardy and the explosive matter that is in solution there. What he disregards is the deference Hardy paid to the novel, not only in its commercial but in its formal aspect.

For *The Rainbow*, the novel that is obviously closest to Hardy, this has an important result. Hardy's characters are, in the first instance, going where the novel sends them, not where a novelist 'with an idea of himself' wants them to go. Their natures are revealed not for their own sake, but in the telling of a tale, which is not about them but takes them in on the way. Scenes like Troy and Bathsheba at the sword exercise in *Far From the Madding Crowd*, or their encounter in the black fir wood when his spur catches in her dress, clearly inspired Lawrence; but they are very different from his own visions of sexual encounter, as in the chapters called 'Moony' and 'Rabbit'. Hardy's have the truth only a novel can achieve which is divided between such imaginative truth and the sober necessities of narrative plot. Such encounters of passion do not reveal the protagonists to themselves but only to the reader, while Lawrence's fuse the awareness of characters and reader together in a single whole.

And are we in life aware of ourselves at such moments as those experienced by Troy and Bathsheba? Not if we are like *them*, surely, but only if we are like ourselves, reading a novel? In Lawrence consciousness as fiction has quite taken us over. There is a moment in *The Rainbow* much praised by F. R. Leavis, and indeed taken by him as a kind of touchstone of fictional authenticity, when Tom Brangwen, as he tends his ewes in the nights of February, 'knew he did not belong to himself'. How did he know it? In what sense was the idea present to him? Surely because it is such an idea that Lawrence suggests to his reader at such a moment and in such a situation? It is a Lawrentian desideratum, present in the magic prose, not present in the farmer as such. Certainly it is a comment which jars me in the reading, like stubbing a toe; and with it my interest in Brangwen as a character in a novel, goes out and is never rekindled.

This emphasis on Brangwen's oneness with the pulse of life on the farm brings into the forefront of fictional consciousness what in Hardy is implicit and held at a distance—the distance between our sense of ourselves and our sense of others. Gabriel Oak, tending his sheep on the same kind of winter night, could not have been recorded as knowing he 'did not belong to himself'. The notion is without meaning, all the more so because Oak's consciousness is one thing and that of his creator another: in their natural relation the two are as separate as objects in nature, cows in a field or trees in a wood. But in *The Rainbow* consciousness impersonates the whole field of nature. In one sense the gain is great, for where any comment of Hardy's is made by one being about another, Lawrence passes through all as if no barrier existed, his genius making open and uniform to us his characters' inward selves and responses. The one thing they cannot be is *separate*: that accomplishment has to be left to the other kind of novel.

4. *Dogma and Fantasy*

And yet, when all is said, Lawrence's own claim—trust the novel, not the dribbling liar with the pen—is justified in his own case. And his sanity is justified, for we are not finally imprisoned by him, however assertive he may be. Since he has himself kicked Birkin in the behind, that character—unlike

Vronsky—cannot 'leave us to learn', for it was the novelist who administered the ritual chastisement and not the novel. What we *are* left to learn, however, is how much we need certain sorts of fantasy, and that fantasy is the most vital part of sex.

Lawrence's rage at this pronouncement may be imagined, but let us try to avoid being kicked by him and look at his novel. All its stuff about 'blood-consciousness', the loins, the buttocks, the solar plexus, are not physical facts but mental projections. Lawrence detested what he called 'sex in the head', but that is where he puts it—has to put it—in his novel. He detested fantasy, whether the art sort in pictures and novels, or the popular sort of the cinema screen, seeing it as the concomitant of furtive and mechanical sex and daydreaming. Yet all the sex acts and situations in his novels are daydreams to a very marked extent; inevitably so.

Somerset Maugham observed that for the artist fantasy is not an escape from reality 'but the means by which he accedes to it'. That is true both of Lawrence and his readers. The hectoring Lawrence, the prophet who said he would change the world for the next thousand years, was also the artist who lived and wished to live in isolation and in himself; who held that in marriage and in every human relation the partners must remain 'constellated' in their separate interdependent spheres. Nothing he says is amenable to logic. To employ commonsense against Lawrence is no more feasible where his work is concerned than it was with the man himself. As Aldous Huxley found, any rational argument would be countered by Lawrence placing his hand on his solar plexus and saying 'he didn't feel it there'. There is no point in responding to what he offers by selecting some of his doctrines and rejecting others: even if we assume that doctrine in Lawrence has become art, that is hardly the way to respond to what he offers, for irrespective of revision and inconsistency his art has an overall unity which is levelled at us and seeks to take us over. Not to be taken over is important, but to differentiate does not help us here; our way to freedom is to recognize how Lawrentian abstraction is in fact working as fantasy, to compare our own with his, to understand in the process the part that such fantasy plays in sexual freedom and civilization, and how misleading is the claim—made both by Lawrence and his disciples—that he has banished it from his own conception and conduct of life. In fact he shows just how much what 'makes for life' depends upon it.

One cannot learn from Lawrence, any more than from any other great imaginative writer, how to live. To be 'liberated' by him would be merely to be constrained into a different pattern of life. But what, at this distance of time, he can be seen to have done is to elevate and diversify sexual fantasy, giving it afresh and anew something of the same kind of open and reverential status that the code of courtly love possessed in the Middle Ages. Like a writer of the Middle Ages he locates his fantasy in the centre of society. Not necessarily in any class sense. In one of his best stories, *The Fox*, fantasy is distanced by belonging to the young soldier who carries off the girl, March, from a relationship with another woman, admirably conveyed, on a war-time farm. Lawrence conveys with remarkable dispassion the disappointment of the young man when his fantasy of triumphant abduction is realized, the sense of frustration that persuades him all will be perfect when he can get the girl right away, abroad. The tale here really is more important than the teller, and what makes it so is the authority of the setting and the propriety in it of this kind of fantasy. This can be equally effective when Lawrence places his fantasy in some image of high society; for at his best he is not only a highly social novelist, as preoccupied as Proust with class observation and observance, but one of the very few novelists who can endow his own sexual fantasy with the conviction of a fully realized social world. There is a marked contrast here with E. M. Forster, just as intelligent and lively a social novelist but one whose sexual fantasy has no part in it but remains unassimilated and unconvincing on its edges. The same is of course even truer of the expatriate American novelist like Hemingway, who in *A Farewell to Arms*, or *For Whom the Bell Tolls*, makes scarcely an effort to naturalize his sexual fantasies in a convincing social context.

Our fact here is that the inescapable incongruity of sex—its containment in a set of physical reflexes and an immeasurable amount of mental image—requires perpetual renewal and rebirth. Lawrence's ideas about it, like his ideas about society, are two-faced (what makes him, like Evelyn Waugh, such a good social novelist, is his capacity for love-hate, for recording both romantic allure and malignant exasperation). The head, where sex consciousness must take place, for all Lawrence's objections, is where Lawrentian fantasy plays its liberating role. We must not submit to it, otherwise we should merely acquire a new mode of conditioning, but we should let it work on us in the same way as other such fantasies in art, disregarding Lawrence's strident denunciation of the genre, which may well conceal his exasperated knowledge of how much his own joins up with it.

'The only thing unbearable', he tells us in the same foreword to *Women in Love*, 'is the degradation, the prostitution of the living mysteries in us. Let man only approach his own soul with a deep respect, even reverence for all that the creative soul, the God-mystery within us, puts forth. Then we shall be sound and free. Lewdness is hateful because it impairs our integrity and our proud being'. So it does, but this is itself an invitation to the head—to the authentic consciousness—to make a newer and finer fantasy about its sexual being. Lawrence's contempt for what he calls 'Aphrodite in elastic garters', for the vulgar male desire for pin-ups, was of course total: the heroine of *The Virgin and the Gipsy* despises her young men because she feels she might as well give them a set of her underwear to divert them as herself. But the point to emphasise is that the distinction here is not one of kind but of quality and degree. The fantasy about Mellors and Connie in *Lady Chatterley*, for example, is concerned with the acceptance of female excretion as an attractive sexual *idea* ('Here tha' shits and here tha' pisses'). Both Lawrence and Joyce were turning the age towards new kinds of sex acceptance in the head, and we should remember that Joyce in *Ulysses* showed forth the same fantasy in relation to the Blooms with much less fuss and for that reason a truer artistic tenderness. Lawrence thought *Ulysses* disgusting, because he shared the common human tendency to be repelled by all mental sex other than his own; but Joyce in his humorous and complex way revealed the freedom and the moral pleasure implicit in the mental sex art of everyman, for to be artist here —rather than to live conditioned in what Forster calls 'little private circles of excitement'—must itself also be a moral activity.

Thus successfully to share fantasy with us, as both Joyce and Lawrence can do, can be an artistic achievement of the first order, and this is surely what we mean when we speak of the art, not the doctrine, in Lawrence, and of not trusting the teller but the tale. Whatever Lawrence's abhorrence at the notion, he is a great artist of sex in the head. Division with him comes between how he saw the thing, and what it is. The point might be emphasized by a reference to the novels of Aldous Huxley, where sex is an occasion not for fantasy but for didactic idea, and the art in consequence is not only a mere veneer, but uses a short cut which makes it incapable of acting on us with depth and indirection. Huxley affected the young of his own generation deeply, much more deeply than Lawrence, because his daring connections and agile exotic intellectualism really offered a kind of simplistic reassurance. Isaiah Berlin has recalled the impression made on some contemporaries and how it was an experience to be 'morally freed (as others have been by psycho-analysis, or Anatole France or living among Arabs) by reading Aldous Huxley'.

> The performance took place against a background of relatively few, simple, moral convictions; they were disguised by the brilliance of the technical accomplishment, but they were there they were easily intelligible, and like a monotonous insistent continuous ground bass, slowly pounding away through the elaborate intellectual display, they imposed themselves on the mind.

Lawrence's imposition may have seemed less insidious at the time but it was in fact more so: it was true art, which may take a lapse of many years to show how it works and what is its substance. The immediate and superficial appeal of Huxley was moral in the worst sense, in that it liberated from uncertainty and fantasy while confirming conditioning and prejudice. Lawrence might be said to have done the opposite.

Huxley, like Lawrence and Forster, was a great emancipator, as concerned as they were to change the expectations and ideas of the age and belonging to the same great 'leap forward' in sexual and social enlightenment. But of the three Lawrence was the only real rebel, and the only one with whom rebellion is transformed into art. In his use of society in art Huxley is as conservative as Peacock, and that is one reason why his cleverness and his advanced ideas seem so dated today while both Forster and Lawrence in their different ways are as fresh as paint, particularly Lawrence. *Women in Love* is not only a sexual fantasy but a social one as well, for Lawrence transposes his friends and connections with abandon, turning London intellectuals into grandee coal-owners and his aristocratic German wife into an English Midlands girl. This may be a rather vulgar way of putting it, but my point is that the social fantasy of *Women in Love*—established with instant audacity and conviction when all parties are brought together in the opening wedding scene—is as brilliantly effective as the sexual one, and as meaningful. New and real possibilities for the social image of the self emerge out of it, just as sexual ones do from that other, though related, side of the fantasy. And again, to criticize Lawrence for 'getting it wrong' socially, as Graham Hough did in *The Dark Sun*, for example, is as beside the point as attacking his sexual views for their male chauvinism, sadism, lack of respect for the female orgasm etc. The fantasy creates and expands irrespective of assertion, which is not quite the same as the usual judgment that vision and art are more important than metaphysic: vision and metaphysic are predictably at one in Lawrence; but fantasy—social and sexual— liberates us from them and leaves behind the self-conscious aspects of both.

It is self-consciousness of purpose and method that makes *Howards End* a far less convincing social construction. The Wilcox-Schlegel confrontation and synthesis remains dependent on reflection and assertion. The lack of assured imagination is revealed in Forster's refuge—or rather weapon—of diffidence: his remarks recorded later for example, that where the Basts were concerned 'he hoped he had brought it off'. Lawrence would not have bothered to hope anything of the sort. But Jane Austen might have, though diffidence with her would have been of a more open kind; and Forster's successes in *Howards End* are distinctly Austenian, as in the blend of fantasy and social comedy at Evie's wedding, with all its preceding horrors and screams of laughter—('Margaret screamed a little too, but without conviction'). Forster enjoys and is a fine hand at the big set-piece scandal, like the scene in *The Longest Journey* where Ansell denounces the ethos of Sawston in the school dining-hall. But what the Russians—*à propos* of Dostoevsky— call the *skandal* scene, depends on what Bakhtin has described as an adroit evasion of commitment—the novelist must not be himself pinned down, as Forster is, by the drama of revelation that he has himself provoked. In this respect Lawrence's social fantasy is surprisingly like Dostoevsky's: he is sardonic at moments of crisis, and non-committal, seeming to step out of the action momentarily with a shrug of cheerful bloody-mindedness. This Forster neither can nor wants to do, for his dependence on the solidity and reassurance of the social scene and social convention is too great. Like the Bloomsbury writers he gives the impression of enjoying the unorthodox in the same spirit in which undergraduates once enjoyed stealing police-men's helmets: a daring act that showed a deep unconscious belief in and respect for the Force.

And indeed it could be said that if Lawrence the artist is self-divided by his refusal to admit the purely mental nature of his sexual fantasy, then Forster is equally—and with equally happy results—undermined by his unspoken reliance on the social conventions and life-style that he attacks. He could not write novels without them: to emancipate himself from them would be to lose the whole dynamic of method, vision and imagination. In order to produce his novels he must be totally compromised with society, not in Jane Austen's fashion, but in a manner that subordinates his personal instinct to an art form which the novels reject even while they depend on it. Forster himself of course perfectly understood the division, or at least came to do so after he could no longer avail himself of it. In 1935, at the age of fifty-six, he is recorded as remarking: 'I want to love a strong young man of the lower classes, and be loved by him and even hurt by him. That is my ticket; and then I have wanted to write respectable novels.'

Today there would have been no division, and the formula for those particular masterpieces could not exist. What does exist in its place is foreshadowed in Forster's posthumous novel, *Maurice*, written about 1912, where the problems and development of a homosexual are openly recorded. The most noteworthy thing about *Maurice* is its abandonment of society: the novel is no longer in collusion with a social situation on which it depends for structure, tension and most important, humour. Instead, social philistinism and the ordinary *mores* of the upper classes are equated with heterosexuality and totally dismissed. Maurice's friend Clive, who becomes a heterosexual, is shown as losing for that reason all claim to the author's and reader's interest, and entering a dead world of convention and joylessness, a world which has lost everything that—to use the formulaic phrase of Lawrence's admirers—'makes for life'. His wife is a non-person, not even like Evie Wilcox, a 'rubbishy little person', not even worth the collusive Forsterian relish of antipathy and exposure. The balance is quite lost that is achieved in the 'respectable' novels by the conspiracy of reticence and indirection. And virtually nothing is gained, for the account of Maurice's love affair with the gamekeeper, Alec, remains as much a fantasy as Rickie's crypto-affair with Stephen Wonham in *The Longest Journey*, but a fantasy which no longer carries the licence and excuse of art and its possibilities of expansion. Like the fantasies in most modern novels it is simply a question of: 'This is what I would like to do'—and not: 'This is how I have managed to reconcile what I would like to do with my awareness of and dependence on art and society'—art and society forming an alliance which artist and social man cannot and do not want to do without.

For, as I have said about Lawrence, the test of such fantasy in art is whether it works for other people, and can be socialized into the wider human setting. *Maurice* remains exclusive and solitary. The paradox is that by means of indirection and dissimulation the artist in such matters can reach a wider audience and find a more sympathetic echo and response than he can by 'speaking out'. The seemingly explicit *Lady Chatterley's Lover* is really not only reticent but—given the nature of its fantasy—ambivalent as well: homosexuals could well identify with, or at least find a real absorption and fellow interest in, both Mellors and Connie; the latter, like all Lawrence's heroines, is not in any conventional or conditioned sense 'feminine'. For both Lawrence and Forster the fantasy of sex was also in large part a fantasy of class, and both are attracted to individuals, irrespective of their sex, who represent the romance of another class—gipsies, gamekeepers, foreigners, aristocrats—in whom sex appears as the attribute of a way of life.

Lawrence was in a sense more fortunate than Forster—it is an aspect of the unity of his life and art—in being able to write about everything that happened to him, sexually speaking, and it is clear that the one thing he could not have written about would have been a normal marriage and a family of children, with someone of his own age, class and background. Such a relation could have had no sort of appeal for him, none of that correspondence with sexual fantasy which filled his dealings with Frieda, Murry and others, or which is imagined in Mellors and Connie, Kate and Cipriano in *The Plumed Serpent*, Somers and 'Kangaroo'. The young Brangwyns, Will and Anna, are the only normal couple on whom Lawrence visits his powers of insight and description, and in spite of its moments of joy their relation is clinically surveyed *de haut en bas*, as one of doom and sterility, empty victory for the woman and inner destruction for the man. It offered no 'sex in the head' for Lawrence; and he seals off and ignores, for fantasy can make nothing of them, the non-sexual intimacy and discourse which constitute married life for persons ordinarily matched.

It must be said, though, that both *Women in Love* and Forster's novel *The Longest Journey* enter with zest into what was then, and perhaps still is, an important practical aspect of the convention and requirement of marriage: the takeover or banishment by a wife of her husband's friends. (Neither author is interested in what the husband might do to the wife's.) Lawrence is recording his own experience when Ursula shows the symptoms; and Forster uses the reactions he must have observed in himself and his friends at Cambridge. Yet when consciousness 'turns turtle' in *The Longest Journey* and fantasy takes over, what is most impressive is the unexpected nature of the truths that emerge. The most incisive fantasy in the book is Rickie's running away with Stephen Wonham, and the abandonment of his wife Agnes, who has tried to neutralize and tame his friends. But this culminates in bitter failure. As Forster makes deviously clear, his hero Rickie discovers too late that his desire and love for Stephen bears no relation to reality, and misinterprets the casual protective friendliness which Stephen has neither the wish nor the means to implement. By presenting these matters crabwise Forster gives them much greater impact and significance in art than they could have in the clinical isolation of *Maurice*. Although her creator has little sympathy for her it is clear that Agnes, too, is as much a victim of misunderstanding as Rickie; and the power of the tale is only diminished by the necessary pastoral ending, which, like that of *Howards Ends*, substitutes a contrived symbolism for the fantasy which is the true means whereby both Forster and Lawrence 'accede to reality'.

CHAPTER II

1. *The Puzzles of Kipling*

Forster saw himself, as he said of Cavafy, 'at a slight angle to the world'. Lawrence too was in a sense at an angle, though it was of course for him the proper and sacred relation to life. Both owe to this the unity and achievement of their writing personalities. A writer like Kipling, scattered among the contingencies of his time, and involved particularly in the technologies of militarism which had come to dominate the European scene, is in very different case. And yet the contrast does not now seem quite so clear as it did. It may even be, as I have been trying to suggest, that the achievement of Lawrence and Forster, as it has survived and matured, depends more than their admirers admit on aspects of their genius which they themselves would disown or refuse to recognize. Compared with Kipling, the black sheep of their era, they once seemed clear cases of enlightenment, of civilization and progress. Do they still?—or rather do their novels as we now read them seem so wholly separated from other sorts of inspired fantasy which have left a mark on the age and on later readers? Freud's favourite reading in his later years, *The Jungle Book*, has impressed itself on readers at one stage of their lives at least as deeply as the works of these more accepted masters.

Edmund Wilson, in *The Wound and the Bow*, suggested that Kipling is one of those artists whose skills attend disablement from a childhood trauma. Yet, though Kipling's desertion by his parents was in all likelihood more traumatic than the prolonged maternal domination to which Lawrence and Forster were subject, its influence on the pattern of his life and ideas seems in fact to have been much less clearly pronounced. Nor would it be true to say that Lawrence and Forster are exiles from their epoch while Kipling is inside and identified with his. All were rather leaders, or associated with leaders, of more or less exclusive groups who sought to influence the age.

51

It is true that Kipling was absorbed by—even disintegrated by
—his age, with more evident completeness than we can forgive
a great writer for being, or accept that he should be, if we are
to think of him as a great writer. He cannot be said to have
belonged to his times in any conventional sense, for though his
temperament and views were those of a great many other persons of his class and kind he went with embarrassing detail and
enthusiasm into what they took for granted. He was always far
too much for 'the Group' to be of it, and he was a lonelier figure
than either Lawrence or Forster, though probably a more
widely influential one.

His influence and his loneliness are closely connected, and
make it immediately necessary to redefine what we understand
by being 'lonely' in his case. For it is no use blinking the fact
that in terms of sensibility he was not lonely at all; his feelings
and responses coincided completely with those of a large and
widespread social and class ethos, not with those of a cult group
or 'inner ring'. The major disconcertment to many people in
Kipling, and especially to *bien pensants* in our time, is to find
so much intelligence in such an unlikely area of sensibility. The
sensibility of that part of the tribe *is* coarse, is repellent—there
is no doubt about it: but it cannot blunt the acuteness and the
powers of observation which Kipling bestows on it. Indeed the
coarser the feeling he shares, the finer the perception of it in
his art—a rare and embarrassing conjunction. And so loneliness
for Kipling is being far cleverer than the people whose sensibility
he shares, and just as clever as the fellow-artists whose sensibilities cause them to shun him.

He fitted, in his own imagination and work, into a category
which Lawrence in his correspondence with Dr Trigant
Burrow (a sociologist rather surprisingly respected by
Lawrence), called 'societal man'. That is to say Kipling took
himself for granted but was fascinated by any social unit he
sought to belong to, or saw himself as belonging to. He had
no interest in himself as such, and had none of the two other
writers' ability to project that self into an imagined social
scene, dominate it and take it over. Why it is interesting, after
this lapse of time, to look at him in the context, not of the
literature of imperialism but of the solitary authentic consciousness in its self-created social setting, is because Kipling's
answer to the problem of Hegelian awareness is not so much

opposed to theirs as complementary to it. Kipling understands, no less than they, the symptoms of social neurosis, alienation and discontent, but the ways in which he puts these things into art suggest remedies of a wholly practical, non-visionary kind. Kipling's fantasies, like the notorious one of *Mary Postgate*, are always rooted in a well observed and understood social situation, and his solutions accept in practical fashion the limitations of that situation.

The odd thing about Kipling is that such a talent, at such a time, should not have been housed in an 'authentic conscious-ness', and in self-estrangement, but in a personality passionately committed to all the honest social and family values. In one sense the paradox was disabling, for it prevented him becoming —what Henry James thought he had it in him to be—'the English Balzac'. In fact it was James himself who can now be seen to qualify for something like that title: he was able to do so because he combined the strongest possible interest in social ties and commitments with an equally strong disinclination to involve himself in them. Kipling's involvement was complete, and it prevented him from standing far enough back to write a novel; the nearest he came to it was *Kim*, in which his absorption of India could be made use of in a superlatively vivid and fantastic retrospection.

Kipling was not only deeply and continuously involved in every aspect of English life and politics but he also believed in and practised the normal family virtues, affections and responsi-bilities. Balzac's form of detachment was irresponsibility. Exploiting his two mistress-mothers, both more than twenty years older than himself, pining for a third mistress who lived romantically on a Polish estate as big as a French department, Balzac was totally involved in those obsessions and appetites of living which he described, but not in its duties or abnegations. Kipling's curiosity in and relish for what made people and society tick was equally great, and so perhaps was his power to describe it—his dimension was as large and as vivid as Balzac's—but his personality was not up to his talents. He used to be considered a monster by liberal *bien pensants*—'horrible old Kipling' as Auden called him—but it would be nearer the mark to say that he was not monster enough, certainly not the kind of 'sacred monster' who could create on Balzac's scale. His personality was not commonplace, but it was kept,

in what was perhaps a peculiarly English way, dutiful, careful, and ordinary. He revered 'the Gods of the Copy Book
headings'.

Yet as an artist he was deeply divided, none the less, and
the divisions may determine what we feel about his art.
Forster's 'Only connect' does not at all apply; the unified and
dominating consciousness, which we may see developing and
forming itself during a writer's creative life, is conspicuously
absent. In a suggestive essay on his later stories W. W. Robson
made the point that his art

> does not in any very obvious sense show development . . .
> Masterpieces as assured as anything he ever wrote can be
> found, at any period of his work, side by side with very
> inferior things; and yet on these inferior things the same
> minuteness of skill and care seems to have been expended.

This is certainly a clue, and it may lead to a deduction that
Robson does not make. For what he calls 'inferiority' is of
strange importance in Kipling. It is not, as it would be with
other writers, a sign of failure of imagination, concentration or
nerve, but is as determined and confident, as full of mastery,
as the recognized excellence. It is a sign of his stature, as it is
with Lawrence: perhaps, indeed, it is *the* sign of a writer who
is important in the ways I have been trying to suggest.

Women in Love, I maintained, does not have the same
qualities we associate with the idea of a 'masterpiece'; it is
loosened and freed in its aesthetic structure by kinds of comedy,
even of absurdity, in language and vision which are wholly
Lawrentian but which yet do not strike us as belonging to
Lawrence in the often oppressive way that his style and ideas
can do. It may be that the gap between this vulnerable Lawrence
and the armed and unified author getting the statue clean away
from the marble is too great: we can't easily, in appreciation,
assimilate the one to the other and find a proper home, as we
do in the 'good' and the 'bad' alike of Hardy or of Kipling.
That is because Lawrence is too intent on forcing everything
into consciousness, and the same certainly cannot be said of
Kipling, who more typically seems concerned to leave matters
below the level of realization. This may be a weakness or it
may not: Kipling is convinced that what is most important to
social man is usually conditioned in him in ways that ought not

to be disturbed or brought to light too much; a conviction difficult to reconcile with the ways in which art works as finding out, exploring and revealing. That is why the pay-off, in Kipling's narrative metaphysic, so often disappoints, seems either meagre or smart, and not rigorous enough.

But this applies more to what is usually thought of as good in his work than to what is considered bad. It is probably true that if we accept Kipling we are not all that much concerned with the difference between the two, granted always that both the good and the bad are concerned with the investigation of a social unit. And ultimately something of the same kind may happen with Lawrence, for the addict of both writers rapidly becomes indifferent to their doctrines—though he may remain very knowledgeable about them—and becomes hooked on something that is not exactly their 'art', but more their individual speech and their particular mode of self-revelation. Like Lawrence, also like Dickens, Kipling was essentially daemonic in temperament, though he preferred to think of his daemon not as the fire in his own belly, but as it were a powerful and senior colleague who lived in the next compound. He insisted, and over-insisted, on being an artist, but his place is more with these other daemonic creators who have no regard for art in the lamp and inkhorn sense in which Kipling liked to talk of it. It was as difficult for him to get outside himself, and to be the detached artist, as it was to get outside the packs and societies which he ran with and believed in.

For the writer who depends in one way or another on divisions, unresolved issues and confusions present in the completed work, detachment is in any case not possible. All he thinks and is shows all the time, and this is as true of the early tales in which Kipling is at school with de Maupassant as in the later ones, with their finicky techniques of the elliptic and absconded narrator. It is significant that Hemingway, who admired and learnt from Kipling, has none of this involuntary presentness. When he relaxed his revolutionary and immaculate technique of narrative mannerism he is revealed as a wordy bore, a mind and being at the end of the road. Kipling, like Lawrence, retains his mystery, his power to make us continue wondering about him. Kipling is too big to present a 'case', as Edmund Wilson tried to make him, and as Hemingway undoubtedly is. He goes on cropping up all over the place, even among the young Soviet intelligentsia, offering—in spite of the lack of bulk fiction in his varied work—his own odd version of God's plenty, and something for everyone, even his own variation on Lamb's ideal of 'the sanity of true genius'.

From his own fastidious angle, T. S. Eliot summed up much of what I have been trying to suggest when he said that the pleasure of reading Kipling was 'the pleasure of exploring a mind so very different from my own'. The compliment implicit in the word 'exploration' is a very considerable one. As in Browning's metaphor in *Love in a Life* (and Browning was Kipling's favourite poet) we go from room to room through closed doors. In such a compartmented mind, of a kind familiar to us from daily human contact but not often met with in great writers—though Milton and Dickens both reveal it—we experience contradictions and prejudices which do not meet and examine one another except through our presence. Impulses like vindictiveness and forbearance, humility and strident assurance, appear to maintain a separate but equalizing pressure on the creative temperament. Though in story and character we are always in the presence, it is a presence that does not necessarily weigh upon us as that of much more enlightened authors may do; for the compartments act like a modern equivalent of what Keats called 'negative capability'. Kipling could certainly feel with an Iago and an Imogen, with a Learoyd and a Liza Rowntree, but the impulse to hate or to love which he depicts in such characters doesn't appear capable of meeting or recognition. To draw a crude parallel, he sometimes reminds us of a loving father who votes for hanging and flogging; and indeed as a man of his time that was what he was, and what he did.

In *The Wound and the Bow* Edmund Wilson compares Kipling, much to his disadvantage, with Yeats and with Henry James.

> Kipling *had* terribly shrunk . . . Whereas Yeats was playing out superbly the last act of a personal drama which he had sustained unembarrassed by public events, and Henry James was now seen in retrospect to have accomplished, in his long career, a prodigy of disinterested devotion to an art and a criticism of life.

A personal drama unembarrassed by public events suggests, rather more than Wilson perhaps intended, the fundamental and self-willed isolation of Yeats; and James, too might have smiled wryly at Wilson's compliment. The truth is, surely, that all three acted as they had to do and as their creative natures required, but the limitations are not necessarily on Kipling's side. His vulnerability was as intelligent as the dedication of Yeats and no less noble than James's abstinence. The loss of his son and daughter; his knowledge of hatred and vindictiveness and of their inevitability in any social group; his involvement in duty and unfreedom; his sense of attachment and forbearance, not as moral qualities or enlightened opinions, but as what was for him absolute needs, like the need to support order and be some kind of snob—these are the marks of Kipling's participation, as of many other persons', and that silent majority would no doubt endorse his view that in this way 'hearts, like muddy streams, cleanse themselves as they go forward'.

James in fact, in his subterraneous way, has an almost wholly deterministic view of the moral world. The hero of his story *The Beast in the Jungle*, knew his fate to be emptiness, not by reason of a noble abstinence, but because of his own egoism: that was the way he was. Kipling's remarkable late tale of a fantastic literary forgery, *Dayspring Mishandled*, resembles James's story in its bleak and subtle suggestion of the inability to be other than oneself. Its hero is a writer of historical potboilers who plans an elaborate revenge on a Chaucerian scholar who has done him a great injury: he composes and forges a superb fragment which he contrives that the scholar should discover; but when his enemy is delivered utterly into his hand he refrains from consummating his triumph, not through any free and virtuous moral choice—such things do not exist in Kipling's world—but because as an artist he cannot bear to see such a piece of work collapsed into the triviality of life.

The story is composed and highlighted with great care and cunning. And as often happens with Kipling this meticulousness emphasizes something both coarse and conventional in the selection of characters and in the concept itself. The woman whom the villain has 'wronged' has no proper specification, which implies that Kipling is too much of a gentleman to give her one; and though his discovery has brought him fame the villain dies of cancer without enjoying the knighthood he has got by it, while his wife, now Lady Castorley, prepares to remarry. We may be chilled by a callousness in the characters' behaviour which Kipling seems quite to take for granted, and perhaps repelled as well by the glib 'nature's revenge' in the ending. James, perhaps, could have given us a more artistic chill by delicately indicating and probing the ugliness in and beneath the seeming decorum of professional literary society. But Kipling's *donnée*, though so much like many of James's, draws us into a more memorable encounter, perhaps because he himself seems not wholly aware of the nature and meaning of the materials he is so meticulously handling—on this, as on other Kipling conundrums, we can never be quite sure. Characteristically he prefers to present himself as a technician rather than a creator: we can sometimes tell if something is important, deep down, from his light and offhand manner of talking about it.

And in fact the technical expertise and knowledge he prided himself on is often much more insecure than his instincts. There is an example in his memoir, *Something of Myself*, which has an odd bearing on *Dayspring Mishandled*, for it shows how sketchy was Kipling's actual knowledge of Chaucer. He relates, in that ebullient manner which is both stimulating and strangely repellent, how the *Manchester Guardian*, always hating his attitudes, managed in their reviews to find fault with everything he published. One of his later tales, *The Wish House*, earned their contempt by having a heroine obviously cribbed from Chaucer's Wife of Bath, down to the 'mormal on her shinne'. Kipling wrote to the paper

> and gave myself 'out—caught to leg'. The reply came from an evident human being . . . who was pleased with the tribute to his knowledge of Chaucer.

What Kipling did not appear to have realised was that he had compounded a howler—the 'mormal' belongs to the Cook in Chaucer's *Prologue*, not to the Wife of Bath. The incident shows not only Kipling's attitude to expertise, and to false expertise, but how some of his fascination comes from a kind of involuntary collusion by the reader in falsity got up so closely to resemble life that it sheds sudden and disconcerting light on Kipling's views *on* life. The gap between hand-rubbing accuracy and an over-casual tone holds the particular flavour of the Kipling experience, and like good journalism (no wonder Kipling felt kinship with the *Guardian* reviewer) it makes an immediate impression without much follow-through. The trouble with elaborations on reporting is that they are only true for a moment, where the 'story' and the reader intersect; and we often feel that what happened afterwards is no affair of Kipling's.

The really bizarre thing about this hypnotically untrustworthy innocence, which earned him in his time as many English-speaking readers as the Bible, is the way it is mixed in with a cunning ceremony—the literary equivalent of freemasonry. It is hinted that only initiates, those really in the know, can understand the Last Effects, the 'overlaid tints and textures', in his Burne-Jones picture vocabulary, 'which might or might not reveal themselves according to the shifting light of sex, youth and experience'. (Just conceivably his story about the *Guardian* man and Chaucer is intended to test the reader, with Kipling knowing what was wrong all the time, for he tells us in *Something of Myself* that he used when he was young to plumb the real knowledge of 'the Men of Letters' he met by misattributing quotations, and was seldom or never corrected.) In one of the South African stories, *The Comprehension of Private Copper*, clues are undoubtedly planted to show Sahibs in the know that Private Copper's captor, a renegade young Boer of English origin, has come in his speech and outlook, his consciousness of inferiority, to resemble a Eurasian, because the true Boers have denied him political rights and treated him as an inferior being. For Kipling (as for Lord Milner) this was the crux of the case against the Boers—to dissolve the reflexes of British superiority was the unforgivable sin—and, as Professor Bodelsen has pointed out, some verses called *The Old Issue* introduce a sexual motif that the story completes. 'Deeper strikes the rottenness in the people's loins', because as helots they lose self-respect, and with it the will to power and the hegemony of race. Kipling was conditioned by his time, and by his varied experience, especially in India, and his understanding of these matters can be seen now to be exact and profound. However acute their intuition of a place—and Lawrence's could be astonishing—Lawrence and Forster were always visitors and tourists, whereas Kipling knew to the bone how men are set and moulded into the place where they must live and the job they must do.

But such knowledge is in its nature unprincipled. Its only real logic is the maintenance of British domination, because that domination was the best thing for the world in general, and for India or South Africa in particular. (As Marlowe observes without irony in Conrad's *Heart of Darkness*, where the map is red you can be sure that good work is being done there.) But in terms of Kipling's art this lack of moral logic or external insight (Kipling loathed principles or beliefs unearned in the conditioning of action) is not important. What is important is that a story which may seem morally deplorable, even indefensible, can none the less be a work of art in the Tolstoyan sense. Kipling's art effects may stop on the page, but not the moral of his art; and its lack of abstract ethic provides a sort of challenge. Why is it wrong for Boers to treat English *uitlanders* as an inferior class, and right for the English to do the same to natives and Eurasians? Why is it right to drop bombs that may kill German civilians, and vile of them to kill our children by the same means? Of course there is no answer and Kipling does not pretend that there is; unlike racial theorists he never tried to justify himself—the feeling of the tribe was what counted. But equally of course we ask the question, because the stories—so far from requiring we should—cannot, by reason of their peculiar power, prevent us.

This, with a vengeance, is to trust the tale and not the teller. A late tale from *Limits and Renewals*, a companion of *Dayspring Mishandled*, is a case in point. *The Tie*, deplored by Mr Robson as 'negligible and unpleasant', is about a fraudulent contractor of the 1914 war who is only saved from violence at the hands of some young officers by the old school tie he is wearing. Conditioning tells, in a manner that is as explosively satirical in effect as it is—presumably—merely genial and admonitory in intention. Such tales are able to reach into us through outrage, whereas the *Puck* series, in which the 'tints and textures' are all methodically and insipidly overlaid, are by this comparison lacking in the secret dynamic, and are parables too consciously intended to be read on more than one level. But in these tales knowledge is not imparted by an author outside; Kipling has no Lawrentian intelligence to place, define and assign from a position of isolated integrity. Light does not come from outside—it dawns inside the locked compartments of assumption and prejudice which the daemon makes us enter, and it is arguable that the more apparently awful the stories, the further they reach in our hearts and minds, if we let them.

One of the Plain Tales from the Hills, as 'awful' as *The Tie* , but written something like forty years earlier, makes much the same point as the later story, and forces us equally to understand by participation in the society described. A young English civil servant is determined to marry a Portuguese Eurasian girl and is 'saved' by his colleagues, who kidnap him before the wedding can take place. There is a gruesome equability in the narration. The Eurasian is both good and beautiful, and the pink and white English girl who will subsequently be chosen for the promising young man will be without interest: between them there will evidently be, as is fitting, no real sympathy or emotion. But things are as they are, and the relation in the tale between Kipling's gleeful acceptance of the situation, and his cool understanding of it, is charged with his special kind of disturbing vitality; just how much so we can see if we compare it with the similar themes that Somerset Maugham was going to handle. In terms of so tricky a theme Maugham's enlightened views are as repellent as his detachment; though he is a far from negligible writer his authorial attitudes are all too simply egoistic. Maugham annoyed Colonials who found themselves and the tales they had told him in his stories; but Kipling must have embarrassed his contemporaries in India very much more, and more subtly. For they had always taken tacitly for granted what he now exuberantly took for granted in print, and the demonstration is far more unsettling than any satire, especially to the community so equivocally endorsed by Kipling's art.

Kipling's involvement here is not so unlike that of Tolstoy in *War and Peace* and *Anna Karenina*. Tolstoy's enthusiasm for the manners and assumptions of his class and kind is subjected to a massive process of self-analysing and self-revealing detail and is both more lyric and more epic to the extent that Tolstoy is by far the greater genius. But the Rostovs' ball, Stiva's lunch-party, the great reception for Bagration, show Tolstoy as emphatically on the side of a way of life as Kipling is, and this emphasis could be said to be just as damaging, not only in retrospect but in the eyes of those associates of his who realized—as which of them, however obscurely, did not?—that such a mode of being depended both for its confidence and for its private validity on *not* being publicized in this way. We know that Tolstoy's peers privately resented his magnificent process, and we may assume that Kipling's had the same reservations about his more specific and workaday one. In both authors there is the same secret sense of the injustice of the world, and of where they stand in relation to it, and to its necessities.

The daemon knew more than the journalist and spokesman for imperialism, and certainly had more human sympathy: when Kipling tries to show sympathy in person he almost always fails and is not infrequently embarrassing. His apologists today make the mistake of supposing that it was Kipling himself—as it might be Lawrence or Forster—who could be an independent judge, accepting, so to speak, the laws of Israel, but retaining and demonstrating his own values—values more like their own. But there are no values for him outside the pack. It has been suggested that a criticism is passed on 'the great game' of the secret service in *Kim*, by means of the figures of the Lama and the Babu, but the Lama is really only a case of self-indulgence on Kipling's part. As a Tibetan monk, of an exotically unknown and therefore uninferior race and religion, the Lama is excused from real participation in society. We can see Kipling clearly— too clearly—in these moments of humanity, but we cannot see him at all when he is writing about what really inspired him.

*   *   *

The queer ratio of his acceptance and awareness goes some way towards explaining why he did not in any ordinary sense develop as a writer, though this claim also has been made on his behalf, even by Wilson, who considers the later stories— 'the Kipling that nobody read'—in some sense penitential, and a kind of saving diminishment. But all such things, good and bad, are really very much of a piece, as I have been suggesting. It is the less characteristic Kipling which in a sense develops, or at least expands, from the formal experiment of *The Light that Failed* (Kipling tells us it was based on *Manon Lescaut* and there seems reason only partly to disbelieve him) to *Captains Courageous* and *Puck of Pook's Hill*. Good as all that side of Kipling is, it does not really contribute to his inner dimension, for the moral perspective—as I suppose it must be called—is flat and plain, and Kipling at his least personally involved. All this open side of him goes with his rather touching desire to write a 'veritable three-decker, out of chosen and long-stored timber', a massive novel that was presumably to be a kind of historical human comedy—'worthy to lie alongside *The Cloister and the Hearth*'. Kipling's admiration for Charles Reade (attributed in *Brugglesmith* to one of his chief engineers) throws an odd light on his own more conscious ambitions, and the difference between them and his real achievements.

I don't wish to overdo this emphasis, because the design of the more open works like *Captains Courageous* is as imaginative as it is memorable. The liner's path intersecting in fog with the frail dory, and the background perspective of Harvey's industrialist father, whose success story was 'like watching a locomotive storming across country in the dark'—these have become classic things, as much a part of literature as—say—*Middlemarch*, or Dickens's Marshalsea, and so too have the world of the *Jungle Books*. None the less the large designs do suffer from a certain perfunctoriness and a lack of all-round vigilance: they lack the faceless inner intelligence of the tales. Henry James's Adam Verver, of *The Golden Bowl*, has the excuse of a deeply pondered English setting for not really being convincing at the level of an American tycoon, but Harvey Cheyne senior loses his reality in Kipling's presentation somewhere between a demonstrated outer ruthlessness and an assumed inner refinement. The real Cheynes, we know, were coarse, dull and brutal; and if Kipling knew this too he is not letting on, because his tale is one of instruction in manliness and high endeavour.

It is here that Conrad, Kipling's master in strength of design, scores heavily. Capitalism in *Nostromo*, and even more significantly in *Chance*, is revealed as innerly hollow, without a soul, full of what Forster calls 'panic and emptiness'. This Kipling exorcizes by substituting for acquisitiveness and greed the poetry of exploration and endeavour. His vision is as true as Conrad's where the spirit of nineteenth-century capitalist achievement is concerned, but it cannot but appear fatally naïve in its engrossed emphasis on a single aspect of those great undertakings. Cheyne's neurosis is evident enough, but its price is not apparent in the same tranquilly awful manner that is so thoroughly and disturbingly conveyed in *Dayspring Mishandled*, or in *Plain Tales from the Hills*.

In those places Kipling is at one with the joints and sinews of the whole process, 'the toad beneath the harrow' who, as he gets on with his job, cannot afford the moral perspective of 'the butterfly upon the road'. How much depends on the nature of that job? Suppose—to take it to a deliberate extreme—it had been the job of gassing Jews? Kipling's views on 'non-Aryans' who didn't fit into the pack are well-known, nor are they much meliorated by his deliberately sympathetic vision of mediaeval Jewry controlling the flow of gold ('that wonderful underground river') in *Rewards and Fairies*. In his essay, *The Inner Ring*, C. S. Lewis suggested that Kipling's group preoccupation is ultimately amoral, and that provided he could feel he was on the inside he would not care what were its aims and methods.

Lewis hated Kipling wholeheartedly, and this is certainly an ingenious way of rationalizing his hatred, but it ignores the implications of the fact that Kipling never tries to get outside the inner workings of a situation. Is it wrong to hunt, to hang, to regard black men as inferiors?—involvement in actual situations dissolves and solves such queries. It may not be the right line to take, but our familiarity with those various masonic-type groups (Disko Troop, Mulvaney, McPhee, Jobson, 'William') whose worth Kipling preaches but whose real virtues the daemon more involuntarily reveals, must at least show the absurdity of Lewis's point.

For the kind of systematic horrors which Lewis had in mind, and which Kipling did not live to see, are not the result of an Inner Ring muddling along and enjoying its innerness: they come from the demands of the ideal, bubbling together in solitude. Like many people of his time, Kipling seems now to have a sort of innocence, which comes from the mannerisms of anecdotage and club-room chat, together with enthusiasm for all the numbers of things that were to be done in the world, progress to be made, burdens carried and new marvels discovered. The Kipling twinkle seems as dated today as his attitude to japes, rags, and revenges; but on practical matters of power he is, within the context of his age, sober, intelligent and well-informed—he was, after all, right about the Boer policy as about the German. Like so many of the men of action of the time whom he admired, he is innocent and open in his address and manners, shrewd and practical in his sense of the way things are run. He quoted with approval Lord Dufferin's dictum: 'There can be no room for good intentions in one's work.' For the Nazis, and for such a frighteningly and genuinely innocent writer and genius as Knut Hamsun, who embraced their creed, 'good intentions' were indeed the road to hell, or to the heaven they hoped for if the Master Race were in charge, the Jews eliminated and the sub-men enslaved. But in Kipling's work and outlook there are no solutions, final or otherwise.

Of course Kipling had what today would be called 'racial' ideas, but they are simply, not to say brutally, empirical: a question of who has the confidence to dominate and rule and who has not. The 'dominant race' (to whom Wee Willie Winkie demonstrated that he belonged) has no god-given right: in the nature of things its self-assertion can only be temporary. Nor is it without significance that Kipling detested the forms of pride in race and behaviour that go today with a concept like *machismo*—fashionable because (as he to some degree foresaw) it would distinguish an American-style dominance. He had an extreme hatred of boastfulness, and of the violence which put an end to his life in America—the superiority of Canada over the United States was amply demonstrated for Kipling, as he tells us more than once, by the law that was upheld and respected there, and the absence of lynching and shooting. It may well be that the modern distaste for his whole outlook (though this would not apply to C. S. Lewis) makes his racial and social opinions the scapegoat for another and deeper reason: the fact that his art dismisses out of hand the more anarchic and anti-social desires and displays of the authentic consciousness. Intellectuals today may tolerate any kind of cruelty and violence—in fact connive in it—provided it is the gratuitous act of the solitary and alienated consciousness; and I suspect that it is not his 'cruelty' that repels the contemporary *bien pensant* so much as his insistence on the disciplines of the pack, their condemnations and retributions.

For the same reasons Kipling is interested in sex not as a personal and physical but purely as a social phenomenon. Here too there are signs of deep concealments, interments and divisions, for although—like Durkheim or Malinowski—he portrays sexual custom in terms of group and caste loyalties and necessities, his sense of the consequences can be profound. He is acutely aware of the part sex plays in racial and social fears and hatreds, and of the forms it may take in times of group crisis and personal disintegration. The amusing side of this comes in a very early tale like *Cupid's Arrows*, in which a Simla young lady jilts a most eligible commissioner who sets up an archery contest in order that she should win it, and he win her. (Kitty's mother makes a typical remark which links the world of Jane Austen and Trollope to Kipling's newer and more stringent world of caste: 'You will take precedence of your own mother, you know . . . think of that and be reasonable'.) The more interesting sides are revealed in stories like *Private Copper*, and above all in *Mary Postgate*.

We experience in both stories Kipling's power of revealing how the virulence of the instinct may work in society; but much more graphically in the latter, for Private Copper is a soldier of straw, and Mary Postgate is very much a real woman. She is one of the few exceptions to the general truth that Kipling is only good at portraying groups and representatives of groups, not individuals; and his normal indifference and even insensitivity to the 'thisness' of a person make the exceptions decidedly startling. Kipling's general tone is an index of his treatment of character: it is usually that of the raconteur in public, taking for granted that only the public nature of his characters will be of interest to the audience. By contrast a writer who sees his creations as individuals will also see his reader as one. With Tolstoy and Lawrence, for instance, we feel that their penetration and analysis of a personality extends to us; we seem to be alone with them, and the experience is a stimulating one, even if on occasion so exasperating that we want to defend ourselves in person against the author. But Kipling is remorselessly unintimate. We are never alone with him but always one of a group, and it is this more than anything that defines his characteristic vulgarity, his insensitivity to the reactions of whatever in us is *wholly individual*. As artist he is all too often oblivious to everything except the craving for what he called 'the loveliest sound in the world—deep-voiced men laughing together . . .'

Mary Postgate, however, is very much a person as well as a social phenomenon, and yet not a person presented as a case history, in the manner of Maupassant's *Une Vie*. As in *The Wish House* and in *The Turn of the Screw* and the best stories of James's disciple in that vein, Walter de La Mare—the key to the tale is that it remains unclear how much in it, particularly the climactic act of cruelty, happens in fact, and how much in Mary's mind. 'One mustn't let one's mind dwell on these things', says Mary (the phrase is discreetly emphasized by repetition) and that is of course why the mind does so dwell, and why the fantasy is so powerful. When young Wynn, her employer's nephew, is killed flying, Mary has what amounts to a nervous breakdown, but being Mary ('I've no imagination I'm afraid . . . As Wynn says, I haven't the mind') it takes a strange form. The play on the word *mind* is almost Shakespearean—'Postey doesn't mind', says Wynn, after a particularly unfeeling jest at her expense. Wynn's multitudinous effects are to be burnt after his death, and Mary goes to the village for paraffin to light the garden incinerator. An aeroplane is heard, a shed is knocked down, and a little girl fatally injured. Mary takes for granted it was a German bomb (Wynn had shown her the bomb-racks on his own machine) but the doctor overtakes her on the way home and tells her the shed collapsed from dry rot. She doesn't believe him and it seems unlikely he believes himself—but uncertainty is the climate of war. She goes down the garden to the incinerator, finds a German airman who has apparently fallen from his plane, and leaves him to die while with closed eyes 'she drew her breath between her teeth and shuddered from head to foot'. (A gruesome unstressed touch is that in spite of her apparently sheltered life she recognizes the onset of death and knows, too, the difference between its preliminary symptoms and the final spasm.) She then has a bath and is found by her employer relaxed and 'quite handsome' on the sofa.

It is not surprising that this extraordinary tale, which sees so much and touches so many nerves of war, sex, love, neurosis and repression should so often have been denounced and denied the sympathy of proper recognition. It is one of the very few of Kipling's stories in which the craft elements—compression, detail, symbolism, a wholly effectual ambiguity—not only pan out exactly but are filled with an invisible depth of sympathy and experience. We are so used to the feeling that Kipling in fact knows *less* than he pretends to about his subject that it is a shock to receive the opposite impression.

It has been customary for apologists to point out that Kipling is not indicating how he thinks Germans should be treated, but how some people felt about the Germans (Conrad's slight wartime tale, *The Northman*, is even more ferocious.) There is some truth in this but it is not the whole story, nor would the creation involved be so remarkable if it were. Mr Robson is nearer the mark when he observes that critics who detect the provenance of Kipling's cruelty in the experiences that befell him when his parents sent him home from India, and which he put into the tale called *Baa Baa Black Sheep*, ignore the important elements of self-diagnosis in that tale. Kipling is clearly very close to Mary Postgate, but at what was for him just the right distance. As himself, as Punch, he was inhibited by group loyalties and family reticences, though in fact it has the ring of total truth that Punch never dreams of resenting his parents' 'desertion' of him or blaming them for his sufferings, any more than did most little boys of the period who were sent into the hell of boarding schools. Kipling had not the social freedom to make use of his parents as Dickens did in *David Copperfield* and *Nicholas Nickleby*: his own daemon had all the inhibitions of the class and the period. But when he enters the character of Mary, the daemon can lift the lid with impunity, to liberate and expiate itself through fantasies which we all share in one way or another, and which his art has made real at this disturbing level.

The triumph of the story is that Mary is a good woman, and she comes across as such in spite of what she does, or imagines she does. She recovers and finds a temporary release through an act of cruelty in which she both possesses and exorcizes Wynn himself through his *alter ego*, the German airman. And not only Wynn. In the most uncomfortable touch of the story the dying airman looks at Mary with the same expression—a drawing down of the mouth—as the little girl torn by the bomb. The war point here is clear enough: victim and butcher are at one in their death agony: but for the childless woman there is something further unspeakably peeping out. There is the power over something helpless and hers, and some unappeasable maternal force is unable not to find this a mode of physical satisfaction and fulfilment. One must emphasize again that this is not wilfully macabre. Mary is a good woman, whose unful-filment in peace is as noble and useful as her fulfilment in war is hateful and degrading. Kipling's fine sense of and respect for such persons is shown by Nurse Blaber of *In the Same Boat*, who says: 'I don't need anything, thank-you, and if I did I shouldn't get it.' The effect of the story, fully digested, is as heartening and satisfying as the release of truth in good art must be.

It is likely that no one but Kipling could have pulled it off, for no novelist could be less suspected of doing it either 'for art's sake' or as a self-consciously objective study in sadistic neurosis. He is never in any crafty sense a detached writer, but here he achieves, despite himself, both detachment and intimacy. Yet in the verses at the end of the tale—a device that Edmund Wilson rightly calls 'tasteless', and an exposure of the excitable poet who was an aspect of the cooler prose daemon—he mouths lines about 'how the English began to hate' as if he were deliberately suppressing the tale's impersonal intimacy and returning to his pack *persona*. Their assertiveness is a way of covering up. And the verse he intersperses with the tales does have this distressing characteristic. It acts like a jolly and uneasy tribal intrusion on some interesting and more thoughtful debate, a defensive habit that Kipling began early—it is equally intrusive at the end of that excellent 'soldiers three' tale *With the Main Guard*—and continued all his writing career.

It is a symptom of our impression that Kipling is apt to be uneasy about his best things, and breezily confident about his worst ones, perhaps because they never give anything away. The chief cause of embarrassment in the stories with an English setting is listening to someone who is making a quite different impression on us from the one he supposes, and in the smoking-room of Kipling's more overpowering craftsmanship we may feel he is strangely unconscious of the effect some of his more genial assumptions produce. He seemed convinced that he understood Sussex rural ways and attitudes, and in *A Habitation Enforced* he invites our jovial participation in the spectacle of an American couple bewildered and fascinated by English country customs. We may feel, however, that it is Kipling himself who is bewildered and fascinated, and not at all as much 'on the inside' of the situation as his narrative manner proclaims. It is he who seems the foreigner, rather than the knowing native, with the odd result that the story's actual effect diverges from the one intended. It seems to be Kipling who is missing the point, not us, and that point is that Americans, and Kipling too, have their own picture of English rural society, which is quite unlike the local one. In fact, to paraphrase the famous query: what can they know of England who when abroad have decided what she is like?

The same kind of thing can be more disturbing when a carefully matured masterpiece gives us, not the real revelation of

Mary Postgate, but a kind of snow-image of it, a simulacrum. I find this in the case of *They*, an elaborate fantasy which many admirers of Kipling place very high, perhaps because its tone is so palpably and yearningly 'good' and humane. But this is no criterion with Kipling. However heartfelt (the death of his own small daughter affected him very deeply indeed) there is something disturbingly glib in his presentation of bereavement ('Bearing and losing come so alike in the long run') which is analogous to his elaborate presentation of how the American couple come to discover themselves and their past in relation to England. He endeavours to treat an entirely intimate and personal experience by the same methods of group response and a group formula. And the unreality of the props in the story seems a consequence of this too group-minded assurance. The superlative country mansion of *They* has no true individuality, but with its topiaried yews, its butler, its Sussex panorama, seems a Platonic form of such a place, a waxwork complete down to the last twig and hair, but with none of the actuality in itself which Forster suggests so well about *Howards End*.

The idea of group-healing works well in the war stories, because Kipling understands how the intolerable pressures on men in a team may be relieved by just those factors of comradeship and shared experience which have made it into one. Yet *The Gardener* (which Edmund Wilson thought Kipling's best) suffers from a device which both brings the author into the foreground and gives him something to hide behind—always for Kipling a most unfortunate type of equivocation. The great cemetery is marvellously done, in his best manner, but the idea left hanging, that the gardener, who in reply to Helen Turrell's question about her nephew's grave says he will show where her son lies, is a figure of Christ—this is of course no ambiguity at all: it is merely Kipling consigning himself and us into other hands. The story is so very nearly moving that the effect is peculiarly frustrating. And the most significant critical point about the tales could be illustrated by the comparison of a First War one—*A Madonna of the Trenches*—with the rather earlier *Mrs Bathurst*, the most cryptic that Kipling ever wrote. The horror behind this tale expands—it is the horror of life itself—and the 'craft of words' seems struggling to contain this fact; but in *A Madonna of the Trenches* the ingeniously obfuscatory revelation of 'the horror' turns it at last into nothing more than the comforting popular sentiment that a great love goes beyond the grave. That is what I mean by Kipling consigning himself and us into other hands, for his final repose in a popular myth suggests—as does his whole philosophy of life and writing about it—that the common man sees things as they really are. It is the view of Tolstoy, but Kipling, with the ingenuity that is his peculiar talent and yet ultimately—as this story shows—his weakness, arrives at it by a process the exact opposite of Tolstoy's: by suggesting that in art supreme sophistication finally arrives at a simple and moving gospel truth.

If it does, then Kipling is not the man to persuade us of it, for his daemon does not recognize such truths. I shall return to *Mrs Bathurst* in a moment but the point to be made about *A Madonna of the Trenches* is that the more elaborately Kipling seeks to show that illusion and 'the possible' are what humans live by, the more he domesticates the mystery and patronizes those who are involved in it. The vulgarity here seems unavoidable as an aspect of art and intention, for Kipling cannot help giving an impression of over-familiarity with the dark mystery of the tale, even as the extraordinary ingenuity of his method pushes its denouement further and further back into the ambiguous. The ingenuity starts with the narrator Strangwick, a private who has been shell-shocked in the war, and who tries to conceal the thing that really haunts him by overlaying it with more obviously gruesome memories, such as a trench floored and revetted with the frozen corpses of French soldiers. It turns out, however, that what has really dispossessed him is the apparition of his elderly aunt, at the time she died of cancer, to another relation of his, an elderly platoon sergeant. The pair have been long and secretly in love, but have scarcely met, except now in the trenches, in a kind of mutual death-pact, with 'all eternity ahead'. The ambiguity of whether the ghost has really been seen is—as in *The Gardener*—no ambiguity at all: the point is that Kipling is intending to awe or amaze us; and in the really successful tales such an intention seems to have been pushed aside by the daemon, whose matter-of-fact sense of things is genuinely and comprehensively disturbing. What makes for our frustration and sense of an ultimate falseness in these elaborate tales that seem nearly to come off is the sense that all Kipling's skills are working together in the under-standing silence of mutual craftsmanship, just as he imagines one of his expert teams or groups at work; and what he needs for real success is not this co-operation but something more like disintegration. *Mary Postgate* and *Mrs Bathurst* impress us involuntarily; *A Madonna* and *The Wish House* by a continual nudging from behind; and the two effects only seem alike. In reality they are very different, and the difference is between the open vulgarity of Kipling's self-consciously mystifying devices, and the secret impersonal distinction of his intuitive powers.

In fact, of course, vulgarity makes him as stimulating and compulsively readable as it does Dickens and other authors; it is not a diminishing or disabling quality but—as with Dickens again—its sudden absence is all the more impressive. But Kipling's use of the supernatural or the 'marvellous' *is* vulgar, because he tries to have it all ways, relishing the possibilities while careful not to commit himself, and depending while he does so on our own vulgar sense of the thrill. It is the kind of device which has a history of facile usage by inferior authors, a mere 'let's pretend' mechanism, and in the stories which use it Kipling does not even have the motives of moral and social ideology which led Forster in his fantasy tales to make use of the Great God Pan and his various myrmidons. In general Kipling's technical borrowings are rarely felicitous: the dramatic monologue he handles brilliantly and with his own innovations, but the specific Bible background of the two Pauline tales is too close to Browning and to George Moore. The line of imitation is not reassuring; but it is impossible to supply any literary origin for *Mary Postgate*, and equally impossible to think of its being copied.

Much of the power of *Mary Postgate*, as of other stories, is in their glimpse into darkness and chaos, the darkness which the stories fear so greatly and image in so many graphic ways. The twist in *Mary Postgate*, ironically rare in Kipling, is that it is the fear and primitive horror which brings relaxation and relief, of however dubious a kind. But it is the strength of Kipling's art that it can never contemplate the horror and emptiness with anything approaching equanimity, and this makes such stories in their way more perturbing than the carefully contrived presentation of 'the horror' by Conrad in *Nostromo* and *Heart of Darkness*, or by Forster in *A Passage to India*. An early tale called *The Strange Ride of Morrowbie Jukes*, one of the most memorable though least discussed of Kipling's *œuvre*, conveys sparely and without insistence the nightmare that Kipling found in India, as in all uncovenanted and unorganized human experience, and which his art fights off in any way it can. Again it is worth insisting that a great part of the effectiveness of his work, like that of Dickens himself, comes from its sheer unevenness, and the different kinds and senses of appreciation to which this gives rise. In one sense *The Man Who Would Be King*, which comes in the same collection as *The Strange Ride*, is as good a story if not better, more dramatically planned, with all Kipling's sense of time and place—the adventurers turning up at the newspaper office is wonderfully stage-managed—but it remains none the less a 'yarn'; while *The Strange Ride* is a real look into the abyss, reminiscent of both Poe and Kafka, but with none of the former's stagy melodrama or the latter's devoted neurosis. Kipling was quite prepared to use his Indian expertise in the service of the deliberately blood-curdling and Gothic—*At the End of the Passage* and *The Mark of the Beast* are the two obvious examples—but it is the background of those stories, and not the contrived horror in them, which continues to haunt the mind.

The writer's literary models and tastes are clearly revealed in this context as not specially elevated; it is typical of Kipling and one of the 'Balzacian' things about him that he combined a sweeping ambition—to record the human comedy of the men who were running the empire and the new technological society —with a very unexigent idea of intellectual specification. We never of course have the sense that his material is matured in the conscious demands of deep intelligence, as we do with the great *nouvelles* of James or Conrad, but on the other hand there is never the feeling which those artists can give us, of intelligence labouring too long and ingeniously at a topic already exhausted or intrinsically too slight. Kipling's tales may be very uneven in their levels of appeal but they never die on him as Conrad's could do: we may recall Conrad's rueful comment to Garnett about this deadness, from which he felt that only such things as *The Secret Sharer* were exempted, and his droll image of the reader of such a failure as like a man under an umbrella, listening to heavy drops strike one after another 'upon the stout distended silk'.

Kipling's daemon was not always in a hurry but it never had time to think. As his fame grew and his sense of the meticulous increased, his practice was to put a tale aside for months or even years, then take it up again and strike out words, sentences, and paragraphs. The daemonic process came thus almost to parody itself: uncertainties, divisions and queries were increased not by intelligent brooding but by a kind of arbitrary operation of the unconscious. There is still no intellectual exploration or self-exaction, and Kipling's aesthetic vocabulary becomes even more exclusively one of painting and joinery. He tells us that *The Eye of Allah*, a superbly decorated but ultimately boring story about the premature discovery of the microscope, would not come alive in black and white but eventually revealed itself as requiring the illuminated treatment of a mediaeval missal; and the aesthetic message promulgated with great insistence in one of the Puck stories, *Hal o' the Draft*, concerns the dangers of the artist supplanting, with hasty and pretentious work done to order, the unvouchsafed epiphany of the true design.

The notion of daemonic inspiration as the natural ally of painstaking craft is significant, but put into a formula like this what it shows us mostly is the source of Kipling's shortcomings. It is too childish, this emphasis on the magician's 'cool and perspicuous eye' whose gaze distracts us from the conjuror's sleight of hand. The expulsion of the real by the meticulous, as in certain pre-Raphaelite paintings, is enjoyable in its way, when we experience it in *They* or in *The Wish House*, but it marries with fatal facility with Kipling's journalist's skill and with his inability to consider and create the individual human being. Kipling's best characters are probably his schoolboys and schoolmasters in the Stalky stories, and they have either not become individual beings yet or—in the case of the masters— have resigned or abstained from any kind of life that would make them into such. When Kipling is not enumerating the pack he evades the problem of individuality in a different way, and a sentence in *They* about 'cross-sections of remote and incomprehensible lives through which we raced at right-angles' gives us the clue to this process. It alienates and distances deliberately by ascribing the exotic to the person on view: X, who was shot in Burma by his own men; Y, one of the three men in the world who can both draw and expound the Great Wheel; Z, who can get his man with a Martini at 700 yards. A variant of this distinguishing technique is to reveal a kind of fairy kinship between unlikely and dissimilar persons: the

India of Kim (how different from that of Morrowbie Jukes) is like a vast and well-equipped nursery full of benevolent mothers and fathers, who are all regarded as belonging to the gang, whether they are prostitutes, healers of sick pearls, polyandrous hill women, or colonels in the secret service. In *The Janeites* Kipling sinks to a nadir of insensitivity when he presents us with persons from all walks of life and varied intellectual attainments who have it in common that they regard Jane Austen's characters in just this fashion.

Our conclusion must be that Kipling's best work is brought out by the confrontation within him between something almost like Wilcox and Schlegel, or at least a pair of warring daemons who have certain family resemblances to Forster's creations. Wilcox is full of panic and emptiness; Schlegel is tough and rational, with a passionate belief in the processes by which civilization is kept up and carried on. One is the weak Kipling; the other is the strong: both need the other, and in the contrast resides the secret of his power over himself and us. One could put the matter in existential terms as an artistic analogue of the human state, between what Sartre calls the knowledge that *il n'y a pas de signe dans le monde*, and the determination to make such 'signs', to create (in Kipling's case) social and imperial organizations, castes and mechanisms. The weak and the mad have no signs, and the strong Schlegel Kipling 'is firmly resolved that signs there shall be'. The quotation is from Alan Sandison's study of Kipling and Imperialism, which demonstrates admirably how Kipling and other public figures of that epoch set about exhorting their fellow-countrymen and each other with what the author calls 'all the paraphernalia of self-reassurance'.

But if the Schlegel in Kipling's make-up is tough it is also feminine. One of the singular things about his best characters, which contradicts in part the general point I have been making, is how many are women. I do not myself think that the heroine of *The Wish House*, who takes her lover's cancer on herself, is any more than one of Kipling's good ideas, though many Kipling admirers have found her moving. In general, as I have been suggesting, such a 'good idea' is the nemesis in a Kipling story, preventing its true operation at a deep dark level, and there seems to me little doubt that the idea in *The Wish House* came before its female embodiment. But Mrs Bathurst, who 'slid into his mind' on an early visit to New Zealand, is another story. Together with Mary Postgate, Liza Rowntree of *On Greenhow Hill*, and even with Maisie of *The Light that Failed*, she demonstrates a creative side of Kipling that can only be called Lawrentian, a deep and involuntary sense—in the Lawrence phrase—of 'what the woman is'. And here Kipling's failure with individuals suddenly becomes a positive strength, a strength, moreover, which gives him authority of a more effortless kind than the sort which is produced by Lawrence's highly conscious diagnostic intelligence. However much they 'are', in the sense Lawrence worked them out for *Women in Love*, his women are all drawn more or less from the life— Mrs Witt in *St Mawr* is a clear case of such a worked-up portrait—while Kipling's seem to have 'got into his head', to use his phrase for what the night did to him during his youthful periods of insomnia. Maisie, it is true, may well have some prototype in what has been guessed of a painful early love affair —the fact that Kipling covered his tracks in *Something of Myself* by affirming her kinship with Manon is not unsignificant—but the other pair are clearly hatched out of the void.

Lawrence, and Dostoevsky, would have seen the truth of Mary Postgate: Mrs Bathurst is more completely and uniquely a Kipling creation. In one sense she is an unnerving case of the absence of 'signs' in the world—the world in its most literal size and distances—in another, of their presence. Colonel Browne of the Kipling Society, quoted by Professor Bodelsen, suggested that *Mrs Bathurst* is a deliberate hoax—the jape as it were to cap all Kipling's elaborate japes—and is full of clues which are not meant to make sense. (Kipling and the Colonel might well, one feels, have had a good chuckle together over this before Kipling slid off the topic and started the Colonel on his reminiscences.) Has the daemon who could find no signs in the world surfaced here at last, to fill the narrative art with daemonic false directions? Perhaps the other Kipling's passion for meaning and order, all the connecting-rods of working society, came to be more and more flouted by something that began to grow inside him during his later days?

It is certainly not a conscious joke. Kipling's passion for jokes, often embarrassing, is an aspect of his passion for meaning: we laugh because there is something to laugh *at*, and the unavoidable point of the hoax is its denouement. Why such humour makes us feel uncomfortable is that we are given *too much* to laugh at; the more elaborate the jest, the more thick with banana skins and burnt cork, the more we deliver ourselves—as the English do—'unreservedly to mirth'. ('Who but Kipling would write a brag about English understatement'? asks Lionel Trilling, and who but he could shame us with this notion of a national sense of humour?) But in this remarkable story there can be none of the hoax humour, because any chain of significance is snapped off, and we are left with the vast indifference of the world and the pathetic isolation of human contacts and human wishes. The backbone of the tale is Kipling's old theme, the preoccupations of men in a team, in this case one of the biggest and most distantly linked that history has seen, the English navy at the summit of its powers and responsibilities, but separated in pre-wireless days by immense stretches of ocean.

The conscious theme is thus swamped at the outset by the more sombre and more general one of human isolation. Distances and random contacts grow in its imagination. It is narrated in a damaged railway-truck in a siding by the bleached dunes of a South Africa beach; and the tale jumps from New Zealand to Vancouver Island, from Tristan da Cunha back to Paddington Station, and thence to a teak forest in the heart of central Africa. This geographical wandering is paralleled by a mechanical invention, the impersonal flickering of the early cinematograph, which registers Mrs Bathurst by chance on a newsreel, as with her 'blindish look' she walks towards the doomed Vickery on the cinema screen and vanishes in its foreground 'like a shadow jumping over a candle'. Vickery, the naval man, has met her in Auckland; they have fallen in love, and in some unspecified way he has betrayed her—the betrayal is as much one of distance and the unreality it breeds as of sundered ties and previous commitments. But she has come to London (or has she?) to look for him; he has seen her intercepted by chance but for eternity on the moving film, and he returns to it as long as it is being shown on the local screen. I wholly agree with Professor Bodelsen's conjecture that she is already dead when the old news film catches up with Vickery: there are no ghosts except on celluloid, and Kipling does not explain how or in what random way she died. What he does make appallingly convincing is the effect of her presence on her old admirer. Kipling had tried his prentice hand on this trite old theme of the haunted and doomed man in *The Phantom Rickshaw*, but here he has found at last the exact setting to make it overwhelmingly genuine in human terms—Camus's story of the Algerian *colon* 'outsider', Meursault, is not more meaningfully related to a particular cultural experience and background.

The final jolt of unmeaning in the story is the finding of Vickery's charred corpse in the heart of Africa, where the railway runs for two hundred miles dead straight through a teak forest. Beside it is another corpse, and the audience is invited to find some significance in this conjunction, while the story itself gives the impression of knowing quite well that there is no significance in it; the other body has no connection with Mrs Bathurst but is that of a casual tramp whom Vickery had picked up in his wanderings after leaving his ship at Simonstown. Both have been killed by lightning setting fire to the bush. But it is the lightning that struck Oedipus; brief as it is, the story is a genuine tragedy. And although she is mocked by worldwide unmeaning Mrs Bathurst remains a real and a good woman. Through what seems a *reductio ad absurdum* of the 'right angle' technique, the distant and flickering picture of her, which is all we have, somehow contrives to distil for us the density and mystery of a single life.

These fine portraits of women, few as they are, provide something like a moral centre in Kipling's work. It is one of the many paradoxes about him that such a centre seems most firm and true in a tale which in terms of a sense of meaninglessness technically induced could be said to anticipate the efforts of the *nouveau roman*. Such a centre of truth makes for an increase of understanding in the reader's mind between his successive experiences of Kipling, and this again is very unlike the way in which the bulk of the material works on us. Though we can read him over and over with pleasure, the impression of each well-done thing is in general that of the bright fixity of an exhibit, something that delights the eye but will never move again. Continued extension and growth of meaning is rare in him but it does exist: the effect is not always that of a machine intricately assembled *in situ*. Even the theme of cancer becomes a strangely life-giving thing, as if the contemplation of this final unmeaning in the flesh helped to bring him back from what James dolefully referred to as his progressive reduction of a dramatis personae down to mechanical parts—'the engines and the screws'—back to human nature and to what is most touching and perturbing in its fate.

Yet even here we have to remember the compartmented side of him, for the theme of cancer is as vulgarized in *The Children of the Zodiac* as that of mother-love is in *The Brushwood Boy*. It would be fair to conclude that both the strength and the weakness of Kipling is in this unpredictability, this difficulty of knowing who or what is ultimately there. We are left reflecting on the difference between the protean being of a Shakespeare, whose anonymity only makes us more confident of his final moral presence, and its ambiguous Kipling equivalent, which is more like being all things to all men. Kipling's kind of anonymity, the official and social rather than the individual face, is as different as could be from the total emphasis that Lawrence and Forster in their different ways lay upon the personal, and yet the three of them are often united by aspects of art which bypass or ignore the obvious coherence of the writer's personality. In one sense Kipling sought to put the clock back. His endeavour to put dynamism and romance—the 'romance' that 'brings up the 9.15'—back into the world of technological and social morality, to put before us new kinds and versions of the *honnête homme* , was perhaps bound to fail at a time when—in the intercourse of art—the authentic consciousness was making for its single self ever-increasing claims and demands. Yet the problem is not as simple as that, for in another and it may be more sinister sense Kipling has won where Bloomsbury has lost. His popularity in the Soviet Union is hardly surprising, for his view of the writer's role was not so very different from that of the Marxists and their sociologist allies. Nine-tenths of the literary production of the Soviet world is concerned with doing exactly what Kipling sought to do: showing people, at work, to each other, humanizing and dignifying different societies, teams and work units by giving them an image and a function in literature.

It is to the credit of Kipling's daemon that it realized the hollowness of all this; and that the hollowness comes out in the work and bestows the characteristic assertiveness and the characteristic unease. It is not the daemon who is alive and at work behind the Iron Curtain, but the naïve ambitious and extroverted talent which has not realized the force of Lord Dufferin's dictum that 'there can be no room for good intentions

in one's work'. Moreover, much that is evasive in the worst
sense in Kipling is potent about us today. Many types of art
today depend on the avoidance of individual communication,
while the film and the drama, no less than advertising and public
relations, work increasingly through jargon and group words.
Something in Kipling foresaw this and perceived its fraudulence;
but if we ask him why and what is the purpose of the fraud he
cannot reply—he cannot talk to us personally, any more than
the Royal Court dramatists can do. In *Something of Myself* he
tells us that the nature of his work, 'to realise all sorts and
conditions of men and make others realise them . . . gave me
no time to "realise" myself.' So much the better for me, the
tone implies. And yet—'to thine own self be true . . .' The
author of *If* might have pondered the conclusion of that even
more celebrated platitude. A late and moving poem on St Paul
at his execution may suggest that he came to do so.

> I was made all things to all men
> But now my course is done—
> And now is my reward—
> Ah, Christ, when I stand at Thy Throne
> With those I have drawn to the Lord,
> Restore me myself again!

St Paul and General Booth (who had told the youthful Kipling
that he would play a tambourine with his toes to win a soul to
the Lord) are hardly the artist's ideal sponsors. Yet Kipling so
often strikes us as on the verge of personal disintegration, and
refers to it obliquely in his work, that he may indeed have felt—
as might the Methodist ministers who were his grandfathers on
both sides—that he had given up himself to bring us the word,
and to make us more aware of national and imperial destiny.
There is an element of tragedy if so, for seldom can a mission
have more oddly miscarried. One can only conclude that a self
may be there—it suggests itself in some of the best stories—to
which it would be worth while to be restored. On the other hand
—and this is the final curiosity of the Kipling conundrum—
whatever its private virtues, that self may have been trivial,
commonplace, blinkered, *borné*, and conceited with the naïve,
secret, and very English conceit which, on the strength of his
astonishing early successes, led Kipling to take himself for
granted as a great man. If this was so, and there is much

evidence that it was, then the actual scope and nature of his achievement may well strike us as being not the less but all the more remarkable.

2. ' We must live as we can '

Kipling's vision of things is ultimately fatalistic. Improvements may be made, but human beings must get along as best they can, determined by their own imperfections and those of the societies they live in. His reverence for Jane Austen, celebrated in *The Janeites*, goes deeper than admiration, for their approach to life was fundamentally similar. A community, whether it was a ship, village, regiment or tribe, they could understand to the bone; and make it the natural setting for their art. 'We must live as we can' is the tacit motto of such a community, and the words are uttered in a novel which has essentially the same attitudes as theirs and makes the same use of society— Elizabeth Bowen's *The Death of the Heart*. This masterpiece deals in the same realities, and may well continue to be read as long as Kipling and Jane Austen are.

Those realities are also brought sharply into focus by brisk kinds of acceptance and non-admission. Though the novel's statutory front defers to a pattern of the feeling and the unfeeling, the creating and the deadening, which is emphasized by the rather overwhelming promise of the title, its actuality endorses a much more subtle imagination of the subject. It is as if Elizabeth Bowen, like Jane Austen, needed a pattern of conventional intellectual and moral reassurance in which her unconscious confidence and hidden knowledge could be licensed to operate.

In a bleak, amused way, which is far more charitable than the protestations of novels that proclaim themselves on 'the side of life', *The Death of the Heart* uses a kind of severity or toughness which, like Tolstoy's about Sonia or Jane Austen's about Jane Fairfax, is the product of an instinctive knowledge that has no need to make up its mind in public, and which liberates both the author's and our own capacity for identification with the arrogant and defensive as well as with the innocent and the vulnerable. 'We must live as we can' implies that the conditions of social existence are both intolerable and needful:

the artist who understand this, or perhaps rather takes it for granted, has no need to appear to judge or to reconcile. Elizabeth Bowen, like Kipling and Jane Austen, can be both readily censorious and shamelessly collusive: the bonds and boundaries of her world make so much necessary sense that she does not have to compromise her own position within it. None of the three needs to be conscious of the division in themselves between moralist and anarch.

Paradoxically it is the romantic presentation of the self and its environment in fiction which has to assume an entire responsibility here. There is a good deal of difference between Lucy Snowe and Maggie Tulliver, but their creators are committed to them both, must stand by them in crises and protect them against the reader as well as against the world of the novel. Because that world is designed for them and their aspirations it must be elastic and extensible; but the more completely it is owned by the novelist the greater the demand it makes on him. Kipling, Jane Austen and Elizabeth Bowen have, as it were, a social and moral contract with the actual world they know and make use of, but are not responsible for; and this frees them—and us—to feel equivocal about it. Only the novel of bourgeois society has been able to produce this division and this balance. The Soviet novel, for example, with its assumption that author and reader are bound by a social and moral contract, and simply and fervently desire to be so, has no chance of achieving the balancing act of the bourgeois novel, which both needs and detests the social bond, acknowledges it and escapes from it. We must *want* to be cruel to Miss Bates, as Jane Austen wanted to, before we can see it will not do—and, conversely, we must be repelled by the Stiva Oblonskys and Daisy Buchanans, by the money in their voices and their knowledge that society exists for their benefit, before we can enter joyfully into them, as we also enter into Elizabeth Bowen's deadening middle-aged couple, the Quaynes.

Even the most responsibly and morally committed novels of today suffer from their authors' freedom to create their own image of society, freedom which is also, as I have suggested, a crippling kind of responsibility. Society must be changed, but first the novelist must control and manipulate it to show why. Heinrich Böll made these comments about his novel, *Group Portrait with Lady*: 'I wanted to write a love story, but it

seemed to me it would be more genuine and realistic if it were
about the love of a man and a woman in an extremely precarious,
politically and socially difficult situation as a result of the war.
For this reason I chose a Russian prisoner as the heroine's lover'.
In such an act of choice the fatality begins, for although Böll is
writing about a real society and its falsities, he is compelled to
make it his own and arrange it to his own specification before
he can offer it to us as an exemplary picture of contemporary
reality. In that contradiction lies the weakness. Inability to
honour the contract between him and us, which would make us
want to speculate and disagree about his personages, comes from
his inability (a very natural and obvious one) to live in the
social contract on the old bourgeois love-hate terms. Böll's own
comments deprive me, at least, of the slightest interest in the
persons of his fiction, and the novel itself cannot seem to me
other than two-dimensional and schematic, however honest its
vision and vigorous its method. Böll involuntarily demonstrates
how compromised this kind of apparently open social novel has
become with what might be called the Graham Greene syndrome:
his own total responsibility for the validity of his society being
a kind of secular equivalent of Greene's assumption of cathol-
icism. Greene's spiritualities are equally deadening, because
they can only repeat, in novel after novel, the same image of a
world, and no dialogue with him is possible because there is no
contract between us on which one could be based.

The equivocation which such a contract makes possible, and
which I have tried to trace the working of in Kipling, and in
my references to Jane Austen and Elizabeth Bowen, is entirely
different from the kind which Wayne Booth queries in the last
part of his study, *The Rhetoric of Fiction*. How can we tell, he
says, what the writer intends when, instead of 'making the
moral basis of his work unequivocally clear', he moves towards
us in a cloud of irony, an irony whose object is itself uncertain?
This characteristic modern situation is the opposite of that free
play between novelist and reader, characters and story, which
we have been discussing—for that carries straight over from
life into art, on the simplest basis, the inevitable limitations of
an area where we must live as we can. Without such a framework the natural and relational aspects of the novel can founder
in multiplying and soon meaningless possibilities. It has taken
too much on itself; and the novelist cannot be free when he is

so weighed down with aims and responsibilities. By contrast
Jane Austen shows how simple are the needs from which the
novel begins—the need to enlarge a narrow situation and to
ease restraint, social and moral, by invisibly indulging the
desires and the impulses which it professes openly to school
by precept and example.

3. Shestov's Law

The scale of these divisions in Tolstoy's novels is, as we might
expect, enormously greater; their metaphysical status corres-
pondingly more impressive. No one has analysed them better
than the Russian philosopher and critic Lev Shestov, and what
he says is so relevant to my general argument that I should
like to say something about him, and his attitude not only to
Tolstoy but to literature in general, especially the great Russian
classics of the nineteenth century. Shestov's ideas are not
original, but he is the only philosopher who has taken imaginative literature as his text for their exposition and justification.
He is the only Russian polemicist who is a joy to read, even
in translation, for he has a limpid style and a dry wit and is a
lucid connoisseur of ideas, unusual attainments in the culture
he formed part of, and notably absent in his friend Berdyaev
who, though better known and more widely translated, was of
altogether inferior intellectual stature.

Shestov was amused by Tolstoyism at a time when it was
universally revered. His admiration for Tolstoy's novels was
of quite another kind. He is never tired of reminding us that
great writers are paid far less attention than they suppose, and
have far less influence. His great target is humanist idealism,
of the Tolstoyan sort; but by way of Tolstoy himself he is kin
to Voltaire, and he attacks it with the same relish with which
Voltaire excoriated the church, or Tolstoy himself the historians.
Sceptical and unexcited, his style has none the less great energy,
and he is often extremely funny at the expense not only of
other philosophical attitudes but also of his own: there are few
sages less self-important, even though—or perhaps because—
his peculiar emphasis on solipsism is the key to an essentially
negative metaphysical position. His intuition is that great
writers are also solipsists, however much they may protest the

contrary, and the real 'message' —and certainly the real virtues
—of their work are thus often very different from what they
are usually taken to be. To put it bluntly, he sees solipsism as
the real dynamism of literature, and its god—above all where
the novel is concerned—as the goal of detached understanding.
The novel goes along with Hegel, however much Dostoevsky
and Tolstoy, too, affected to despise him, in 'seeing gnosis,
understanding, as more important to it than eternal salvation:
what is more, in understanding it finds eternal salvation'.

Although without their inner fires, Shestov has much of the
stylistic vitality of his two heroes, Nietzsche and Kierkegaard,
whom he sees more as novelists and dramatists of the inner life
than as philosophers, and as closely akin to the two great
Russian novelists. But Shestov himself has no pretensions to
anguish. He did not go mad; there was no Regina in his life;
he underwent no tormenting spiritual pilgrimages like those of
Tolstoy and Dostoevsky. Utterly rejecting 'reason and the
good' he remained himself a model of sanity and common
sense. There was no humbug in this: it was the result of a
remarkable and unique kind of cultural balance. A Jew, Shestov
inherited that ancient and unshaken imperturbability in the midst
of chaos, and the age-old scepticism of Christian idealism in all
its forms; a Russian, he was on the inside of the greatest of new
literary cultures; a European settled in France for the later half
of his life, he exercised a direct influence on Sartre and Camus,
both of whom knew and respected his work. He lived on other
authors, but his interest in them was an evangelist's rather than
a critic's. His first book, published in 1898, won him a reputation
among the Petersburg intelligentsia; Rozanov and Merezh-
kovsky in particular recognized ideas congenial to them. *Shakespeare and His Critic Brandes* denies that the rational humanist
critic can begin to understand the nature of Shakespearean
tragedy. It was followed by *Good in the Teaching of Tolstoy and
Nietzsche* and *Dostoevsky and Nietzsche: the Philosophy of Tragedy*,
Shestov's most brilliant polemical performances.

As a critic Shestov wastes no time on style or form or literary
device. What interests him is the gap between what a great
literary artist thought he was saying and what he was actually
saying as a creator. In *Shakespeare and His Critic Brandes* he
rejects the notion that 'Macbeth is a criminal who feels all the
pangs of conscience on earth', even though this may have been

Shakespeare's conscious idea and intention. But the imagination of Macbeth is of a man in extremity, mind at the end of its tether, unable to find the conviction in himself without which life signifies nothing, and this has nothing to do with the ethics of crime and punishment. Shestov perceived the dilemma of art in a Godless age, its need to search for and reveal salvation while showing that no such thing existed—a function that art alone can perform, and one for which Russian literature was peculiarly well qualified, since it found its true voice and purpose only in the nineteenth century. The Russian novel, according to Shestov, is founded on a continual process of striving against the grain, one masterpiece of hypocrisy succeeding another. In the second part of the novel, Gogol proposed to reform the hero of *Dead Souls*. Futile hope! What he had created was *sui generis*, the product of his own fantasy, the misshapen masterpiece of his own assertive needs, and this had nothing to do with what merely *ought to be*. Goncharov's *Oblomov* is of course so tailormade to Shestov's insights, with its portrait of a hero whose real justification is to do nothing at all, that he hardly bothers to notice it; in fact Oblomov's outraged cry that he is being compared with *other people* could be the epigraph to Shestov's argument about imaginative writers and their real work.

Even Chekhov does not escape impeachment. Nothing wry, nothing gentle, nothing humanist here, but another 'cruel talent'. According to Shestov, 'for almost twenty-five years Chekhov did one thing only: in one way or another he killed human hopes'. Humanist hopes, that is. In his essay 'Creation from Nothing', written after Chekhov's death in 1905, Shestov tells us what was the basis of his real achievement.

> As long as a person is settled in some job, as long as he has something ahead of him, Chekhov is completely indifferent to him. But when a person becomes entangled, so that he can in no way be disentangled, then Chekhov begins to come to life . . . then an upsurge of creative force appears . . . Before the character lie hopelessness, helplessness, the sheer impossibility of any action whatever. Yet the character continues to live: he does not die . . . In the end he is left alone with himself. He has nothing, he must create everything himself.

Of course Chekhov tries to complete many of his plays and

stories with some idea of human betterment, but this is not what they are really about.

Tolstoy searched endlessly for the good and identified it with God. Maybe so, but what his characters want and strive after is rather different. What they desire above all, and what the lucky ones get, is contentment and assurance, even at the cost of smugness, even at the cost of hypocrisy. We leave Pierre, that one time restless and tormented seeker after the truth, smugly content in his marriage, aspiring to the condition of Rostov, the real hero of the novel, 'who knew how to live and was therefore always stable'. And Rostov's wife, Princess Mary, with what Tolstoy calls 'her profoundly spiritual nature', is in reality indifferent to everything except her own marriage and children.

Such an attitude, says Shestov, is for Tolstoy the real law of life, and, almost unique among authors, he is able to combine an appearance of telling the absolute truth with a passionate reverence for the lofty, the beautiful and the good. In reverencing hypocrisy he does not cease to revere the ideal. In his superbly impassive celebration of what makes for life 'he has told the truth, and yet the truth has not undermined life. Before Count Tolstoy idealism did not know such subtle techniques . . . in him the lofty and the beautiful do not end up in question marks.' (Shestov is of course speaking of what he feels to be Tolstoy's greatest and truest achievement, but this would be true of the ending even of such a story as *The Death of Ivan Ilyich*.)

As for Levin in *Anna Karenina*, 'the more he withdraws into the narrow sphere of his personal interests the more brazen he becomes in praise of "the good"'. Shestov has a good ear for the nuances and the dead-pan touches of meaning.

'You're married, I hear?' said the landowner.
'Yes', replied Levin with proud satisfaction.

It is a meaning that Tolstoy cannot help himself putting in. Why 'with proud satisfaction'? Because, for Tolstoy-Levin, to be married, to have a family and an estate, and not to care a straw for anything or anybody else, were the *summum bonum* which held the individual in the confidence of life 'as a plough is held in the earth'. This gives him the same 'proud satisfaction' that Dostoevsky's Underground Man has in being an Under-

ground Man, in the teeth of the rest of the world. For Dostoevsky, in the eyes of Shestov, is akin to Tolstoy in this
marvellous kind of creative hypocrisy. The 'compassion' of his
book based on his own experiences of prison and exile, *The
House of the Dead*, moved all Russia, and continues to move
every reader today. But Shestov detects in it the same hidden
dynamic of solipsism which drives Tolstoy's great masterpieces.
Dostoevsky is careful to invent a narrator whose suffering is to
be 'permanent, obscure and dark', the equivalent of the eternal
pains of the outcast and imprisoned; a narrator who is a stalking-
horse behind which Dostoevsky can conceal his own creative
response to the challenge of adversity.

Why, asks Shestov, did the author abandon this concocted
narrator, Goryanichikov, 'buried alive' in Siberia and 'lost to
hope''? Why? Because he himself *had* faith and hope: like all
good Russian solipsists he lived by his own internal sense of
himself, and he wanted to go on living. At moments he forgets
his 'compassion' and his narrator, and gives to the problem of
such suffering what Shestov calls an 'ingenuous but wholly
conclusive answer': 'I won't be here forever, only for a few
years'. That is what really matters, what really keeps him sane
—to leave these dead and return to his own life. This is to be a
man of faith, in the real sense; and when Dostoevsky returns to
Russia he shows as much by his invention of that ultimate man
of faith and anti-humanist, the Underground Man, the man 'for
whom the world can drown in blood as long as I can drink
my tea'.

As can be seen, Shestov's sardonic but passionate anti-
humanism leads him to find the real 'Knight of the Faith' (as
Kierkegaard called him) in the solipsist who has complete, if
hidden, assurance; and then to claim that all great novels and
works of art are produced by such persons. If they were not,
they would not be works of art at all but mere tame humanist
tracts. As it is, they are saved for our illumination by what is
deeply equivocal in them. Dostoevsky preaches compassion, but
really lives on—and by—the gusto of his own cruelty and
malice. Tolstoy preaches selflessness and renunciation but really
believes in grabbing and holding what one can get, in the
success of every kind of secret exploitation.

In fact, of course, Shestov exaggerates his case, insists too
much on the absolute validity of his own undoubtedly shrewd

perception. What he misses out is the appeal to us, in Dostoevsky as in Tolstoy, precisely of their search and aspiration, their passion for the good. That passion, often anguished, always genuine, may in many senses be unavailing: it may not convince us, it may not overcome or transcend the realities of themselves, and of their truest imagination of our existence. But it is essential, it guarantees their stature, it is the real pledge of their authenticity. Shestov implies that the true, in these great giants, underlies and is revealed by the false. But it is what he thinks of as false that gives the truth its justification, almost its dialectic. The world of *War and Peace* and of *Anna Karenina* would be utterly dead if living were a matter secretly solved and revealed by Tolstoy's 'true perception', instead of being a process always redissolved, always carried on by the force and urgency of the inescapable question: how should a man live? The fact that this question cannot be answered openly by idealism, but only tacitly by the arts and possibilities of self-assertion, does not mean it was not worth asking, or that art and life would be of any interest if it were not asked.

For all Shestov's insistence on true faith and religious understanding having nothing to do with virtue and knowledge, with reason and the good, we may feel that he is too complacent about the grounds from which desire for these things—in art as in life—arise: contingency and its ensuing dissatisfactions. He perceives the aesthetic repose in great art, and traces it —surely rightly—to a profound equivocation in the personality of the artist: but he does not allow that this equivocation leads inevitably to new search and new struggle. We may feel that great literature, for Shestov, is not a living and dividing process, but a waxwork museum of ideas and evasions of ideas, over which he presides like a sardonic but seductive curator.

Such a museum image, and what it implies, is in fact more suited to the appreciation of other kinds of literature than the Russian—to the deliberate, even ponderous equivocations of Thomas Mann for instance. Mann is himself Shestovian in the meticulous way, but it is possible that the philosopher would not have cared for the German ironist's all too careful renunciation of irony. Shestov preferred diplomacy in the novel to be as inadvertent as it was revealing. Yet while revelling like a connoisseur in the two-faced *démarches* of the great creators (he treats Princess Mary, and Tolstoy's collusion with her, for she was based on how Tolstoy wanted to picture his own dead mother, almost with reverence), he will not admit that the official version, the cover story, is as important as the giveaway. Tolstoy's portrayal of the truth about society is only what it is because of his passionate desire to reform it, and himself. Both sides are strengthened by the other, neither discredited.

It is the same with Dostoevsky, who is both Underground Man and sanguine, bustling polemicist, full of passionate idealism and faith in the *narod*, full of hope that the Russians will one day have Constantinople. Between the two there is a kind of muffled, never completed dialogue, for the Dostoevskian personality, as Bakhtin remarks in his study of the author, can never come to terms with himself through speech (that is, art) but can never for a moment give up speaking. Dickens, too, fascinates us by such different speeches from two very different sides: the imagination haunted by childhood and by violence, haunted by the success of its own cruelty, can still speak with the voice of the gaily and ardently outgoing Victorian ameliorist.

4. *Dickens and His Critics*

Dickens offers a good case to Shestov, who, as the arch 'anti-intentionalist', takes it accordingly, though less lyrical about the forms and pressures of Dickensian inconsistency than he is about those of his fellow-countrymen. Like the two great Russians Dickens was the child of his age, and particularly in the sense—applying variously to all three—in which hypocrisy was the breath of life in their nostrils, the great force and dynamic of the age which nourished them even as they revealed and denounced it. Dickens's first biographer, Forster, was quite aware of his hero's inconsistency and of how it came about, calling him a man of one idea at a time, 'each having its turn of absolute predominance'. Dickens, interestingly enough, seems to have possessed intermittent but gradually growing and maturing powers of self-diagnosis. He knew his powers depended on something wildly erratic and unstable in him—what he himself referred to as 'the wayward and unsettled feeling which is part (I suppose) of the tenure on which one holds an imaginative life'.

His capabilities, none the less, were always infinitely more spacious than his own critical sense of himself or of society. As with Shakespeare, so with Dickens: the critic has to come clean about his own attitudes in order to emphasize some part of this space of genius. Shestov of course presents a genial domestic figure concealing the diabolic anarch, the Quilp beneath. But there are many other Dickenses, like G. K. Chesterton's jolly Falstaff who hated nonconformist self-righteousness and knew there are no pleasures like the pleasures of the poor; or Humphrey House's producer of valuable social documentaries, who had the misfortune, none the less, to be less knowledgeable about Victorian social conditions than was House himself. These have been followed by various sorts of intellectuals' Dickens: Lionel Trilling's haunted and perceptive nature, alembicating deep and delicate allegory, and creating in a villain as stagy as the Blandois of *Little Dorrit* an evil as profound as Iago's. Rather late in the day, Dr Leavis has mutated a Lawrentian Dickens, who opposed the brilliant symbols of feeling life to utilitarianism in the solitary master-piece of *Hard Times*, into a master of both Blakean and Jamesian social vision, 'placing', diagnosing, and showing forth with conscious and intricate artistry—and for his pains still being dubbed the great entertainer.

The special interest of this from my point of view is the total contrast between the Shestov and the Leavis Dickens. For Leavis Dickens is in no possible sense a divided figure, but an incredibly sensitive, meticulous and thoughtful novelist, who was sometimes guilty of writing down to his public, but who was never taken in by the fact and never identified with popular work below his best. Can we believe in this? It is true that Dickens's own remark about the 'tenure on which one holds an imaginative life' reveals a capacity for self-diagnosis which is far from characteristic of the popular mind. Mrs Jellyby, no less than Wemmick and Mr Jaggers in *Great Expectations*, objectify and reveal common aspects of social inconsistency: while David Copperfield and Pip, in no sense self-portraits, are masterly examples of Dickens's power to extrapolate and generalize his own increasing self-knowledge. Her analysis of this process makes Q. D. Leavis's essays on *David Copperfield* and *Great Expectations*, in *Dickens the Novelist*, by far the best and most detailed of recent studies; and F. R. Leavis's essay on *Little Dorrit* in the same volume is equally suggestive and penetrating.

And yet both Dickens and Dostoevsky are far more sensitive to their audience, and involved with it, than the Leavis concept —at least of Dickens—can allow for. Dostoevsky's involvement is most clearly shown in his immense respect for melodrama, and for the taste for murder and detection which went with it; and in the deliberation with which he used such scenes as Sonia's reading of the gospel to Raskolnikov in *Crime and Punishment*. There are plenty of such things in Dickens too, but the popular taste and the popular consciousness was deeper in him, more engrained, intimately bound up with the knowledge of how 'things have worked together to make me what I am'. What the Leavises cannot admit is Dickens's capacity to see the same thing with an extreme hardness and an extreme softness too, to be—in the same act and seizure of the imagination—both utterly sentimental and utterly cynical. Nothing is more important to his work, and nothing is closer to and more in keeping with the popular response. That instinct that Dickens was a part of, and which he satisfied so completely in his audience, is to laugh without shame and to cry without shame—at the same thing. Oscar Wilde expressed it in his remark that one must have a heart of stone not to laugh at Little Nell; and in his recent study of Dickens, *The Violent Effigy*, which makes a forceful case against the excessive intellectualization of Dickens, John Carey observes that most of his critics have come to employ 'a species of discourse and a mode of thought quite distinct from that in which Dickens's powers operate upon us'.

That is it—once we ignore the way he works, the vision becomes subtly denatured and in a sense emasculated, however much more penetrating and intelligent it is made to appear. Shestov perceived this in his claim for Dickens's unique ability to turn an extreme horror of life into an almost hysterical enjoyment of it. He assumes the authenticity of Dickens's inadvertent self, the Leavises emphasizing above all the slow but certain delicacy and maturing of intention. The two views are not incompatible, but it seems worth bringing them together in order to enlarge our understanding. *Little Dorrit*, the text most recently favoured by F. R. Leavis, gives scope for illustration of how such viewpoints reveal the conflicting powers at work.

Dickens was a tough case—the toughest conceivable: that is

the impression most directly made on us in *Sketches by Boz*. The moving thing about *Little Dorrit* is the way it shows how Dickens has learnt what this means, to himself and to others. His inexorable hilarity is never far off (as Carey says, 'once Dickens starts laughing nothing is safe, from Christianity to dead babies') but its implications, though no less uncontrollable, are now far more interesting. Dickens's capacity for success made him desire above all to escape from failure, from its symptoms and its victims. He escapes it through derision, through patronage, through fierce attention to neatness and order, through hatred and fear. And above all by making effigies of it, to use Carey's suggestive word. I once remarked in an essay on *Oliver Twist* how curious it was that the boy who befriended Dickens at the blacking-factory, whose name was Fagin, should have been transformed into a villainous grotesque. It was a way to get rid of a relation that in its nature compromised the desire to get right away; a kindness which, if given in to, might have threatened to naturalize Dickens in some lower circle. All the more moving that in *Great Expectations* Dickens should have in so many more subtle ways revealed the impossibility of escape from one's past, from Magwitch into the dream of total independence and success. It is an important point stressed by Q. D. Leavis, that Magwitch's possessiveness about Pip is presented in the novel for what it is, a nightmare thing, pathetic and horrible, from which Pip shrinks (for which *bien pensant* critics who don't feel the nightmare call him a snob). In *David Copperfield*, Daniel Peggotty's maudlin possessiveness about his errant niece is equally revolting, and equally understood and feared by Dickens. Peggotty and Magwitch are far more interesting figures than Fagin, but they too are effigies, creatures whose power is the product of a strenuous imaginative attempt at exorcism. Like that of the real boy Fagin, their benevolence is a form of ownership, an assumption of its object on a degraded level, and this is the direst threat Dickens's unconscious knows.

'How does he know these truths?' asks Q. D. Leavis, going on to take them as 'indication of the novelist's full consciousness of the living material he works in'. Admirable as her analyses are, one may take leave to doubt the soundness of this conclusion, which goes with the significance of one of her titles: 'How we must read *Great Expectations*'. Her Dickens is not only armed with complete understanding and dispassion, but with a feeling of injury that most of his readers don't realize how complete these are. She severs, in fact, his continuity with readers and his instinct for their responses, powers his sensitivity confers but which a self-dispassion so much greater than theirs would take away. And in fact when Dickens *is* being dispassionate and serious the effect is too obvious, oddly embarrassing even, and false. He cannot assume the virtues Q. D. Leavis wishes upon him without jeopardizing his true powers. These are not only products of ruthlessness and sentimentality, but require that these two responses are not aware of each other. It is for this reason that his effects of clarity, neutrality and perceptive meditation never sound quite right.

Q. D. Leavis champions the 'happy' ending to *Great Expectations* which Dickens adopted, where most critics have preferred the 'unhappy' one. Her reasons for doing so are cogent and yet curiously unreal, as if it really mattered, in a deep way, to the pattern and meaning of the novel. In fact both endings are equally satisfactory, as switches which close, so to speak, the popular circuit in the novel. Like so many other such things in Dickens neither ending need be, or can be, taken very seriously, as Q. D. Leavis must surely feel if she attended to the tone of the thing instead of concentrating on her own interpretation of character and event, illuminating as these are—brilliantly so when she traces the modern Pilgrim's Progress element in the book. But whether Pip is being glad that suffering has given Estella a heart like 'my heart used to be', or seeing in 'that broad expanse of tranquil light' no shadow of another parting from her, the elegant elegiac fall is really in both cases Dickens merely coasting, the switch-off completed. This becomes all the more evident in the suggestion of another critic, A. O. J. Cockshut, that the last words may contain the possibility that Pip has yet another travail of disillusionment in store. What a happy idea, but just to consider its intelligent felicity is to admit that such good ideas have no place here. Such an ending would be Jamesian, as in *The Bostonians*; it could not be Dickensian. The harshness and the vulnerability that give the novel its edge (the invulnerable Jaggers and Wemmick, and self-protecting Estella, and the undefended Pip) need the deep sea of the novel's movement under them to show Dickens's power at its most disturbing. That power moves easily inside its popular bounds but cannot, even at this stage of maturity, be goaded by them into real exigence. Like Shakespeare, Dickens is always ready to relax at such moments.

The more so because the real engagement with the public is underground and elsewhere. Though we shy away from the utter hardness of Dickens (Carlyle remarked on his youthful features, as if made of steel), I suspect it was the thing to which his Victorian audience gave their most secretly abandoned response, just as they responded to its reversed and uncommunicating image in abjectness and pathos, in waifs, strays and outcasts. Dickens only really identifies with the weak in so far as they may become the strong, able to make effigies and assert rejections of power and knowledge. Dostoevsky may well have detected this, and been impelled in reaction to the heartfelt identification with the insulted and injured which in any case came naturally to him (the steely Dickens had no Achilles heel like epilepsy). The underground convulsion occurs when hardness finds how helpless it is, as happens in *Little Dorrit*. Dickens comes as near, below the level, to identifying with Dorrit, and with his inflexible will to survival and self-respect, as he does with any other character, and Dorrit's success— playing the great man in meaningless Italy and yet dying looking back to what has really given life its meaning, the Marshalsea prison—is both horrifying and deeply moving. In Dorrit and his daughter Dickens both confronts and transforms his own awareness of limitations with the maximum intensity. I cannot agree here with Carey, who in a general and vigorous attack on the fashion of large-scale symbolic interpretation of Dickens, suggests that 'if the novel is really designed to pass on such message as that "All the world's a prison", it fails'. The message about prison is surely a message to the self, showing— through the experience of the author himself—how limited are our real powers of response and receptivity. The novel confronts the frontiers of success and personality—prison limits most of us come to acquiesce in—in a manner unique in Dickens, showing how much remains outside, never to be entered. One of its themes, perhaps its main theme, is our sense of the rest of the world, the world from which Dickens was debarred by the nature and conditioning of his own genius, but which yet could not, in the characteristic Dickensian way, be *got rid of*.

The powers of the unexpressed and the unexperienced that brood over so much of *Little Dorrit* remind us how much Dickens normally grabs everything, as if the world's contents were waiting, bursting with expectation, to be superlatived by his prose. That seizure of things is not only a part of his confidence in comedy, of setting up and getting rid of effigies, but is nowhere more apparent than in the way he grasps the utilitarian nettle in *Hard Times* and turns against it all his powers of effectively specious symbolism. F. R. Leavis formerly thought this the only book of Dickens worth taking seriously, a point of view ingeniously modified by the omission and rephrasing of a few sentences when the *Hard Times* essay was reprinted in *Dickens the Novelist.* Certainly the world of *Little Dorrit* could hardly be more different from that of *Hard Times*, and for the reason I have given: *Hard Times* is in the best sense a flashy work, while *Little Dorrit*, in some mysterious way that much enhances its potentialities, can imply in its metaphysic a sense of exclusion and incomprehension, even a loss of confidence. Odd though such a word may sound of Dickens, and inapt as it may be to describe his style, there is something *tentative* in *Little Dorrit* which may remind us of Hardy's novels. All the more surprising that the Leavis who continues to reject Hardy as a great novelist should direct his attention to this work in particular. Hardy, we may suspect, does not appeal to Leavis, because of something opaque and baffling in his art which inhibits the critic's occasion to evangelize, to show forth on his own ground the message and meaning inherent in the creative pressure of genius; while all Dickens's later work, and not *Hard Times* alone, turned out to be well adapted to this process.

But in enlarging his appreciation of Dickens's novels Leavis does not alter his method; and it is this, I feel, which causes him to misrepresent the feel of *Little Dorrit* as he did not that of *Hard Times.* We may disagree over *Hard Times*, but it is a novel singularly well suited to his methods and to his kinds of perception. These are well summed-up by his comment that 'in *Little Dorrit* we see very potently at work a process that it seems proper to call definition by creative means'. This might apply very well to *Hard Times*, but I challenge its application to the bigger novel, or that of the other phrase Leavis uses to describe it—'Dickens's inquest into Victorian civilisation'.

Leavis maintains, surely rightly, that Little Dorrit herself is a remarkable and interesting creation, in no way to be compared with Little Nell, who as a character is simply not 'there'. But this is not because Dickens has become less self-indulgent; he continues to separate love and sex, and his fantasy continues to feed on the image of the wholly reliable, wholly unselfish child-woman, with whom the question of sex relations does not exist. But Dickens's capacity to handle his pleasure has become more fastidious and more mature. His complicity now demands as part of the day-dream that she shall be very much a real person, but this is hardly 'definition by creative means'. Leavis is superlatively right about the prison organization that is everywhere in the book, and so intended to be—each significance joining up in the *Hard Times* manner, what Leavis calls 'the Blakean suggestiveness of the Marshalsea, closed in upon by the city "where the chartered Thames doth flow"'

> The prison is the world of 'the mind-forged manacles'; it is Society with a big S, as well as the society we all have to live in; it is Mrs Clennam's will and self-deception (figured also in her arthritic immobilisation and her wheeled chair); it is Henry Gowan's ego; it is Pancks's 'What business have I in the present world except to stick to business? No business'; it is for the great Merdle the Chief Butler's eye; it is life in our civilisation as Clennam—as, more inclusively, the Dickens of *Little Dorrit*—registers it.

Absolutely. That suggests the richness of the organization and the closeness of the linkage. And one would agree also in dismissing Edmund Wilson's simplistic Freudian discovery that Dickens, obsessed with his own childhood experiences in the Marshalsea, is 'working the prison out of his system'. But if *Little Dorrit* really existed to 'enact for us' an inquest into Victorian civilization, it would be work with all the limitations of *Hard Times* and, owing to its greater technical elaboration, some extra ones as well.

For the fact is that Dickens's real genius is not to be found in such an inquest, nor in organizing the machinery for it. His conscious social purpose is, frankly, rather a dull purpose— obvious enough, and this makes the imaginative organization that serves it ultimately rather dull too. This sort of thing, one might say, does not *need* a Dickens: the real and ever-enlarging

fascinations in him are not to be found there. Once we have
seen the point of the prison analogies and symbols, as those of
Sleary's circus in *Hard Times*, our appreciation is distinctly
finite. The writing that nudges us at these moments is not vital
enough to survive the establishment of its point. (One might
compare the equally explicit Moony and Rabbit scenes in
Lawrence where the writing can do just that.) Merdle's suicide
is grippingly done, its preliminaries and aftermath suitably
macabre, but who wants to read it again, or to ponder the lesson
about money and wickedness involved? Its panache and well-
done effect is lowering on re-acquaintance, like Madame
Tussaud's the second time. And this necessarily applies to the
whole 'chartered Thames' purport, in other late novels as well
as *Little Dorrit*.

The inwardness of the novel, and what I have called the
tentative quality which gives it its peculiar scope and long-term
fascination, are much more in Dickens himself, and in the
undeclared aspects of his creative voyage. The refinements and
revelations of *Great Expectations* are well brought out by the
Leavis method because they are more progressively coherent—
more things to be seen about the same preoccupation each time
we make the journey. But the directions of depth in *Little Dorrit*
are more obscure, less clear to creator and contemplator alike.
Why should the figure of Little Dorrit herself be so compelling
to Dickens and us? Here the suggestions are not so much that
society is a prison, but the senses in which consciousness is
always compelled to make one—either for living or for dreaming. Hamlet's exchange with Rosencrantz and Guildenstern,
often read or heard by him in the theatre, must as often have
been below the surface of Dickens's imagination.

In one sense, then, the book projects the author's acknowledgement, unproposed and undiagnosed by himself, of the imprison-
ing bounds of our dream wishes, in this case the image of the
selfless and self-effacing, the devoted and perfect girl. It is in
our own imaginations that lack of freedom begins, unvisited
by 'winds and the wings of birds', and it is here that we are
'made what we are'. The agent of revelation, the Italian journey,
impinges on and infects us all alike, Dickens, the reader and
Little Dorrit herself.

If we agree that Little Dorrit is 'unquestionably there for us',
it is not her virtues but her limitations which disclose her, and

these the author does not voluntarily exhibit. Leavis fastens on
a key exchange between Little Dorrit and Arthur Clennam on
the nature of guilt and justice. She asks if her father will pay
all his debt, now he can, before he leaves, and when told that
he will, ventures to say that it seems hard that he should have
lost so many years in suffering and have to pay as well—pay
'in life and money both'. She knows she is wrong, she says;
and the comment is made that 'the prison, which could spoil
so many things, had tainted her mind no more than this'. It
seems that Clennam and Dickens agree at this point, but Leavis
is quick to insist that 'if we take Dickens's irony' we realize that
the judgment is on Clennam for having such a thought, that she
is the unconscious judge. 'She understands enough to be
infallible in response.'

The passage—it is a marvellous one—does indeed give us a
shock, but hardly one of gratification at Dickens's meticulous
irony and Blakean judgment. We rather realize, surely, just
what it is like to be Little Dorrit, to whom life and money—
life *as* money—is the whole shape of meaning and experience.
Little Dorrit is a dream figure, but one who is as much the
product of a real environment as are Madame Bovary or
Eugénie Grandet. So far from admiring, as Leavis wishes us
to do, an irony which expresses Dickens's unerring 'affirmation
of life', don't we rather admire how inimitably he has things
both ways? To do so is the privilege of such art, nor is it self-
indulgent: it both expresses and emancipates a real human
truth. We all want—Dickens more than most—to feel emotion
and indignation about imprisonment for debt; and we all know
that debts have to be paid, one way or another. Leavis expresses
lofty scorn for A. O. J. Cockshut's comment, in *The Imagination
of Charles Dickens*, that Little Dorrit's experience cannot show
her what hardship unpaid debts may cause the lender, but this
is indeed exactly what the passage implies. Leavis cannot bear
to think of Dickens raising to the level of his mature art the
popular sentiment Dickens so fully shared: heartfelt sympathy
and indignation on behalf of the debtor, coupled with the
disinclination to be out of pocket oneself.

What Dickens does not 'know' himself, one feels, but records
at a different level of his understanding, is the fact that Little
Dorrit is *not* a self-effacing and self-excluded angel, without
will or passion except at the service of another, with the mystic

omniscience of a small female Jeeves. Such a stereotype of comfort and reassurance was indeed gloated—positively gorged on—by his readers and by Dickens himself. The indications that his art gives of how she came to be as she really is, why she can be nothing else, is bound therefore to come with the force of revelation. In so far as she can, Little Dorrit is speaking as much of herself as of her father, with whom she has become identified in order to survive. Beneath the prescribed compassion for her father is a cry of pity for herself, muffled and made timid by Clennam's scrutiny and registered by his startled awareness of something in her which is really *her*, which he identifies as the taint of the prison. She has the sense of having 'to pay in life and money both', because of her equally obscured knowledge that she can never be other than these conditions have made her. Her marriage to himself will presently have to repeat her identification with her father.

An artist who reflects and organizes with the meticulous care Leavis attributes to Dickens would certainly have taken the trouble to give Little Dorrit a few touches which would show her 'not too bright or good for human nature's daily food'. Both Trollope and George Eliot knew well how to supply such corrective verisimilitude, in the detailed setting and in the commentary they would have given on the girl's consciousness, no doubt shown as harbouring an occasional irritation against her sister, as well as the wish that her father would now and then recognize, between them, the completeness of his dependence on her. But Dickensian dream intensity has no need to bother with establishing this kind of human nature. With nothing to hide, Little Dorrit has Cordelia's blankness: nothing for author and reader to overhear and look in at. For Dickens and his public such a heroine must be outside the conversation of criticism, and portraying her in this way actually augments —as it does with the complementary Clennam—the large shadow of the pressures which have moulded them into what they are.

Another treatment, invoked by Leavis as affording a close comparison, would be Henry James's of Maisie in *What Maisie Knew*. But Henry James's care over the 'case' is worlds removed from Dickens; in spite of all his serpentine sympathy he fails utterly in establishing Maisie as existing at all in the sense that Little Dorrit exists. Leavis's admiration for the art of

Maisie is to me as incomprehensible as his introduction of her into the Little Dorrit context, for the real 'thereness' of Little Dorrit shows no symptom of being under Dickens's direct control, and is frequently overlaid—as if deliberately—by the more assertive and dominating aspect of his powers.

This shows most on the Italian journey. It is clearly a part of Dickens's purpose to show us that Dorrit and his daughter cannot escape from prison, any more than Mrs Clennam does as she looks out of her window at the Marshalsea—'looking down into the prison out of her own different prison'. But intention gathers strength until its direction and movement seem uncontrollable, as the words tumble out to reveal the kaleidoscopic foreign background, where 'the more surprising the scenes, the more they resembled the unreality of Little Dorrit's own inner life as she went through its vacant places all day long'. Has anyone but Dickens ever conveyed so well not only the inner oppression conveyed by marvellous scenery, but the implications to the self of what such oppression means? 'Little Dorrit would wake from a dream of her birthplace into a whole day's dream.' This is profoundly moving, not only in relation to Little Dorrit herself, but to Dickens and to us.

For it is Dickens's own experience, at an undisclosed level, that we are being offered here. Confronted with Italy he must have had this reaction, been confounded in himself by his own negative and defensive response. Not admitting this, he responds to the challenge by making something dynamically felt and perceived, even though it is felt and perceived as a kind of anti-scene and anti-experience. The artist makes vivid drama out of the paralysis itself, its accompanying deadness and defensiveness. His open attempt on the scenery, in *Pictures from Italy*, shows his failure to register appreciation at the conscious personal level—it is merely banal. But in *Little Dorrit* this is transformed into a new kind of internal drama.

One aspect of the overwhelmingness of sight-seeing which Dickens must have felt, and makes the Dorrits feel, is that there is no role to play in the face of it. In fact William Dorrit soon finds another version of the one he has always played—having been the gentleman with such persistence for so long it should not be difficult to sustain the same role under the languidly correct auspices of Mrs General. Though Dickens has great fun with Mrs General and her prunes and prisms, as with Mr

Eustace and the attendant guides, we are aware of an enormous relief in the way in which he can fasten on the kinds of familiar pretentiousness they stand for. This section of *Little Dorrit* is the most concentrated instance of a vitality recurrent in his novels—the division between a great surface drive and gaiety and an underlying uncertainty of a much more intriguing and revealing kind. By making scapegoats of the parasites who hang about the Dorrit family he can repossess the initiative and the assertiveness that the narrative seemed to be losing in a trance: the strange record of his own loss of identity merging with that of his heroine.

Leavis asserts that this recovery by Dickens of his most characteristic vitality is 'central to the author's wholeness and profundity by possession of his human theme'. Can this really be the case? Confronting Italy and its culture, Dickens makes wonderful use of the Dorrits' predicament in order to get rid of what is in an important sense his own.

> Everybody was walking about St Peter's and the Vatican on somebody else's cork legs, and straining every visible object through somebody else's sieve. Nobody said what anything was, but everybody said what Mrs General, Mr Eustace, or somebody else said it was. . . . Nobody had an opinion. There was a formation of surface going on all round her on an amazing scale, and it had not a flaw of courage or honest free speech in it.

Leavis feels that this expresses 'Reality, courage, disinterestedness, truth, spontaneity, creativeness, and, summing them, life' —and that 'these words, further charged with definitive value, make the appropriate marginal comment.' It seems to be saying, in fact, that sightseeing is a fraud, and that any show of interest in the monuments of the past is just a cover-up. Of course we can all pride ourselves in producing 'honest free speech' on these occasions—Dickens is as usual in close touch with a popular response—but Leavis's claim is surely more than usually millennial. What is really there is something characteristically divided and dramatic. Dickens alternately gives in to the vision of emptiness and non-meaning, from which the individual dispossessed of habitual reality recoils, and shouts it down by attacking the 'tongue-tied and blindfolded moderns' who are being introduced by their keepers to the sights of travel. His art is not 'on the side of life': it is dramatically in the grip of life itself. We might in these terms compare this whole section of the novel, and much else in Dickens, with the careful organization of opposing responses and reactions in *A Passage to India*, *Howards End*, or *Women in Love*, works to which Leavis's technique of appreciation would, in this instance, be very much more applicable.

And these instances are hardly trivial, for they serve to show the radical difference in dimension between Dickens's world and that of other and later novelists. Dickens's genius is not concerned with consistency, and its divisions carry him over them by the very obviousness of their existence. He needs them as he needs his public. One of the most singular features of his art, seen in *Little Dorrit*, is the alternation, as natural but much more dramatic than the succession of moods in an ebullient human being, between the normal intrusive and bustling presence of the 'inimitable', and its eclipse in a dimension which seems to reduce him to silence even as he writes at his best. It is the inimitable who bids us observe the dead mother and baby, frozen in their 'grated house' at the summit of the St Bernard, and who remarks of the Dorrit convoy that 'the living travellers thought nothing of the dead just then'. The death of William Dorrit is not like this. It is like Lear's death, in the sense that Little Dorrit's lack of human nature is like Cordelia's. And it depends on the unadmitted dream relation that Dickens had with both daughter and father.

Uses in Poetry

CHAPTER I

1. Reality in Division

'Reality' is a hopeless word in the context of literary criticism, and one to be avoided if possible. But it is a word that must be admitted to have a special importance in any discussion of Keats's poetry, because it meant so much to Keats himself. He belonged to a culture which had become aware—rather suddenly—that its imagination fed on literature rather than on life—on Scott and the Middle Ages rather than on the activities of the new and prosperous post-war industrial society of England. And so the word had begun to mean what it now means to us: that is, a place that one cannot afford to be too far from, an idea the spirit needs in order not to be outside.

The feeling that reality may be elsewhere—this is surely a characteristically modern kind of uneasiness, and one which we find neither in the eighteenth century nor in Keats's predecessors in the romantic movement. Bagehot called Keats 'the most essentially modern of recent poets', a comment that results from the same line of enquiry as Matthew Arnold's judgment that he 'did not apply modern ideas to life'. While Bagehot perceived a characteristically modern division in Keats between what he wanted to do and what he thought the realities of the age required of him, Arnold—in a discussion of Heine, with whose combative and committed spirit he contrasts the Keatsian luxuriance—is the first of many critics to suggest that what is Keatsian is also, in a jargon word of the modern age, 'escapist'.

It is revealing to compare Keats's anxiety and self-distrust with the serenity of Blake and the confidence of Wordsworth and Coleridge, all in their different ways 'explaining metaphysics to the nation'. What may strike us in this context about the great poets is the sheer worldliness of their powers, their conviction of being in the centre of things and taking part in change, radical change. It is a confidence that even appears in the garrulous ease with which Coleridge seeks a subject for a poem 'that should give equal room for description, incident, and impassioned reflections on men, nature and society, yet supply in itself a natural connection to the parts, and unity to the whole'. True, of course, that for all its easy projections, the spacious reference to commerce and politics, to mountains and the moral life, this poem *The Brook* never actually got itself written. But even Coleridge's Gothic masterpieces, *The Ancient Mariner* and *Christabel*, give no impression of anxiety on the score of distance from 'real life'; the 'willing suspension of disbelief' they ask for is emphatically not a suspension of our ordinary sense of reality. Shelley, too, is as matter-of-fact as are Cowper or Coleridge in this respect, however airy his fantasies: perhaps because what Keats called his 'magnanimity' leads them straight into the tumult of human aspiration and desire.

Keats, then, is the first of the romantics to reveal the kinds of anxiety and guilt about the relations of art and reality which are still with us today; though, oddly enough, there are hints of the same sort of thing in Byron. As we might expect, the giveaway with him is an exaggeration of defiance and swagger, the insistence that his poetry is at last presenting unvarnished truth. 'It may be profligate but is it not *life*, is it not *the thing*?' he writes to his friend Kinnaird. 'Could any man have written it who has not lived in the world?' We might set this beside Keats's claim: 'The imagination may be compared to Adam's dream—he awoke and found it truth' (the almost suspiciously exact converse of the Knight-at-arms' experience on 'the cold hill side'). We might compare both with the claim that Dickens would be making in a few years' time, that however extravagant it might seem what he wrote was TRUE! The three assertions are all early warning signals in the progress towards what has been today termed *realism*. 'Truth', as Stendhal and Tolstoy show ('My hero is Truth' claims the latter in his preface to the *Sevastopol Sketches*) is the direct object of the claim to set down things as they really were.

Such assertions are a long way from the assumption of the earlier romantics that what they felt and wrote could not be otherwise than true. The world within and the world without were for them manifestations of one wholeness of being, not potential rivals and claimants for the title of truth, a claim which Keats's famous comparison of dream and truth only draws attention to and does nothing to settle. The uneasiness involved here has nothing in common with that exuberant guilt about his moods of dejection and loss of faith and zest in living nature which haunted Coleridge; moods exorcized by Wordsworth in the *Immortality Ode*. It is rather the kind of uneasiness which compels its victims today (if they happen to be literary spokesmen) to dwell on a poet's 'essential relevance to living', or a novel's 'central human truth'; which in Victorian times impelled Tennyson to write *The Palace of Art*, and Matthew Arnold to emphasize that poetry must be 'a criticism of life'. It is also recognizably the same sort of awareness that provokes a counterattack, like that of Yeats and his deliberate conversion of external 'reality' into a personal myth; or a compromise like that of Auden, who dwells on the poet's freedom and irresponsibility in the world of art, and his quite different obligations to the real world, 'in which you have to live whether you like it or not'. One curious result of this preoccupation with the division between life and literature is that 'life' itself comes to figure virtually as a literary concept, and is used by such influential critics as Dr Leavis purely as a criterion for the evaluation of books. To be 'on the side of life' does not mean to live in a particular way but to write in a particular way.

In 'the hateful siege of contraries' which often oppressed Keats's sense of his own creativity, poetry was both the whole of life and a dream that had to be woken from into life. His ambitions never sound so unreal—to beg our question for a moment—as when he is striving for some new image of reality and rejecting as fantasy some former mode of poetic being. From dreamer to poet, from fancy to truth, from luxuriant ignorance to deeper understanding, from feathers to iron— these are the kinds of contrast by which he sees himself educated to a knowledge of things as they really are.

> Ye tranced visions—ye flights ideal—
> Nothing are ye to life so dainty real!

Keats suppressed this exclamation of Endymion in the published poem, but it never left his own consciousness. And the same passion for the real strives to make words give the feel of physical experience to imaginary longing.

> —one human kiss!
> One sigh of real breath, one gentle squeeze,
> Warm as a dove's nest among summer trees,
> And warm with dew at ooze from living blood.

The words are most real—embarrassingly real perhaps—when fantasy is most apparent. *La Belle Dame sans Merci* has often been called a perfect example of the romantic temper, but these contrasts between reality and dream are much more intimately and painfully personal for Keats than that phrase implies; and his preoccupation with them continually reveals, in the *Letters*, his special and vulnerable and endearing sort of intelligence. It is not in the nature of the *Letters* to reveal a poetic pilgrimage, though the critics have fashioned the appearance of one.

> While he was writing *Endymion* he had realised that the poet must bear the burden of the mystery, and he knew he could not shut out 'the still sad music of humanity'. In *Isabella* and *The Eve of St Agnes* he luxuriated in the world of romance, but his imagination had been enriched and disciplined by his experiences, and he was fully aware that these poems, describing events of far away and long ago, were only a temporary escape from the pressure of reality.

In this quotation from one of Keats's most sympathetic critics* we may feel that the poet, like the Shakespeare of the Victorians, is being gravely escorted by posterity from the Forest of Arden, into the depths, and perhaps onward to the serene heights.

It may be objected that if Keats himself saw his poetic life as a pilgrimage it is the job of the critic not only to document the stages of it but to acquiesce in Keats's own implied judgments about it. I cannot feel this. There are many indications that Keats was not himself a good judge of his own poetry, and unlike T. S. Eliot he had no Ezra Pound to reveal the true direction and outlines of a poem to him. Instead he imposed on it and on himself patterns of romantic aspiration that do not fit. And to discuss the poetry as if the patterns did fit leads us ever further into abstraction, into the regions where Keats himself was only too anxious to go, but where his poetry obstinately refused to follow. For instance, the whole question of *identity*, of what the poetic identity was and should be, exercised his speculation, and has in consequence been exhaustively examined by the critics, but it is an impasse that leads not to what is of

* From the Introduction to *John Keats, A Reassessment*, edited by Kenneth Muir.

excellence in his poetry but to a bewildering number of contradictory ideas about Keats.

His sense of himself, and our sense of him, certainly begins in what Verlaine called *littérature*, in 'a lovely tale of human life'—

> the silver flow
> Of Hero's tears, the swoon of Imogen,
> Fair Pastorella in the bandit's den
> Are things to brood on . . .

So they were for the Elizabethans, for Spenser and Chapman, for William Browne and for Shakespeare himself; but the Elizabethans did not feel, as they brooded, that they were escaping from life as they did so, or letting it go by. Keats did; and did consciously prepare himself for a personal and poetic progress.

> Then will I pass the countries that I see
> In long perspective, and continually
> Taste their pure fountains. First the realm I'll pass
> Of Flora and Old Pan . . .

'An ocean dim, sprinkled with many an isle' stretches before him. He is himself, be it noted, experiencing the standard romantic poetic hero's voyage, the voyage of Alastor or Laon or his own Endymion; but again it is worth emphasizing that Shelley's poetic development did not include any *personal* sense of moving from youthful fancy into mature reality. In *Sleep and Poetry* and the *Epistle to Reynolds* Keats sees himself as a figure in poetic romance, but though the agonies, the strife of human hearts await him, and the thought fills him with excitement and awe, the geography of his imagination is wholly literary. If it ceases to be, he loses himself, loses the power to *be* himself in the poem.

> A sense of real things comes doubly strong,
> And, like a muddy stream, would bear along
> My soul to nothingness.

It looks as though 'real things' are not only Keats's enemy here but ours, for the success of the poem depends on our vivid sympathy with him in it, and that sympathy is felt for a person, a particular young man who is expressing here the fear that he may lose that particularity which he has in the nurturing 'lap of legends old'. Like Saturn in *Hyperion* he fears that

> I am gone
> Away from my own bosom, I have left
> My strong identity, my real self—

but lose it he must if, like Apollo, he is to undergo the fierce but abstract anguish of 'dying into life'. The trouble is that there is a world of difference between our informal and engrossing communion with a young man and his ambitions and ideas, in *Sleep and Poetry* and the *Epistle to Reynolds*, and the spectacle of the same young man renouncing his nature in terms of grave heroic allegory. Paradoxically it is the *renunciation of self* that strikes us as self-absorbed, even solipsistic, while *Sleep and Poetry* and the *Epistle* do not.

The business of identity distracts Keats. He must renounce it as a poet, and yet find his true identity as a man. 'The world is a vale of soul-making', he writes to his brother and sister-in-law, 'and souls are not souls till they acquire identities, till each one is personally itself.' The unidentified poet must end as an identified soul? It is a sterile quibble for the critic, but it was no contradiction to Keats. As well as being a genius he was the best of men. His humility was seraphic; his loving-kindness inexhaustible. He can speak of a vale of soul-making in a way that both moves and shames us, for he had the right to speak. His humour, even on this vexed question of striving to know himself, is delightful. 'Perhaps I eat to persuade myself I am somebody', he interjects to Woodhouse, just before copying out the *Ode to Autumn*. He could never say like Yeats:

> Now shall I make my soul,
> Compelling it to study
> In a learned school . . .

And he could never 'remake himself' by remaking a poem. Although he had to 'o'erwhelm' himself in it, he had too true a sense of the unimportance of poetry. 'I have no faith whatever in poetry, sometimes I wonder that people read so much of it.' The sanity in that is a part of his goodness, the goodness which, for all his insistence on the poet's delight in an Iago as well as an Imogen, is so transparently revealed in his poetry.

And yet his obsession with poethood does run like a flaw

through the sound intelligence of his insights, surfacing most conspicuously in his attitude to Shakespeare. 'Shakespeare led a life of allegory; his works are the comments on it.' It is not only untrue, it shows why Keats's relationship to Shakespeare is in fact so profoundly deceived. 'Lord Byron', he goes on, 'cuts a figure, but his works are not figurative', a comment he may be said to gloss in a later letter by saying of Byron: 'He describes what he sees, I describe what I imagine.' The briskness is the tone of Keats at his best, but it is disconcerting that the prime activity of the imagination, lacking to Byron as a mere observer of the outward show, should be assumed to be a kind of allegorizing of the inner life. Keats cannot help seeing the Bard's progress as 'full of symbols for the spiritual eye', a progress from the maiden thought of comedy to the tragic deeps and up to the serene heights—an allegory of supreme poetic mystery. 'His plan of tasks to come were not of this world—how tremendous must have been his conception of ultimates'. It is the Victorian image of Shakespeare (and it has not become for many critics the image of Keats) but more important it is the image in which Keats confided his hope of writing 'a few fine plays'.

A drama like Shakespeare's is the opposite of allegory, for the characters cannot be identified as embodying some experience or preoccupation of the author. They do not represent him: they do not even represent the 'uncertainties, mysteries, doubts' in which Keats feels that the 'writer of achievement' has the 'negative capability' to live. The notion of 'negative capability', like that of 'a life of allegory', ignores the reality of the drama by concentrating on the personality of the dramatist. Keats is not really rejecting the usual Romantic emphasis on the poet's ego, but offering a different version of it. Shakespeare, the diffident and neutral-minded genius, is no more credible or necessary a hypothesis than Shakespeare the authoritative sage, for in both versions the dramatic point is missed. Even when he is stressing its 'camelion' nature, Keats cannot help but emphasize the poetic personality, perhaps because his own is so important to his poetry. His uncertainties are as characteristic and in their way as obtrusive in his poetry as are Wordsworth's certainties in his. The thrush of the Letter to Reynolds, the Grecian Urn, the narrator of *The Fall of Hyperion*, are no less earnest about the truth of what they tell us than the Pedlar and the Narrator of *Peter Bell*.

Certainly Keats has no trademark of identity as a critic. He was no phrase-maker: he never referred to 'negative capability' again, and he did not retain it in his critical quiver for further use. When he deputized for Reynolds on *The Champion* he subdued his pen wholly to the outlook of his friend and the enthusiasms of their set. He proposed to ask Hazlitt 'in about a year's time, the best metaphysical road that I can take', but it does not seem necessary to defend him against the imputation of excessive reliance on Hazlitt, as Professor Muir has done, by maintaining that 'Hazlitt is a good critic: Keats is a great one'. In setting up as a critic Hazlitt made himself the embodiment of an attitude which it became his business to define and defend. Keats needed to do neither. His passion for 'truths' is for himself, not to convince others, and if Hazlitt could help him so much the better. He 'cared not to be in the right', and he was always ready to admit that 'I and myself cannot agree about this at all'. He has no wish to testify publicly: 'everyone', he said, 'has his speculations, just as everyone has his troubles'. And his speculations were troubles to Keats, not possessions.

And yet as a poet his identity is unmistakable. We must continue to say 'poet' with some emphasis, for it is true that his life and letters have been dredged to provide an ideal poet figure, who can either be transferred into the poetry and worshipped there, or else can be severely ignored by readers who prefer the *vates absconditus* of negative capability, the poet whose rather unfortunate early manner vanishes into a grave maturity, which gives promise of still more mature and impersonal things to come. Because we know so much about Keats's life we are unable or unwilling, to accept as it is the distinct life of his poetry— distinct and different because Keats's own personality was in the most impressive sense *provisional*, which that of his poetry is not. He is not like Byron or D. H. Lawrence: his self and his work are not an inseparable and completed whole. Few readers seem prepared to accept the personality of his poetry in the way that we accept Chaucer's, about whose life we know little. But the reality of his poetry is to be found in its personality, if we are not in search of what we think the poetry should be, or what it might have become. What then is this personality, which seems to me so vital and in a way so neglected?

2. The Vulgar and the Heroic in 'Bad Poetry'

The decisive ingredient is a kind of vulgarity. What is most real in his poetry is also what is vulgar: indeed 'Keats and Vulgarity' would probably be my right title. There is something sublime about Keatsian vulgarity; in the 'material sublime' of his poetry it acquires a sort of metaphysical status which is almost self-defining. It goes down into the root and sinew of the poetry's language—not just the surface genteelism of cockney spellings and words like 'dainty'—and is vulgarity in the heroic sense in which Antony and Cleopatra are vulgar, in which the dung we 'palate' is 'the beggar's nurse and Caesar's'. It is the true commonness which in German is called *das Gemeine*, a term which retains more obviously than its English equivalent the sense that it is what we have in common that can make us 'common' (an ambiguity delicately employed by Paul Klee in the title beneath one of his exquisite small pictures—*Ein Fetzen Gemeinschaft*—'a scrap of commonness'). In German Romantic writing, and even for Goethe, it is the earth which drags down Pegasean poetic thought, the distinctive, the lofty, and the ideal. And the paradox, so typical of Keats, is that it is precisely what is 'common' in his poetry that makes it so uniquely and distinctively Keatsian.

Keats's poetic personality is magnificently *gemein*. In it the earth reveals the rift of ore; it turns what might appear mean and embarrassing into what is rich and *disconcerting*: for at his most characteristic Keats always disconcerts. Now a mark of the man of poise and breeding is to object beyond all things to being disconcerted, and it was no doubt for this reason that Byron hated Keats. 'Burns is often coarse but never vulgar', he observed, implying that the cockney school is too vulgar even to aspire to coarseness. (There is the further implication that Burns knew he was coarse and did not care—indeed took a pride in it—but one cannot take a pride in vulgarity.) And Keats came to detest Byron. Their personalities reacted violently against each other, and this gives the clue to a point of some interest to which we must return—the point that Keats and Byron are in fact more closely related to one another than to any other Romantic poet. Both transform poetry by their personality, though one exploits the process and the other seeks to evade it. Byron was ready enough to extend a tribute to the safe, depersonalized Keats of *Hyperion*.

Byron is the most easily self-conscious of poets; by contrast, Keats is vulgar when he does not know what he is doing, uneasy when he does. Vulgarity cuts both ways: an author may be vulgar when he is unaware, like Keats or Dickens, of the disagreeable impression he is creating; or when, like Hugo, he is making sure that we notice an effect which yet does not impress us as he seems to think it should: in Goethe's phrase, one sees the intention and one is embarrassed. Keats's brand of vulgarity is as far as possible removed from such an appearance of deliberation, of 'the artist's humour'. His language continually strikes us as fulfilling Yeats's requirement of 'the right word that is also the surprising word', but never in a way that suggests contrivance: the word would not be right for anyone except Keats, and is often right for him only in the most impossible way. Even less does he practise the 'studious meanness' of language cultivated by James Joyce; and still less again—to push our necessary point to an *ad absurdum*—does he revel in the ritual of linguistic vulgarity for its own sake, like an original and personal poet of our own day, John Betjeman. No, like Chaucer's Squire, Keats deploys style 'with ful devout corage'; like that innocent rhetorician he puts his heart and soul into it. Keats is most fully his poetic self, most wholly involved in what he is writing, when he is, in the usual and technical sense, 'bad', or on the edge of 'badness'. One might say that the full reality of his poetry is revealed in the presence of this badness; the poetry needs it. Its greatness, its heavy truth, is profoundly involved with badness and cannot seem to exist without it.

My use of 'bad' here begs many questions, its meaning is more easily demonstrated in Keats than defined. The clue is, I repeat, that Keats's language is right only for him, and even in him will only seem right after we have accepted his poetic nature whole; it is no good 'by naming the faults to distinguish the beauties'. Keats's badness reveals his kinship with Shakespeare more clearly than his agreed excellence. In both we can find the same apparent lack of close scrutiny and sure taste. Who but Shakespeare could have brought off the repetition in Macbeth's speech?

And with some sweet oblivious antidote
Cleanse the stufft bosom of that perillous stuffe
Which weighes upon the heart?

Early editors did all they could to remove or emend it; to us it seems the only possible word. Keats often echoes this primal Elizabethan certainty, though the *gemein* in him is also his own. He describes Isabella after Lorenzo's disappearance as

Spreading her perfect arms upon the air
And on her couch low murmuring 'Where? O where?'

In most poets such an epithet at such a moment would be merely vacuous—in Dryden a routine insensibility, in Hunt a routine archness (it is applied, in *The Story of Rimini*, to Francesca's waist)—but is it not, in Keats, intensely moving? Keats assumes with such *corage* that a 'cliché' is the burning word for him that it becomes so: everything works together for good, even when Isabella turned up Lorenzo's 'soiled glove'

And put it in her bosom where it dries,
And freezes utterly unto the bone
Those dainties made to still an infant's cries.

The congruity between the genteelism and the situation is uncannily touching, as far removed from banality as the apparition of Lorenzo out of the 'kernel of the grave', which,

past his loamed ears
Had made a miry channel for his tears

is removed from any suggestion of the ridiculous. *The Story of Rimini*, of course, subsides continually into both, but Hunt's 'trusting animal spirits', as he archly describes them in the Preface to his *Poems*, are not entirely unselfconscious—he gives us a sidelong glance as he plays the eager enthusiast. Keats's temperament transforms his attitude without altering its idiom.

This 'badness' in Keats, then, might be summed up as a devout, 'unmisgiving' (Hunt's admirable word) acceptance of the first eager brainwave, and a subsequent unawareness that it might be modified or corrected. Keats of course alters much, but he does not polish. His alterations do not, as it were, take the bloom off his characteristic efforts, but show them in a sharper relief. The 'deceitful elf' of the *Ode to a Nightingale* is changed to 'deceiving', but the disconcertingly Keatsian entity remains (all his 'self' rhymes are unsuspiciously clumsy) weighing down with its queer passionate awkwardness the last stanza of the Ode, an awkwardness marvellously in contrast with the nightingale's invisible departure

> Past the near meadows, over the still stream,
> Up the hill-side . . .

I do not want to suggest that his diction is always unself-conscious: of course he had a most attentive ear for the varieties of English poetic diction. Chatterton whose memory was honoured by all the Romantics, was admired by Keats as a poet by whom English—poetic English —had been 'kept up'. When in *Isabella* Keats says that he writes to salute Boccaccio and 'thy gone spirit greet', he is using, I think, a conscious Chattertonism; and so also, perhaps, is the phrase 'husky barn' in a cancelled line of the *Ode to Autumn*. He refused his publisher's plea to restrain the dolphins who 'bob their noses through the brine' in *Endymion*, but allowed 'tip-top quietude' to dwindle into 'utmost quietude'. By the time he came to revise, he was more confident of Chatterton's English than of Hunt's, but here he did his friend less than justice, for Hunt's preface to his own poems—far less lofty and more empirical than Wordsworth's famous document—shows an acute sense of how the spontaneous and 'animal' impulse might be brought back into the diction of the poet who, in Hunt's phrase, 'knows his station', and who would otherwise use the kind of dead language which Wordsworth deplored. Hunt had a theory of poetic diction, and in his Preface defended his use of odd words like *cored*, which he used in the excellent couplet:

> And so much knowledge of one's self there lies
> Cored, after all, in our complacencies.

Further evidence that Hunt's use of naïve neologisms was systematic turns up in a letter of Byron to Thomas Moore (June 1818): 'I told him [Hunt] that I deemed *Rimini* good poetry at bottom, disfigured only by a strange style. His answer was that his style was on a system—or some such cant.'

We cannot say of all poets that they are at their best when at their most characteristic, that their excellence is inseparable from their personal diction. It is true of Hardy, as it is perhaps true of Keats. It is less true of Shelley than of any poet, and it is certainly not true of Spenser or of Hopkins, who might be thought to be enclosed within a poetic idiom of their own creation. Perhaps because they have so obviously fashioned it for themselves, their manner can be shed in favour of a fine simplicity that might have come from anywhere. It is the simplicity we meet in *The Faerie Queene* in lines like

> Thus do those lovers with sweet countervayle
> Each other of love's bitter fruit despoil.

Or in the fragment of Hopkins which begins

> To him who ever thought with love of me . . .

However impressive, this power of achieving a great and plain anonymity need not be taken as touchstone. I comment on it in order to emphasize by contrast how indispensable Keats's personal idiom is. Unlike Wordsworth or Shelley he cannot cease to be immediately himself without losing his peculiar poethood. The early verses *On Death* show what I have in mind; it is one of the few little pieces of its period which his more squeamish admirers can read without shuddering.

> Can death be sleep, when life is but a dream
> And scenes of bliss pass as a phantom by?
> The transient pleasures as a vision seem,
> And yet we think the greatest pain's to die.

Imitative no doubt, but with a simplicity that is rather beautiful, and yet because the thought has not Keats's own linguistic stamp it achieves no wide poetic dignity, it remains banal. But this is not banal—

> O to arrive each Monday morn from Ind!
> To land each Tuesday from the rich Levant!
> In little time a host of joys to bind,
> And keep our souls in one eternal pant!

It is *gemein*, but it is not banal. It has the true devotion of Keats in it.

Of course he can make other styles into his own, the Elizabethans' above all, but they must *be* made his own: insubstantiality and nullity occur when he cannot work the change, when —to borrow his own phrase about Milton—what is life to another poet becomes death to him. An illuminating instance of failure in adaptation is *Daisy's Song*, where Keats takes the form and manner of a lyric by Blake, but gives it, most incongruously, a vulgar touch that is all his own. Even at its most unpropitious, *Endymion* is packed with borrowed life which has become Keats.

> There are who lord it o'er their fellow-men
> With most prevailing tinsel; who unpen
> Their baaing vanities, to browse away
> The comfortable green and juicy hay
> From human pastures; or, O torturing fact!
> Who, through an idiot blink, will see unpack'd
> Fire-branded foxes to sear up and singe
> Our gold and ripe-ear'd hopes.

This is apparently terrible, but let us compare it with the opening of the second *Hyperion*.

> Fanatics have their dreams, wherewith they weave
> A paradise for a sect; the savage too
> From forth the loftiest fashion of his sleep
> Guesses at heaven: pity these have not
> Trac'd upon vellum or wild Indian leaf
> The shadow of melodious utterance.
> But bare of laurel they live, dream and die;
> For Poesy alone can tell her dreams,
> With the fine spell of words alone can save
> Imagination from the sable charm
> And dumb enchantment.

The passage seems to be treading gingerly, with a precarious confidence, secured by a careful abstention from anything that may jar. We miss the deplorable rhymes which wrench the sense so nakedly in their direction, and yet which—like Byron's—in fact give a greater vigour and forcefulness of meaning to the *Endymion* passage than the opening of *Hyperion* can show. In the latter, Keats's greater caution seems to blur and weaken sense; his voice survives only in the thoughtful, colloquial note of 'pity these have not . . .'; and the metaphors (*weave, spell, enchantment*) lie limply, and indeed decoratively, without pressing their conviction boisterously in upon us. Without gathering

itself consciously together, the animation of the *Endymion* style
can leap into the discovery of

> Innumerable mountains rise, and rise,
> Ambitious for the hallowing of thine eyes.

('Rise, and rise'—the rhyme takes the mountain range in its
stride; and *ambitious* is a perfect example of Keats's power to
make use of a grand word without reflecting on it, as unself-
consciously as he uses *baaing* or *comfortable*.) Or into a typically
Keatsian argument:

> And, truly, I would rather be struck dumb
> Than speak against this ardent listlessness;
> For I have ever thought that it might bless
> The world with benefits unknowingly;
> As does the nightingale, upperched high,
> And cloistered among cool and bunched leaves—
> She sings but to her love, nor e'er conceives
> How tip-toe night holds back her dark-grey hood.
> Just so may love, although 'tis understood
> The mere commingling of passionate breath,
> Produce more than our searching witnesseth.

(The movement of that line—'the mere commingling of passionate breath' is as subtle as anything in Pope or Tennyson,
but is given without pretension or pause; and the nightingale,
in its characteristically awkward setting, is far more real than
Clare's more graceful bird, 'lost in a wilderness of listening
leaves'.) Or it may be into a passage like this—

> Staying about, yet cooped up in the den
> Of helpless discontent,—hurling my lance
> From place to place, and following at chance,
> At last, by hap, through some young trees it struck,
> And, plashing among bedded pebbles, stuck
> In the middle of a brook.

—where being young has all the force that it might have in
Byron, together with a most un-Byronic sense of the *feel* of an
event, the moment in the wood when the spear clattered into
the stream. (Contrast this, or 'the sodden turfed dell' of the
murder in *Isabella*, with the Claude landscape of *Hyperion*.) Or
Keats may launch a *sententia*:

But this is human life: the war, the deeds,
The disappointment, the anxiety,
Imagination's struggles, far and nigh,
All human, bearing in themselves this good,
That they are still the air, the subtle food,
To make us feel existence and to show
How quiet death is.

The passage rises into a greatness of generality and at once presses onward; while the opening of the second *Hyperion* seems to be feeling its way, forward towards the plotted moment of a great line, followed by an appropriate rest for appreciation:

When this warm scribe, my hand, is in the grave.

It is moving, and impressive, but it is also in a damaging sense aesthetic. We have seen it coming. Keats is no longer the Squire, writing with 'ful devout corage', but a nineteenth-century poet, nearly a Tennyson, feeling deeply and fashioning a line out of the feeling; the pause between feeling and making can be felt, and in the hush our sense of craftsmanship at work is embarrassingly strong.

*   *   *

Does it matter? Is this a philistine reaction, and should not I just say I *prefer* the more immediate and emotional manner of *Endymion* to that of *Hyperion*, as one might prefer *Maud* to *In Memoriam*? I think, though, there is something of real critical significance here. The wary, meticulous artistry which seems natural to Arnold and Tennyson does indeed matter to Keats, because it inhibits the play of his linguistic personality. *Hyperion* is, so to speak, not *bad* enough, too full of hard-won decorum. Keats distrusted art, because 'human nature' was finer as he felt, but perhaps more because his nature was spontaneously artful. The sad dilemma of his genius is that when he tries to express reality he becomes abstract; when he turns towards the discipline of art he becomes Parnassian. In *Hyperion* both things occur and Keats knew it. He invited Woodhouse to mark in the poem 'the false beauties proceeding from art and the true ones from feeling'. It is a fatal distinction for his poetry and it should be a meaningless one—the whole force of his language and personality should make nonsense of it. But the Keats who abandoned

Hyperion because it had so much of Milton and 'the artist's humour' in it, is the Keats who had come to make such a distinction. He stifles his personality in order to make the necessary calculations for the major philosophical poem, the playing up, or playing down, of 'beauties', to enhance the paragraphing and the overall effect. *Hyperion* thus becomes the prototype of what might be called *Romantic correctness*, the effect displayed in Saturn

> whose hoar locks
> Shone like the bubbling foam about a keel
> When the prow sweeps into a midnight cove . . .

or

> Proserpine return'd to her own fields
> Where the white heifers low

no less than in lines of Tennyson like

> And see the great Achilles whom we knew

or

> While Ilion like a mist rose into towers.

In *Ulysses* and *Tithonus* Tennyson perfects the model; portentous and yet truncated, it makes a kind of poem which seems more deviously intimate the more grandly generalized it is in style, and the more it appears to universalize the burden and the sorrow. It is ideally suited to Tennyson's genius. But is it suited to Keats?

> Then saw I a wan face
> Not pin'd with human sorrows, but bright blanch'd
> By an immortal sickness which kills not;
> It works a constant change, which happy death
> Can put no end to; deathwards progressing
> To no death was that visage; it had passed
> The lily and the snow; and beyond these
> I must not think now, though I saw that face—

In its admirable movement there is something withheld which makes us wonder if Keats has in fact anything to withhold, an impression not uncommon in Tennyson (we have it in *A Vision of Sin*). Superb as Keats's passage is, our view as spectators is

one of abdication, of great curtains rippling together. Very
different from Moneta is the Niobe of *Endymion*.

> Perhaps the trembling knee,
> And frantic gape of lonely Niobe
> Poor lonely Niobe! When her lovely young
> Were dead and gone, and her caressing tongue
> Lay a lost thing upon her paly lip,
> And very, very deadliness did nip
> Her motherly cheeks.

The words here are 'unmisgiving' and alive (compare the potent
word *gape* with *wan* and *blanch'd*). This is the real anguish of
the human heart. It is typical of Keats that even the repetition of
very and the loose feminism of *paly* in no way enfeeble the
passage or add a note of hysteria. The contrast between *caressing*,
with its firm sexual meaning, and the terrible disregard for itself
of this face in torment, would be almost too painful, were it not
that the intensity of the image 'causes all disagreeables to
evaporate'. It is the same brief, almost unregarded intensity
which marks Keats's vision of the brothers' activities in
Isabella—

> Half-ignorant, they turned an easy wheel

—and his expansion of the metaphor into brutal images of blood
and suffering. It is the world's 'giant agony' in a graphically
realized form, as meaningful as the glimpse Shakespeare gives
us of the officer in *King Lear* who was ready to hang Cordelia—

> I cannot draw a cart, nor eat dried oats;
> If it be man's work, I'll do't.

These touches on the nerve are far more effective than a grave
allegory of human suffering, but Keats's sense of guilt made him
feel that one who was a true poet and no dreamer must prepare
himself for a direct assault on 'the mystery'. He did not know,
perhaps could not afford to know, that for him it had to be
revealed indirectly, almost inadvertently, and that he was continually revealing it in this way. *Isabella* struck him as a 'weak-
sided' poem. But like *Endymion* it is as real as anything he wrote.
And *Endymion* has as much life in it as *Don Juan* itself.

Byron thought otherwise, as we know, and in spite of himself

Keats cared much what Byron thought. When in the recast *Hyperion* he made his frontal assault on the human condition he could not forbear—from the height of his new seriousness—a side-swipe in Dante's manner at those critics and 'careless hectorers in proud bad verse' who had dismissed him earlier as the 'drivelling' Keats.

> Tho' I breathe death with them it will be life
> To see them sprawl before me into graves.

The notion of his Lordship, for all his poise and *savoir-vivre*, tripped up and toppled into his own grave, is as gloatingly good as anything in *The Vision of Judgment*. 'Sprawl' is the old Keats: the bizarre picture expands into our mind's eye; but though he had the impulse to 'trounce Lord Byron' in a satire, he would have been ashamed to nurse it up for a long enough period, and become a 'self-worshipper' himself in the process. Satire is no more his *forte* than the grand manner. Though his vulgar native style often has the disconcerting force of good satiric writing (and we might remember that curiously Keatsian line in *Don Juan* about 'cooks in motion with their clean arms bare') it is precisely the element of the *gemein* which gives it its total modesty, and total lack of the keen but complacent self-appraisal which poised satire must have.

The vulgarity which Keats's worldlier critics find hardest to stomach is the lack of this kind of self-awareness: no more than the Squire's does his poetry keep a sharp pleased eye on itself. And not only is Keats too full of the milk of human kindness to maintain the satiric appetite; he was going to drop the passage from *Hyperion* because in the context of the poem's intended seriousness, and select diminishment of effect, it would not do. He had lost the innocence which could include and enjoy so much. One of the reasons *The Cap and Bells* makes depressing reading is that he seems to be exposing and exploiting, with a kind of determined frivolity, the vigour and innocence with which he began, and which Hunt had inspired in him. We can see the process at work in Stanza 62, where Keats is parodying Hunt's style of narration. When he rejects honest vulgarity, and all that for him goes with it, he parts from a great deal. The evidence of this makes it perplexing to know what T. S. Eliot had in mind when he suggested that in the second *Hyperion* we see 'signs of a struggle towards unification of sensibility'.

Does 'unification' here mean the disappearance of so much that makes sensibility in Keats's poetry so worth while?

Both the second *Hyperion* and *The Cap and Bells* show us, in their very different ways, Keats's growing awareness of, and distaste for, his poetical character. In one poem he seeks to evade it in a grave anonymity, in the other in a flippant cynicism. The former is a heroic but desolating attempt, and it might have led him to silence. For his disgust with the idea of the writer carving out a principality for himself—as we say, 'Richardson's world', or 'a Browning character', or 'Trollope country'—was on a typically heroic scale. 'Each of the moderns,' he notes, 'like an Elector of Hanover governs his petty state.' His outburst against the storm in *Don Juan*, if correctly reported by Severn, sounds oddly priggish to us, who find it spirited enough; but Keats's revulsion was, I feel, against Byron consciously making a good thing out of a new mode of fashion of insight into human nature and human conduct. His protest was against the growing pretension of the romantic novelist, and it reminds us that Keats, for all his affinities with Dickens or with Byron, could never have mustered the solipsistic assurance of such a novelist. He writes of the people at a Scottish inn: 'I was extremely gratified to think, that if I had pleasures they knew nothing of, they had also some into which I could not possibly enter.' That is delightful and characteristic, and all the more so from the emphasis with which he records it. We might remember, too, how he noted for his sister the 'old French emigrant with . . . his face full of political schemes' he saw from his Hampstead window; and the curious respect with which he observed the old woman at Belfast—'with a pipe in her mouth and looking out with a round-eyed skinny-lidded inanity, with a sort of horizontal idiotic movement of her head. . . . What a thing would be a history of her life and sensations!' But for all his sharpness of eye and pen he would never have made anything out of it. He was (it was his own highest term of approbation) too 'disinterested' to do so.

It is bitterly ironic that even the *gemein* goes bad on him when he attempts to refine it to the standards of *Hyperion*. One of the curiously intimate apprehensions he is so good at, touches that seem to knit the innerness of the body with the imagination—'ears, whose tips are glowing hot' or, 'eyes, shut softly up alive'—is merely otiose here.

> I had no words to answer; for my tongue
> Useless, could find about its roofed home
> No syllable of a fit majesty
> To make rejoinder to Moneta's mourn.

In the gravely classic context, 'roofed home' is no more alive than 'fleecy care' or 'finny tribe' would be. And the simile

> As when in theatres of crowded men
> Hubbub increases more they call out hush—

anticipates the fatuity of Arnold's in *Sohrab and Rustum*—'As some rich woman on a winter's morn . . .' That close and potent co-operation of the bad and the good which triumphs in *Melancholy*, *The Nightingale*, and the earlier narrative poems, is nullified in *Hyperion*, so that we merely shake our heads when Apollo wishes 'to flit into' a star, 'and make its silvery splendour pant with bliss'; and we sigh with relief when Keats cancelled his metamorphosis

> Into a hue more roseate than sweet pain
> Gives to a ravish'd nymph when her warm tears
> Gush luscious with no sob.

Compared with the sleepwalker's sureness with which he found the alterations in *The Eve of St Agnes*, there is no other word than tinkering for the changes Keats made between the two *Hyperions*. When he takes this kind of pains he becomes conventional, as if convention were an earnest of maturity.

For T. S. Eliot and other critics the *Ode to Psyche* is the finest of the Odes, and Keats himself said it was the first poem 'over which I have taken even moderate pains'. But he is more at home with the linguistic innocence of the Elizabethans: the sheer efficiency of Milton and Dryden is not a happy model for him. The concluding stanza of the Ode is indeed a *tour de force*, but not one of a Keatsian kind; it has the flat Augustan brio which we find in the description of the snake in *Lamia* (so like Pope's pheasant), and the landscapes of his imagination are formalized and parcelled out incongruously—Keats cannot inform the mixture with his own disconcerting truth.

> Yes, I will be thy priest and build a fane
> In some untrodden region of my mind
> Where branched thoughts, new grown with pleasant pain—

We notice the lapse here as we might in Gray or Dryden, and again I take this as a sign that Keats is not fully himself. In the adroitness of the stanza the bad rhyme jars as it should not, and as a similar rhyme does not in the *Sonnet to Homer*.

> Aye, on the shores of darkness there is light,
> And precipices show untrodden green;
> There is a budding morrow in midnight;
> There is a triple sight in blindness keen;

In both poems the adjective *untrodden* makes its distinguishing mark, but while it seems to draw the sonnet into a unique and intense locality, its power in the Ode remains in the air. The sonnet earns the characteristic word, and moves us where the Ode does not.

Keats's endings are worth a study in themselves. He *may* have been like Shakespeare in this respect: that he attached little importance to what he could do supremely and naturally well; this casualness (if it can be called that) fathers what we associate with Shakespearean greatness. *The Nightingale, Autumn,* and *The Eve of St Agnes* 'slipped idly from him'; he does not bother with their 'imperfections', and they do not so much end as complete elsewhere their cycle of fruition, moving without disturbance into their season in our minds. This prolongation of his finest endings is in sharp contrast with the aggressive full stop of others. Keats's sincerity, his almost embarrassing tendency to mean what he says, is bothering (or at least has appeared to bother many critics and readers) at the conclusion of the *Ode on a Grecian Urn*, because it is put in the kind of poetic language which usually does *not* mean quite so intensely what it says. Compare 'Beauty is truth, truth beauty', with the line in *Endymion*—'I loved her to the very white of truth'— where the abstract word is brought home to us through the medium of the graphic kernel image. Phrases like 'the feel of not to feel it', 'a sort of oneness', 'one smallest pebble-bead of doubt', show how effectively and with what accuracy the Keatsian *gemein* can deal with propositions and ideas if it is allowed to do so in its own way, by means of the 'plump contrast' of sense. To generalize for Keats is not to be an idiot, but to run the risk of losing the necessary contact with his physical self.

Although one is abstract, and the other has all the Keatsian reality and weight in it, the ending of *Lamia* does have something of the over-conscious finality we find in the last couplet of the *Grecian Urn*.

> —no pulse, or breath they found,
> And, in its marriage robe, the heavy body wound.

We know that Keats had difficulty in completing *Lamia*; that he wished to end it even more abruptly by cutting off the last twenty lines or so; and that—as Professor Garrod plausibly suggested—he replied to the protests of his friend and publisher by telling them to finish it off as they wanted. He valued *Lamia* much more highly than his other two narrative poems, and for the usual disquieting reason: he thought it had more toughness and reality in it, and he had tried hard to put them there. He wanted it to end with a flourish, a defiant full stop, but—to adapt his own comment on poetry—we might say that if a poem of his does not end as naturally as the leaves fall from a tree it had better not end at all.

The Eve of St Agnes does end like the seasons and the leaves; it is Keats's most moving ending to what I consider his finest poem. Yet he insisted on altering the last lines 'to leave on the reader a sense of pettish disgust'. (The account is Woodhouse's.) 'He says he likes that the poem should leave off with this change of sentiment—it was what he aimed at, and was glad to find from my objections to it that he had succeeded.'

> Angela went off
> Twitch'd with the palsy; and with face deform
> The beadsman stiffened, 'twixt a sigh and laugh
> Ta'en sudden from his beads by one weak little cough.

We can only uphold Woodhouse's objection. But Keats felt that this was more wry and worldly, less romantic and 'weak-sided'. Was it a final gesture towards Byron and to the kind of expectation in the reader which Keats felt that Byron had created? Certainly Byron's most terrible gift was to dissolve the selfhood of his victims, to make those under his spell feel that reality was in him, not in themselves, and he made Keats feel it. He made Keats want '*to write fine things which cannot be laughed at in any way*'—perhaps the most significant admission in his letters. It was a desolating ambition for himself, though it reveals an astonishingly shrewd insight into Byron's own social and poetic obsession. It is like Keats to be dismissive of his poem once written, but it is horribly unlike him to try to give it an all-round reality, a Byronic sort of reality, by adding this touch. And it is in marked contrast to the typically effortless and natural relation which he had with romantic mediaevalism. 'They are not my fault', he says of the names in the poem, 'I did not search for them.' Mrs Radcliffe's world was native to him, Byron's was not.

None the less, the thread that obstinately though incongruously links the two poets is that of personality: and it is Keats's fate that the elements of greatness in him, of aspiration and virtue, all make against the personal actuality of his poetry, negate and extinguish it, are bent on passing it for 'a higher life'. In Byron these elements are in complete harmony with his personal style and show themselves through it. Keats is always in danger of losing himself, either to another kind of 'truth' or to his own ambition. His personality is not self-renewing—it is not ruthless and egocentric enough. A poet like Yeats or Byron can abandon to his following the attitudes which have served him—and yet remain even more richly and recognizably himself; but with Keats the processes of 'maturity' are those of real impoverishment and sacrifice, of muting and muffling. The realities of Calidore and Endymion, of Isabella and Porphyro, are disowned, together with the vocabulary and the sexual imagination that made them real. Reality *changes* for Keats, as it never does for Byron, and the eclipse of reality in his poetry is the eclipse of sex.

3. Keats and Sex

The most emphatic aspect of the *gemein* in Keats is, of course, the way he writes about sex. I do not think that any critic, not even Leigh Hunt, has found himself able to praise Keats's treatment of the subject, and I feel some qualms in attempting to do so now. But considering the general agreement that his poetry is full of sex, and the equally general agreement that he is a fine poet, this negative attitude is odd, to say the least. How does this side of Keats come to be so customarily dismissed—as indeed Keats himself was only too ready to dismiss it—with epithets like 'mawkish' and 'adolescent'? The critic's route of

escape from the topic seems to be that Keats outgrew all that
nonsense when he became full of flint and iron, or that it is in
any case of little importance, something sloughed off in his finest
poetry. Distrust of it unites the most dissimilar critics. It moves
D. G. James in *The Romantic Comedy* to say that 'the most
serious side of Keats does not emerge in *The Eve of St Agnes*';
it annoys Bernard Blackstone so much that he curtly dismisses
one of the most striking and characteristic passages of *Endymion*, in his book *The Consecrated Urn*, as 'hardly relevant to our
purposes', the purposes of thematic interpretation; Professor
Muir takes refuge from it in the study of *Hyperion* as a political
and spiritual allegory; and H. W. Garrod, debarred from that
outlet, in his study of the poet, by his own robust refusal to
admit a growing maturity and reality in the later poems, fell
back on the world of 'pure imaginative forms' which Keats ideally
inhabits.

Garrod, indeed, disposed of the problem most honestly. He
would not make the often implied contrast between the 'serious'
and the sexual or 'adolescent' side of Keats, but he made
another between Keats's supremacy in these 'pure imaginative
forms', and his unfortunate 'relapses upon the real'. Imagination,
he suggested, is as far removed from the erotic in Keats as can
well be: the first produces his 'characteristic perfections', the
second 'assails him with the old hunger and thirst for reality'.
And with disastrous consequences.

> Let the mad poets say whate'er they please
> Of the sweets of Fairies, Peris, Goddesses,
> There is not such a treat among them all,
> Haunters of cavern, lake, and waterfall,
> As a real woman—

'That the same man', wrote Garrod, 'could write like that, and
elsewhere write poetry, we can only believe by finding it to be
so.' This seems to me to go the root of the matter, and though I
take the opposite view and find in these lines the most characteristic evidence of Keats's unique gift, Garrod's vigorous
reaction does challenge us to decide what is good and bad in
Keats, and why. 'Upon whatever page of the poetry there falls
the shadow of a living woman,' he continues, 'it falls calamit-
ously like an eclipse.' Again the emphasis is in the right place,
though again my own feeling would be that when it is indeed a

living woman that Keats writes of his poetry is never more real. Moneta and Mnemosyne are not real precisely because they are not there as women, in the sense that Cynthia, Lamia, Isabella, and Madeline are; they have a function doubtless, a serious and symbolic function, but they do not exist, and it is this kind of existence, the existence that Keats can give to sexual fantasy, that is the kernel of his poetic achievement.

The *Ode to Autumn* is usually considered his most perfect poem, the most free from any 'mawkish' or personal intrusion, and I suppose that Garrod would not have considered the great personification of autumn there to be in any sense 'a living woman'. But in fact she surely is? The poem's weight and substance depend upon her sisterhood with those other ladies about whom the critics prefer to make no comment. Take the second line of the poem,

> Close bosom-friend of the maturing sun;

and the seventeenth,

> Or on a half-reap'd furrow sound asleep . . .

There is not only weight and perfection here but also the *gemein*, the warmly domestic. *Sound* asleep—the phrase expands and withdraws from the mythology of the classic seasons into the more intimate mythology of family and home. More perfect and more generalized as the phrases are, they are none the less cognate with the 'mistress' of the *Ode to Melancholy*, with her 'rich anger', 'peerless eyes', and the 'globed peonies' that are associated with her; with Lorenzo's Isabella, whose 'full shape did all his seeing fill'; with the Niobe of *Endymion* whom I have already mentioned, and with the picture of Cybele in that poem.

What the psychologists might make of this is both obvious and unimportant. The sexual psychology of Byron or Dostoevsky is clearly of the greatest possible significance to the critic of their work: there is no need to concern ourselves with that of Keats because it is in every sense so commonplace. Nor would it be relevant to dwell on the sexual reality of these figures if such a reality was all they possessed. The sensuous weight of Keats's language is evident enough, and its heavy condensation at these moments (like the boat in *Endymion* that 'dropped beneath the young couple's weight') also goes without saying. No, the real importance of such passages is their power of expansion and universalization. Keats is, I believe, unique among English poets in his power of generalizing the most personal and the most intimate sensuality back into a great and indeed an august idea of nature and life. It is a peculiarly Romantic power: the Elizabethans, from whom he learned so much, do not have it. Keats can endow an intimate sensuality with the same power of expansion and suggestion with which Wordsworth, in *Resolution and Independence* and elsewhere, endows his own spiritual and poetic predicament. In both cases we share in something that seems deeply and universally relevant. But unlike Wordsworth, Keats is not aware of the process, or aware of it only in the context of his feeling both antipathy and envy for Wordsworth's more conscious power of generalization. The irony with which we are by now so sadly familiar is that he assumed, as his critics have been ready to assume, that sex was for him a refuge, a *cul-de-sac*, a veritable chamber of maiden thought. His poetry shows otherwise: its power of expansion lay in the very 'mawkishness' which he felt he must grow out of. Sexual vulgarity is the matrix of a generalizing greatness.

'Perfection' in Keats is for this reason never a pure, elevated, separable affair. When his poetry is alive it is never 'perfect' in the sense in which Garrod observed that 'it is hard to conceive more perfect speech' than the first six lines of the 'Bright Star' sonnet, the remainder being 'in painfully inferior contrast'. The end couplet of a Shakespeare sonnet may be inferior to what precedes it in the sense Garrod had in mind, but this kind of perfection or inferiority just does not occur in Keats. The sonnet is a seamless whole, but it reverses the usual order of Keats's great effects; the expansion and the breadth are manifested at the opening, and in the conclusion we can see where they had their source. Professor Garrod felt the perfection began to 'waver' in the couplet:

> Or gazing on the new soft-fallen mask
> Of snow upon the mountains and the moors.

—significantly, because the image of the snow is marvellously balanced between the intimate and the spacious: in its erotic overtone 'the real woman' is beginning to appear.

In its small compass the 'Bright Star' sonnet has the same latent scope, the same promise of the illimitable, that we find in *The Eve of St Agnes*. (Consider, for example, the significance in

line six of the adjective *pure*—Keats first wrote *cold*—and
human. In themselves they contain two worlds.) Although Keats
has no outstanding gift for verse narration, in the traditional
sense, his art holds the seed of that form which was to flower so
conspicuously later in the century—the form of the short story.
It is a form which demands for its highest success a deceptive
slightness of setting combined with the utmost expansion of
meaning, and, as I shall hope to show, we find these in *The Eve
of St Agnes* as we find them in a masterpiece like Joyce's story
The Dead. How that characteristically romantic form, the allegory
of spiritual quest and struggle, is as ill-suited to Keats as it is
suited to Shelley, we have already seen: allegory sinks under
the weight which Keats gives to his own apprehensions of
intensity, but such moments are the life of the short-story form.

I have already mentioned *Resolution and Independence*, and
Wordsworth's poem has indeed this same quality, embodied in
the place or person who provides for the narrator and hence for
ourselves what Joyce called 'an epiphany'. It does not seem to me
absurd to compare the leechgatherer, who is seen not only as a
man but as a vision, as a creature of unknown age and provenance,
with Keats's beadsman, or even with an apparition of similar
intensity in *Endymion*, that of Cybele.

> Forth from a rugged arch, in the dusk below,
> Came mother Cybele! alone—alone—
> In sombre chariot . . . four maned lions hale
> The sluggish wheels; solemn their toothed maws,
> Their surly eyes brow-hidden, heavy paws
> Uplifted drowsily, and nervy tails
> Cowering their tawny brushes. Silent sails
> This shadowy queen athwart, and faints away
> In another gloomy arch

As well as being a Wordsworthian apparition the leechgatherer
is a fully human figure (this gives the poem its force as a story)
perhaps because Wordsworth here (and Keats habitually)
combine with ease the intimate with the frankly literary or
mythological, a mixture that, surprisingly, combines to make
their visions like a portrait from life—perhaps life inheres in
the very incongruity of the mixture? In stanza, spirit, and
vocabulary, the leechgatherer joins with the world of Spenser,
fully evident in such a phrase as 'the sable orbs of his yet vivid

eyes'; and Keats can produce his Cybele as if in the garish
background of the pantomimes he delighted in at Drury Lane,
whisk her on as if with wires and away into the wings again.
That the pantomime was in Keats's head at this point comes
out still more clearly a few lines later when Endymion has put

> Into his grasping hands a silken cord
> At which without a single impious word
> He swung upon it off into the gloom.

Keats afterwards substituted 'a large eagle' for the silken cord.
Keats's essentially vulgar embrace of mythology (about which
he became sensitive as the critics took care to assure him of its
vulgarity) is triumphant in its eclectic and unselfconscious
vigour: he is as familiar with his Andromeda in the *Endymion*
chorus as with the bride in his Galloway Song. No lively use
of mythology can come of an anxiety about good taste; Keats
here is in the company of Chaucer and Shakespeare.

In the passage from *Lamia* which has been so much deplored,
we can see a similar and splendid combination of the Keatsian
gemein with a neo-classic vitality straight from Dryden. Dryden's
worldliness is replaced by Keats's 'devout corage', but his
energy is fused with it admirably in such lines as

> —a real woman, lineal indeed
> From Pyrrha's pebbles or old Adam's seed

or

> With no more awe than what her beauty gave,
> That, while it smote, still guaranteed to save.

This is not to say that *Lamia* is successful as a poem, as are—in
their different ways—*Endymion* and *The Eve of St Agnes*. Its
failure is indeed best shown by the importance which we, and
Keats, have to give to its 'meaning' (which yet neither he nor
we can take seriously) and by the helplessness with which we
find ourselves comparing its thematic tendencies—the fatal
woman, the destructive infatuation, and so forth—with comparable themes in other poems. Failure in Keats, we might
almost say, can be measured by the extent to which there seems
nothing for it but to appraise the significance which his themes
might seem to have, particularly in relation to one another.
Such an analysis is a sign of failure, though where *Lamia* is

concerned of permissible failure, in our response to what he
can best do.

*   *   *

It is a measure of the success of *The Eve of St Agnes* that if we
respond to it we do not feel any need to make this kind of
analysis. If we are determined to analyse we can call it another
example of Keats's wish-fulfilment fantasy, pointing out what is
certainly true, the way in which Madeline's awakening,

> Her eyes were open, but she still beheld,
> Now wide awake, the vision of her sleep—

illustrates Keats's own deep yearning for the imagination to be
like Adam's dream: 'he awoke and found it truth'. But this is no
more relevant than Garrod's description of the poem as 'an
exquisitely coloured tapestry', 'a beautiful piece . . . which fences
us elaborately from all infection of reality' etc. It is not a
psychological conundrum with mediaeval trappings, like
Christabel, or a picturesque labour of love of the past, like *The
Lay of the Last Minstrel*, from which much of its material is
taken. It is the most remarkable instance in romantic poetry
of a poem based wholly upon literature and yet expanding
wholly into life. Just as we are surprised, and yet wholly
persuaded, by Wordsworth's literary vision of the leechgatherer
in a line like 'the sable orbs of his yet vivid eyes', so it is a
shock to find Keats's hero 'brushing the cobwebs with his lofty
plume', but a shock that reminds us just how far from Mrs
Radcliffe we have come; how completely realized, in human
setting, the fantasy has been made to be. In Keats, literature
can become the most effective vehicle of reality.

The best insight into the true nature of the poem is also the
earliest, that of Leigh Hunt. For me, Hunt is a wholly benign
influence on Keats's poetic make-up, notwithstanding that
Keats's own repudiation of him has been fervently echoed ever
since; and I think him Keats's best critic as well. When he
remarks that Keats 'sympathized with the lowliest commonplace', we feel that this is the real bond between the two writers
and that it unites them with a third, whose sympathy with the
commonplace was indeed meticulous—James Joyce. Hunt not
only writes of 'the present palpable reality of *The Eve of St
Agnes*', as opposed to 'the less generally characteristic majesty

of *Hyperion'*, but he also understands the nature of Keats's language in the poem, and how its 'beauties', so far from being merely luxuriant and richly coloured, have a penetrating and revealing power that draws out to indefinite limits the perspective of the actual.

> Northward he turneth through a little door,
> And scarce three steps, ere Music's golden tongue
> Flatter'd to tears this aged man and poor . . .

In *Imagination and Fancy, or Selections from the English Poets*, Hunt has this to say of these lines about the Beadsman. 'A true poet is by nature a metaphysician: he feels instinctively what others get at by long searching. In this word *flatter'd* is the whole theory of the secret of tears, which are the tributes, more or less worthy, of self-pity to self-love. Whenever we shed tears we take pity on ourselves, and we feel, if we do not consciously say so, that we deserve to have the pity taken. In many cases the pity is just and the self-love not to be construed unhandsomely'.

I suppose this might be felt to be a mere flight of critical garrulity, typical of its period, and telling us more about Hunt himself than about either the Beadsman or Keats's poetry. I must admit to being both impressed and delighted by its shrewd warmth—'more or less worthy' is particularly neat—but the special interest of it for us is surely its close resemblance, as critical appraisal, to the way in which Coleridge, Hazlitt, and Hunt himself, were recording at this time their perceptions about Shakespeare. It is a type of criticism that illuminates both authors but which would be lost on any other Romantic poet; a type of insight whose value lies in exhibiting and expatiating on a general truth implicit in a concentration of artful language. A general truth, for it tells us nothing of Keats himself, just as the similar perceptions of Coleridge and others seemingly tell us nothing about Shakespeare. In the poetry of Wordsworth or Byron there are concentrations of meaning which can be enlarged on so as to tell us much about those poets, and hence perhaps about the human situation, but they lack the anonymity which is so complete here, and to which Hunt unconsciously pays the greatest compliment he can by reflecting on a meaning as he would reflect on one in Shakespeare.

In showing the scope of the poem, these meanings that reveal themselves through the nature of Keats's language are even

more important than the evident symbolic setting of warmth
and cold, darkness and light, ecstasy and deprivation. As in most
great imaginative works which we agree for convenience to call
'symbolic', the perspective of linguistic meaning elaborates the
more elementary and static significance of symbol. A phrase
like 'bright dulness', for example, with which Keats describes
the revelry in the castle, contributes as much to the epiphany
of the story as the snow outside. As Hunt admiringly implies,
it is by meanings of this sort that the Beadsman becomes a
human being, and not a mere symbol of age and renunciation.
And so it is with the other characters. Their individuality is all
there in embryo, and it surrounds them with the freedom and
the scope which would be a condition of further more detailed
characterization. Madeline herself is not 'what the woman is',
in D. H. Lawrence's sense, but a particular girl in a general
situation, created from literature—the 'lap of legends old'—and
from the intensity of Keats's vision of warmth and love in the
dark night of human destiny. When

> She danc'd along with vague, regardless eyes

we see her as we see Natasha and Jane Bennet, yet the brilliant
stanzas open to reveal an impersonal glimpse into the divided
nature of the dream of love, the simultaneous attraction and
recoil.

> Innumerable of stains and splendid dyes,
> As are the tiger-moth's deep-damask'd wings;
> And in the midst, 'mong thousand heraldries,
> And twilight saints and dim emblazonings,
> A shielded scutcheon blush'd with blood of queens and kings.

Blush'd has a typically Keatsian weight; it universalizes the
erotic not only among the living but back into the past, calling
up the fears and desires that once warmed the dead. It concentrates Madeline's livingness, as Porphyro's is concentrated in
'The carved angels, ever eager-eyed' who '*star'd*, where upon
their heads the cornice rests'. As well as being the perfect
oxymoron for the two sides of desire, *tiger-moth* has a similarly
uncontrolled metaphorical life: it reminds me of images of
attraction and pursuit in the 'warm darkness' of the later novels
of Henry James. The girl's impulse of withdrawal from this

dangerous world, into the old safety of sleep and childhood, carries us too on the wings of metaphor.

> Flown, like a thought, until the morrow-day;
> Blissfully haven'd both from joy and pain;
> Clasp'd like a missal where swart Paynims pray;
> Blinded alike from sunshine and from rain,
> As though a rose should shut, and be a bud again.

Though stilled for now by the echo of *Venus and Adonis*— 'Love comforteth like sunshine after rain'—the words *clasp'd* and *blinded* promise the struggle and tears, the necessary onset of life, promise it, as it were, without speaking of it. The precision—in a stanza which has been called escapist and sentimental—belongs not to Keats but to his story.

The distinction could be illustrated by comparing such effects of universalized life, and sexual life in particular, in Keats's poem with those in Valéry's *Le Cimetière Marin*. There the peremptory, indeed jaunty, precision of Valéry's language—in the sixteenth stanza, for example—strikes me as only just pausing on the brink of a really disheartening and mechanical vulgarity.

> Les cris aigus des filles chatouillées,
> Les yeux, les dents, les paupières mouillées,
> Le sein charmant qui joue avec le feu,
> Le sang qui brille aux lèvres qui se rendent,
> Les derniers dons, les doigts qui les défendent,
> Tout va sous terre et rentre dans le jeu!

It emphasizes the presence of the poet, and does not initiate the anonymous tale of humanity that seems implicit in every word of *The Eve of St Agnes*. Keats thought the poet must 'die into life'; and here he is indeed 'dying into' the life of his story, though it is very different from his imagination of the process in the weighty symbolism of the second *Hyperion*. It is perhaps in the nature of the true process that he could not realize when it happened.

I will not continue to labour this significance of meaning, but in view of the critics' deprecation, and Keats's own inevitable modesty, I would emphasize how wholly dramatic is the balance it makes between the particular and the general, the real persons and the universalizing vision. Consider Madeline's simplicity of action, her apparently random involvement in commonplace detail.

> Her falt'ring hand upon the balustrade,
> Old Angela was feeling for the stair,
> When Madeline, St Agnes' charmed maid,
> Rose, like a mission'd spirit, unaware:
> With silver taper's light, and pious care,
> She turn'd, and down the aged gossip led
> To a safe level matting.

The last word drags a weight of the commonplace that is almost sublime. It is a commonplace that gets into the heroine; her kindness is immensely ordinary. She is the girl whose lover will advise her to put on 'warm clothing' before they make the escape; the girl whose destiny, whose womanhood and death, are shown forth in the last stanza, a coda that seems to play without a sound the chords of some majestic fictional ending, like, say, the last sentence of Henry James's *The Bostonians*. 'But though she was glad, he presently discovered that, beneath her hood, she was in tears. It is to be feared that with the union . . . she was about to enter, these were not the last she was destined to shed.'

> And they are gone: ay, ages long ago
> These lovers fled away into the storm . . .

The rumours of warmth and cold, the living and the dead, echo backwards and forwards and vanish in darkness.

> Out went the taper as she hurried in;
> Its little smoke, in pallid moonshine, died.

It may be objected that a story cannot tell us so much of human life when it has day-dream and fantasy at its heart. But Keats was never more successful at realizing the interdependence of the two. The dreams of Madeline and Porphyro are brought together; their fantasies coincide, but the pathos of their isolation is inseparable from the warmth of their meeting, is at one with the storm and the snow and the motionless figures in their icy hoods and mails.

> For on the midnight came a tempest fell.
> More sooth for that his close rejoinder flows
> Into her burning ear—and still the spell
> Unbroken guards her in serene repose.

With her wild dream he mingled as a rose
Marryeth its odour to a violet.
Still, still she dreams—louder the frost wind blows
Like Love's alarum pattering the sharp sleet
Against the window-panes; St Agnes' moon hath set.

Well after the poem was written, and in a truculent and self-protective mood, Keats found it necessary to insist to his friend Woodhouse that the physical union of the lovers is described here. It is possible to wonder whether the imagination of the poem, as written, really bears him out? 'More sooth for that his close rejoinder flows'—it is this line, with its marvellous Keatsian concretion (*sooth* has a double meaning, echoing 'jellies soother than the creamy curd') which gives us the lovers' embrace. What follows—if Keats's own interpretation be insisted on—is figurative, and feebly so; and Keats's love-scenes are never figurative, nor is anything in the rest of the poem. If figurative, the lines are vulgar in a sense alien to Keats (we find it in Rossetti's *The House of Life*) and I suspect that the distaste for much of the poem which is apparently often felt nowadays, has its origin here. In 'The Stealthy School of Criticism' Rossetti's answer to Buchanan's attack on 'The Fleshly School of Poetry', he tell us that in the sonnets (e.g. *Love-Sweetness*) 'all the passionate and just delights of the body are declared—somewhat figuratively it is true, but unmistakably—to be naught if not ennobled by the concurrence of the soul at all times'. The point is fair enough (D. H. Lawrence himself would have wholeheartedly agreed with it) but the word *figuratively* goes a long way towards explaining the modern misunderstanding of, and antipathy for, the Victorian poetry of sex.

Once again the influence of Byron, of a queasy compound of Byron and Keats, has a disastrous effect. Nothing is worse for Keats than the convention, already stirring in his time and tyrannical in our own, that the truth must be told, that it is 'weak-sided' and cowardly to leave anything out, especially anything so apparently important as this. But it is an illusory importance, for the intensity of the poem's imagination of love is conveyed by vision and not by fact; the relation of the lovers is imagined in terms of their wishes and their dreams.

The Dead seems to me an achievement very close to *The Eve of St Agnes* in the nature and power of its vision: I should be tempted to call them the most remarkable, and in the broadest sense poetical, short stories in English. Joyce's mastery is of course entirely poised and self-conscious; the weight he gives to the commonplace is as elegant as in Keats it is instinctive, and yet the intensity of impersonal meaning in the language is as remarkable in the story as in the poem. Both have a ritual solidity of description, which somehow pledges that what one dreams and yearns for and regrets is as much a part of life as what one eats, that one's fantasies are as real as one's food. Joyce's dinner laid out is one for the dead to remember; his loving account of a Dublin musical party is the equivalent of Keats's tranced exploitation of the mediaeval and picturesque. The hero and heroine of *The Dead* dream of their past, which divides them as individuals and yet which in a strange and touching way also unites them and the others in a communion of living and a corresponding awareness of death. ' " I love to see the snow", said Aunt Julia sadly', a phrase which compresses the same meaning as the extinguished candle in *The Eve of St Agnes*. Like the lovers, she is on her way to join the vast hosts of the dead. We cannot apprehend death, but we can perceive our relation to it here, with an intensity that does indeed, for the moment, 'make its disagreeables evaporate'. Both Joyce and Keats knew that what *is*, can and must be made beautiful by art, and Joyce's *credo* of the principle of beauty, where it has not yet been imagined or apprehended, is an echo of Keats's own. *

So far from its being 'elaborately fenced from all infection of reality', I have tried to show how *The Eve of St Agnes* takes its place among moving and memorable fictions, and how its reality is of the same nature as theirs. It has supremely what Arnold called the power of natural interpretation, the power that 'calms and satisfies us as no other can'. Yet this phrase has its dangers —not much less so than Joyce's picture in *Portrait of the Artist as a Young Man* of 'the luminous silent stasis of aesthetic pleasure'—for the point about the interpretative power is that it does *interpret*. The aesthetic diagnosis of art is irreproachable, but in concentrating on the end state it suggests—disastrously —that we can take a short cut. We can certainly agree that his poetry ultimately gives the rich calm of aesthetic satisfaction,

---

* See in his early essay 'Drama and Life' the paragraph beginning 'A yet more insidious claim is the claim for beauty'

but we must none the less beware of taking the aesthetic view of Keats. The Pre-Raphaelites did so, concentrating on his 'exquisite detail', and for them a line like 'My sleep had been embroidered with dim dreams' was the choicest example of his art. But it is the kind of line which, in Robert Bridges's phrase, 'displays its poetry rather than its meaning'.

Keats's poetry is in the meaning, and it is in a story which is filled with such meaning that he seems to me to achieve his masterpiece. But we must not forget that for him the poetry had to be in the meaning in a different and more direct sense, the sense in which for Wilfred Owen, a true descendant of Keats as Rossetti and the late Romantics were not, the poetry of war could only be 'in the pity'. Owen's rich and Keatsian talent is in sharp contrast with the experience of war to which he felt that poetry must be offered up—'above all', he wrote, 'I am not concerned with poetry'. But his art transcended the use he wished to make of it, and became a majestic celebration of the eternity of man at war as well as a denunciation of the futility of war. 'Calm and satisfaction', 'the luminous stasis', cannot ultimately be kept out. His rich art has achieved a meaning much wider than the one required of it, and yet this greatness still depends on the urgency and simplicity of his purpose. There is a lesson in this for our reading of Keats.

Owen's poetry, like that of Keats, is inevitably on a grand scale—the scale of his feeling for those 'hearts grown great with shot'. It is this generosity, transcending the art of poetry, which antagonized Yeats, a firm believer in the need for a poet to be master in his own house. But it does not need to express itself in a conventionally 'grand' form, and I must admit to experiencing something of the same doubt about Owen's last and most evidently impressive poem, *Strange Meeting*, that I feel about the second *Hyperion*. It is a doubt which I hope takes the form of humility, and in conclusion I should like to suggest that our most disturbing apprehension of greatness in Keats (and, as an illuminating parallel, in Owen) may be the singular kind of uncertainty we have to feel about these poems, an uncertainty which is not fully answered by the fact of untimely death.

For notwithstanding the conventional supremacy of the Odes (and they are really far less homogeneous, more typically *Keatsian* than the convention implies) there is astonishingly little general agreement about his best-known poems. Nothing is more finally disconcerting about this most disconcerting of our poets than our lack of decision, and of accepted standards of judgment, at moments when some sort of unanimity might be expected. Is the passage from *The Fall of Hyperion* which I have already quoted, and which ends with the comparison of Moneta's eyes to 'the mild moon'

> Who comforts those she sees not, who knows not
> What eyes are upward cast

—is such a passage, which Middleton Murry calls 'an apprehension of an ultimate reality', and 'a wonderful symbol of the unspeakable truth', the finest poetry or not? I have to confess my sense of not knowing, and I can only hope that other readers have experienced this peculiar kind of awed discomposure. It is certainly not just good poetry, and however unaffirmed, our confidence in our own ability to tell the great from the good in poetry is really pretty strong, but Keats upsets it. That he does so seems to be not only because what I have had to call 'badness' plays so strangely important a part in his total meaning, and we look in vain for any trace of it here, but also because here is the final proof that he has no poetic world of his own, no aesthetic enclosure where he is a law unto himself, and where we can recognize and appreciate at once his own special kind of performance. His reality is not, after all, to be found in one place. He does not 'know his station'. His power of loading words with meaning is changed here into quite a different sort of potential, which remains enigmatic.

But one thing is certain—Keats could never have made the most of his genius. However good *The Eve of St Agnes* may be —and I believe it to be his masterpiece—he could never have continued to write more poetic tales, or more Odes, each richer and more full of satisfactions than the last. Nothing held him to the *mode*, as Shakespeare was held to the theatre, and whatever may appear to the contrary his lack of belief in writing poetry, just because he had the genius to write it, was fundamental. It has been argued that unless we believe in his emergent power to express what he so directly and deeply felt about 'suffering humanity', we degrade him to the status of a 'minor poet'*. No poet, perhaps, can be labelled minor who does not in some sense

---

* *John Keats, A Reassessment* (introductory note).

acquiesce in being so, and Keats did not, but—and this is the truth that must shape our last understanding of him—he did not acquiesce in the status of being a poet at all. It was the status that Wordsworth came to rely on, and that Browning took pride in when he formed the resolution, after the uncertainties of his earlier career, to 'keep his poethood ever before him'. For Keats, being a poet was a destiny as momentous but far less manageable than anything expressed in such acts of will and affirmations of role.

It was also a tragic destiny, in that tragedy involves what is most contradictory in human genius. Keats is never immanent in his own achievement: its very perfection ensures his absence. The stillness of his poetry must always appear becalmed and isolated from the onrush of his being. The stasis of Tennyson's poetry, pausing, circling, slowly eddying ever round on itself, is in a kind of domestic harmony and accord with his nature, which it expresses, and releases. He is at home in its verbal movement, as he became in his relation with his public. Tennyson's poetry perfectly 'understands' as it were, Keats's; but it is an understanding that demonstrates the difference. Where Tennyson's poetry is a reconcilement in and to himself, Keats's cannot but emphasize and foreshadow a heroic separation.

4. *Another View of the Question*

Two colleagues who came to the reading of the paper on which this study of Keats was based have since produced longer and more detailed studies, working out their own views on related aspects of his poetry. In *John Keats's Dream of Truth*, John Jones investigates in scrupulous and sensitive fashion questions of 'feel' and sensibility, analysing the static quality of Keatsian narration, and what he suggestively calls the 'end-stopped effect'. In *Keats and Embarrassment*, Christopher Ricks is—as he handsomely acknowledges—even more directly concerned with my main thesis, and with just what is involved in what I called the 'embarrassingly real' aspects of Keatsian language and fantasy.

His interest is particularly significant because it brings out the uneasy quality of the contemporary which is at the elbow of Keats's readers, which disconcerted them in his own time and has not ceased to do so now; and which is at the back of

Bagehot's verdict, quoted at the beginning of my lecture—'the most essentially modern of recent poets.' However much it partook of the properties of the age, Gothic and romantic and sensational, there was something new—socially new—in the world of Keatsian 'beauties'. It disturbed as things do disturb whose appeal cannot be quite comfortably defined, and makes the reader uneasy in his own response.

For the new area and meeting-ground of class and sex had a special sensitivity. The unexpected aspect of the poetry is the way it comprehends and explores—as raptly, though involuntarily, as Wordsworth had explored the childhood intimation of 'unknown modes of being'—the inward dream gentilities of a new urban social class. As G. M. Matthews observes in the *Critical Heritage* compilation of Keats, both Crabbe and Wordsworth had made the domestic emotions of plain people a fit subject for poetry. But not the sexual fantasies and feelings of those who were not so plain, but were the people beginning to enliven the expansion of urban middle-class culture and manners with a corresponding inner world of desire and inhibition, fantasy and wish fulfilment. This is the world of Dickens, as it is also, with allowances for difference of sex and background, the world of *Jane Eyre*. Both gave offence, in spite of—even because of—the avidity with which they were read and responded to.

Even so they offended less than Keats, and the nature of his offence is exactly defined in Mrs Carlyle's comment that *Isabella* (obviously she meant *The Eve of St Agnes*) 'might have been written by a seamstress who had eaten something too rich for supper and slept upon her back'. In its mere prose that comment is as suggestive as anything in Keats's poetry, as suggestive *of* the poetry. It gives in one sentence what is social in Keats's poetry, and what is carnal and infantile as well as sexual; but it also suggests its sexual identification of viewer and viewed, of masculine fantasy and feminine embodiment.

For when Keats explored consciousness, as Wordsworth and Coleridge had done, he explored the hinterland of mental fantasy and physical sensation, the 'fallings from us, vanishings' of the sentient as well as intellectual being. He made words into adepts of previously unexpressed internal movements, the 'thought' of the body. This was never put better than by Aubrey de Vere in 1849, who remarked that 'his body seemed to think, and on the other hand he sometimes appeared hardly to know if he possessed aught but body'. Two years before, William Howitt had put it more bluntly: 'The worldly and the worldly-wise could not comprehend him. To them his vivid orgasm of the intellect was like madness.' And indeed Keats's most embarrassing faculty is to seem to embody in words the capability and animation of erectile tissue. In his letters he speaks of ideas 'swelling into reality'. The 'bodily intuitions' for which this poetry so astonishingly finds words, bring together—virtually identify—the flush of inspiration ('The faint conceptions I have of poems to come brings the blood frequently into my forehead') with the stirrings of sex—

> Sudden a thought came like a full-blown rose
> Flushing his brow . . .

The whole could be said to be signalized, in terms of poetry, of sex, and of class, by the phenomenon of the *blush*, whose displacing shocks and surprises of poetic meaning I noticed in my lecture—'a shielded scutcheon blush'd with blood of queens and kings'. Christopher Ricks has some fascinating and diverting things to say about the comparative study of the blush, and several times cites the work of the learned Dr Bergler, a psychologist who has engagingly defined it as a 'displacement from below upward which phallicises the face'. This is not the language of Keats, or even of any possible gloss on what is happening to us and to Keats, but it certainly reveals in the most basic manner possible the source of embarrassment and— if the reader is not himself stirred, or resents the imminence of such a potential intimacy—distaste.

It also reveals the ultimate source of Keatsian stasis. Somewhat like the seaweed which 'feels all about its undulating home', the body which, in this secret aspect, is the centre of Keats's poetry, can move, but it cannot progress. Nothing can succeed the moment of 'purple riot', of joy's grape against the palate fine, but the anticlimax of deflation, the cold hillside of truth, not as the consummation of Adam's dream but of inspirational detumescence. The poetry holds off this moment, but at the cost of converting it into the felt and feeling picture of the Grecian urn. 'Bold lover, never, never canst thou kiss, Though winning near the goal—yet, do not grieve.' But the grief is there, the truest and most devastating source of the body's grief, for as Keats had read in *Troilus and Cressida*—'This is the monstruosity in love, lady, that the will is infinite and the execution confined'—confined, as all human experience knows, to Tourneur's bewitching or bewildering minute. The rapt intensity of the poetry cannot but admit this, in itself and in its implication.

Another kind of poetry seeks its strength and its renewal from shrugging off such a moment and leaving it behind. The almost hysterical revulsion Byron felt for Keat's 'p-ss-a-bed poetry' was caused not only by the objection of a man of worldly experience and breeding to the presumption of this perpetuated moment, but also because Byron's poetic vigour depends on an exactly opposite view of the process. Like the experienced womaniser Barnby in Anthony Powell's novel sequence, Byron simply did not 'notice' the phenomena of sensuality.* A gentleman was above such things. The source of awe and wonder for Keats was for Byron, as for most womanisers, matter for a joke. For him sex was not a sacredly intimate matter but a social one. Copulating—'on a table, or under it'—was a sport, an exercise of the will, an aspect of the social contest and a continuation of diplomacy by other means. Byron was no Don Juan; he preferred to leave the girl to run the seduction, and was affectionate and obliging while it lasted, but like other things sex for him was to be had, and then on to something else. For Keats, the virginal intensity of the moment meant there could be no 'something else'.

The moment of truth and of annihilation for Keats is when the intense reality of the interior vision ends, and ends in goodbye. Life goes on at the end of Keats's greatest poems, but not the poem itself: it remains enchanted, rooted on the spot. In the Nightingale Ode it is the bird who leaves the poem—

> Past the near meadows, over the still stream,
> Up the hill-side . . .

---

* Or if he did, did so with a jocular worldly ease, which draws us pleasantly into the same atmosphere. Mr Ricks gives a fine example from Canto 9 of *Don Juan*:

> Those movements, those improvements in our bodies
> Which make all bodies anxious to get out
> Of their own sand-pits to mix with a goddess,
> For such all women are at first no doubt . . .

not the poem who takes leave of the bird. Moreover the bird is itself, in a fashion very typical of Keats, both the bird of romance and legend and the bird of reality. The immortal bird is held in suspense, like the Grecian urn or the autumn evening, while the actual nightingale takes its invisible departure, in words as haunting as the magical phrases of the preceding stanza, but as significantly in contrast with them as is the cold hillside with the elfin grot of *La Belle Dame sans Merci*. The weight of the poem is in Keats's 'sole self', the centre of its breathless enchantment and the reason why it must vanish and be dissipated.

So, in the *Ode to Autumn*, weight is concentrated in the motionless female figure—'on a half-reap'd furrow sound asleep' —and disembodied in the valedictory lightness of the close. Like Mariana or the Lady of Shallot, potent figures in a later poetry of arrest, the figure of Autumn cannot move from the situation which the poem exists to fulfil. There is the poignant contrast between this helpless self-centredness, so much a part of the weight of sexuality in Keats's poetry, and the power to enter into a life that is not suspended, the nightingale, the swallows, the sparrow on the gravel. It is the familiar paradox, tragic in its diagnosis of life, though life-giving to the poem. The sexual self becomes what it sees and what it 'yearns' for, like the carved angels of St Agnes Eve, but it cannot melt with them into a further kind of life which would extinguish the breathless moment. Shelley in *The Cloud* does not in the least persuade us of entering the *being* of a cloud, as Keats enters that of a minnow, a rock-pool, a seed of corn, a billiard ball. Shelley's cloud is a metaphysical entity, and a highly successful one; and in fact it is the power of Shelley's poetry to bring us in some sense into a universal relation with things, which does not involve being imprisoned in their thingness. 'I change but I cannot die' is pure anti-Keats, as is Shelley's asexual anthropomorphism, and it is ironic that it is Shelley and not Keats who has the freedom that seems implied in the phrase 'negative capability'.

My chief quarrel with Ricks is the varied mileage he gets out of the concept of *embarrassment*, and his general, though not directly declared, thesis that everything is fine with Keats, embarrassment included, and that all works together for good, and for the consummation of those beauties which Ricks is so good at spotting and analysing. The contradictions, which among

them produce the impression of embarrassment, seem to me both
more desperate and more divine than Ricks's cheerfully brisk
treatment can allow. 'Verse likes despair,' as William Empson
observes, but Keats did not: his temper was irrepressibly
opposed to it. As I remarked at the end of my lecture, despair
was meat and drink to Tennyson, and his poetry fulfils his
nature's greatest need. Something not dissimilar is true of a
poet of our own time, Philip Larkin, who is more fully discussed
in a later chapter. Indeed, with Larkin a poetry that is arrested
and powerless to move contains a subtle joke against itself, a
rich consciousness of its own despondency. It makes fun of the
situation and the stance which it requires in order to function.
It is thus a very *intime* poetry, as Keats's so singularly and
completely is not. Keats himself had a gift for intimacy of the
most joyous kind, which his letters reflect, and Ricks demonstrates its details with warmth and perception. But *embarrassment* is the point which he takes up—rightly as it seems to me
—and embarrassment does not arise from intimacy but from its
opposite, from our being drawn into a relationship of the closest
kind which yet is *not* intimate.

In his poetry Keats's imagination can only come close to us
like another body in the dark (one of the raptest day-dreams in
Endymion is about just this). His attempts at public intimacy
and 'to write fine things that cannot be laughed at in any way'
produce *The Cap and Bells*, endearing and jocose, and with
delightful things in it, but not great Keats. Yet when the
vulgarity in it stops digging us in the ribs and becomes breathless, virginal, and unaware of us—that is Keats at his greatest.
The daily and social Keats was aware of this vulnerable and
virginal self—his 'smoakeability' as he called it; but to destroy
it in himself would have been the end of him as a poet, and this
also he must have had an inkling of. The idea of serving on
board an Indiaman shows, among other things, a readiness to
part company with his genius, to undergo a fundamental change
of personality.

The rich social and intellectual ferment of Keats's London
was the society that produced Dickens, and Keats moved and
was happy in circles that were to give Dickens his best things.
Dickens, too, has something virginal about him—the young
girls of his imagination are nested there, as Keats describes how
young girls he had seen lived in his own consciousness without

knowing it. But the sharp adroit young Dickens could keep things in their proper compartments, and that was to make him instantly popular with all classes, while Keats set so many teeth on edge. Keats's imagination put everything helplessly together —Dryads and 'real women', Poussins and perfume bottles, statues and stays, perspiration and sweat, the feel of feeling it and the feel of not to feel it. He shares with Dickens the fascination with sexual purity and gentility as enhancements of sexual daydream—these are nineteenth-century attitudes of a common kind, just as Keats's nudes, like Etty's, seem to have stepped out of some interesting underclothing, and are naked in the titillating sense which D. H. Lawrence couldn't abide. So much the worse for D. H. Lawrence would be my reaction, but Ricks feels one has got to make much more of an effort than that, and that sex in Keats must not be just enjoyed but must be made conformable with the best modern practice. He goes about this in two ways, and both, I think, denature—even neuter—the poems' life.

The first is to suggest that Keats knew quite well what he was at. Ricks remarks, as if to give the gravity of the charge its full weight, that 'the focus for a great deal of the sense that Keats is sexually perturbing is the accusation that there is something voyeuristic about his art'; but he then ingeniously implies that this was deliberate, that Keats himself, like a fairground operator, was setting up the mechanism to draw the crowds to see what the butler saw. He does this by scoring off *The British Critic*, which in June 1818 reproved Keats for his Pan, 'whom he represents rather indecorously, as a god

> Who loves to see the hamadryads *dress*.'

Ricks points out that this all-too-British critic should have been watching his own voyeuristic tendencies before making this objection, and intensifying it with italics, for the lines in fact go

> Who lov'st to see the hamadryads dress
> Their ruffled locks . . .

Nevertheless Ricks claims—and here he shows his hand—that *The British Critic* was not altogether wrong. 'With cunning humour and decorum Keats did intimate a glimpse of nakedness before rounding the corner into the perfectly proper thing'. There is no doubt about the glimpse of nakedness, as so often in Keats, but 'cunning humour and decorum' seems to me to take us about as far from the truth of the poetry as it is possible to go. Ricks brings to the *effects* of Keats's words—'sluicy', 'gummy', 'ooz'd' ('the ooze-born Goddess' of *Endymion*)—the same freshness and excitement of perception as he brought to the characteristic Miltonic and Tennysonian vocabularies, but he never faces the issue of conscious intention.

Of course *curiosa felicitas* in all great poetry must be something less than deliberate: it happens, it arrives—but the way it arrives is of such importance in Keats because it is one with the nature of his vision, and that cannot be *shared* with us, as in Milton or Tennyson it can, at the level of intellectual sophistication and well-taken reference. If we are with Keats we are with him in his raptly devotional physical perceptions, and these are encapsulated at the moment of experience; they are not and never can be viable throughout the range of our reasoning and critical awareness, which is why *Endymion* and *Hyperion* cannot progress into the abstract sphere of argument and meaning, and why Keats's greatest poems are 'left behind', as it were, when other kinds of consciousness and response take over.

For the second way in which Ricks seeks to save all appearances in Keats is to ignore what I would call tragic, in the big sense, because ultimately divided. He smooths over all the difficulties, and suggests this is what we can do and should do, both with Keats and in life. To put it at the crudest, Ricks implies that Keats peers and sniggers *with* us, at what the butler saw, and that this is desirable. It certainly dissolves embarrassment. Pope and Boucher snigger with us, in their elegant way, and whatever else it may be the effect is not embarrassing. For the essence of embarrassment is the perception that the other person is not with you in your own perceptions. And this is precisely what Keats cannot be: for his poetry confines him to the adorational moment, while we are free to speculate, to wonder, to steal covert glances, even to snigger not *with* but *at* him, in any and every way. This divine height of vulnerability is the real source of embarrassment, for vulnerability is always embarrassing to the onlooker who, because he sees it in another, cannot feel it in himself.

Ricks should have sub-titled his book: 'How not to feel embarrassment when reading Keats', which is the equivalent of saying 'How not to have the real Keatsian experience'. He suggests we should learn to overcome all such feelings, to rise above the sense of being 'located elsewhere' and join Keats in the experience of embarrassment as a kind of social and moral therapy. The question still remains: we may be meeting Keats but is he meeting us? However accurate Ricks's sense of the Keatsian, he cannot persuade Keats to join in. Here is an example.

> One sigh of real breath—one gentle squeeze,
> Warm as a dove's nest among summer trees,
> And warm with dew at ooze from living blood!

Ricks says:

> I think it not right for the modern editor to annotate the last line—'an elegant periphrasis for the Indian maid's perspiration'. If I wished to be elegantly periphrastical in a lady's company I do not think I should speak of anything about her as 'at ooze'. The teasing quality of Keats's periphrasis or euphemism is its strange combination of an encompassing indirectness with a directness which is indeflectible.

This is surely a crucial summation, but I cannot resist quoting further:

> John Bayley said of the lines: 'The words are most real, embarrassingly real perhaps, when fantasy is most apparent'. A pity that 'perhaps' flinches from the truth which it needed to be importunate about. But certainly much of the case for Keats is the case for a proper embarrassment and a proper fantasy, not kept on a tight rein but on a rein nevertheless.

I hope the grapes are not sour, but after so much happy perspicuity in Christopher Ricks I find that conclusion deeply discouraging. How in the world can Keatsian fantasy be kept on a rein, by himself or anyone else? How—after we have been Madeline and Porphyro looking at Madeline—can we ration our mixture of sensations when we turn round, as we cannot help doing, and watch Keats devouring them with the eyes of his language? No doubt Keats's ardent intensities are of a kind that 'makes for life', as Dr Leavis would say, and Ricks, like myself, has probably spent many hours trying to persuade undergraduates that *The Eve of St Agnes* is not the 'escapist' poem they sometimes feel safe in calling it. But enjoyment in

Keats and of Keats is worlds away from the brisk enlightenment
of the sex clinic. If Keats had married Fanny he would no doubt
soon have given up watching her undress, as he watched
Madeline, but then he would not be the same person, or the
same poet. He would have left the chamber of Maiden Thought,
and its characteristic creations, for good and all. It is we who
can come back there as readers: he could not have done so as a
poet. Sex in Keats is not—as Ricks seems to imply—good training for being a husband and father. Those roles may come later,
but this poetry of sex will know nothing of them: it will have
been left behind.

Keats knew all this. He wanted to be happy and to live; he
had the gift for life and happiness. He had humour. (There are
moments when he might have compared Ricks to the gentleman
he met at the Elgin Marbles who said—'I believe, Mr Keats,
we may admire these works safely'.) He wrote that 'the genius
of poetry must work out its own salvation in a man'. But the
intensities of his own poetry have nothing to do with all this.
In its rapt self it does not meet us, as his letters meet us and
his friends. There will always be the division, which we could
not do without, between this happy intercourse with Keats and
our distance from him when he is in the grip of his sensual
magic. With Wordsworth we gravely confabulate; with Byron
we join in an amiable antagonism on the 'I know you know I
know' basis; but our relation with Keats is more radically
divided. Would Ricks really wish it otherwise? Doesn't he
ignore the crucial fact about the voyeur, as he ignores the real
crux of Keatsian embarrassment? In this poetry we want no one
else to be there, not even the author, and after our first 'bodily
intuition' of it, embarrassment begins with our sense of the
senses in which he *is* there. And long live this embarrassment!
It is a richly human aspect of this art, but it does not deserve
to be given a civic function and set to work for the community.

Literature recently has taken to embarrassing us, or trying
to, in the interests of just such a social therapy. But the intention
to shock, disturb, or make uncomfortable—as in the 'theatre of
embarrassment'—is a wholly different process, and indicates
quite a different commerce between author and reader. How
often and how tediously today can we see the would-be embar-
rasser working on us, and hoping for our blushes, or discomfort,
our capitulation in yearning or shame. Keats is not trying to

embarrass us: on the contrary we are embarrassed by his lack of any such intention, by the fact that he is so 'unmisgiving', and out of this flows our real intuitive sympathy—and humility too, one hopes.

Ricks takes up from my lecture Leigh Hunt's suggestive word, and uses it often. But he still seems unaware, as he quotes Sartre on viscosity and Beckett on oral sex in public, of the confusion he has created by his failure to define. Keats's distance in his poetry from Beckett and Sartre, as from Dryden and Byron, is as wide as could be, for Keats is not aware of the problem as they are, and has none of their calm satisfaction in dealing coolly with warm subjects. As I have already said of Pope and Boucher, none of these artists can genuinely embarrass us, because they are so well aware of the possibility of doing so. But Ricks, though he stresses the difference between Keats and these others ('Keats is one of the very few erotic poets who come at embarrassment from a different angle of necessity; from the wish to pass directly through—not to bypass . . . the hotly disconcerting, the potentially ludicrous'), steadily refuses to grasp that his term can rightly apply only to a process that is accidental. Keats cannot have had the 'wish' to 'come at' embarrassment, because if he had he would not have succeeded, and his poetry would not have succeeded either. The majesty of his 'ooze-born Goddess' depends on the sublime innocence in that reverential epithet, an innocence which in Keats's world of the poetic imagination can never become experience. 'Really, without joking, chaste weather . . .' However touching, however engaging, Keats's fellowship in sexual knowingness could not touch his imagination's virginity. There it must always have been that 'Lord Byron describes what he sees, I describe what I imagine'.

Like most of Keats's recent critics Ricks is really seeking, though by unusual means, to bestow a gloss of unity and respectability—the kind of respectability which goes with the moral climate of our time. He has brought his own sorts of perceptive emphasis to the crucial question, as Leavis called it, of 'the relation between Keats's sensuousness and his serious-ness', which might be more exactly defined as the relation be-tween sexual excitement, with its own rapt craftsmanship, and a controlling intellectual self-consciousness. Keats's intelligence knew all about the excitement, and sought increasingly to control it; but his intelligence could not be 'unmisgiving' in the way his excitement could be, and was. What is moving, and truly Keatsian, is the gap between them. All Christopher Ricks's understanding and humanity cannot close it. Indeed, derision takes more cognisance of it than sympathy: the *Quarterly Review* had more respect for this reality of Keats's poetry than Ricks has.

CHAPTER II

1. The Self as Available Reality

'Poetry', said Thoreau, 'is a piece of very private history, which unostentatiously lets us into the secret of a man's life.' This could only have been said by an American, at once the orphan and victim of Romanticism. But in modern poetry to let us in unostentatiously usually means to be confiding; as Wordsworth and Byron in their different ways were, as Keats was not. That Keats's poetry is at once close to us and separated from us is an aspect of its stasis. 'Poetry', said R. P. Blackmur, 'not only expresses the matter in hand but adds to the stock of available reality', a comment that came as something of a revelation to the young John Berryman ('I was never altogether the same man after that'). Reality for the modern poet becomes more and more a question of the ways in which the poet reveals himself, of the idiom he finds to do so.

The relation with us of much of the best contemporary poetry is that of a kind of deadpan drama, as in Keats it is a drama of arrest. It reveals but does not confide: the divisions remain absolute. Keats, as we have seen, did not will the arrested effect: and so the devotional stasis of his great poetry seems unconscious of our scrutiny. Both stasis and scrutiny are taken for granted today by the poet who wishes to reveal without confiding: we are drawn, with him and by him, into a very complete and yet equivocal relation. Berryman has done this; so has Robert Lowell; and in England the most distinguished exponent of this kind of poetry is Philip Larkin, about whom in this chapter I shall have most to say.

To confide simply, and in a spirit of unity, is much commoner in contemporary poetry; also easier, usually less effective. Elizabeth Bishop's famous poem *Fish*, for example, seems to me on re-reading to have lost all its power, perhaps because it only *seems* to be concentrating with such meticulousness on the phenomenon of the fish: it really turns out to be both confiding

and self-justifying, involuntarily enclosing the poet herself.
The same may be true even of such a typical poem of Wallace
Stevens's final period as *The Planet on the Table*. Stevens himself
has defined the impression such a poem makes: it is of the poet
in it becoming 'too exactly himself', and one can turn his own
words against Stevens, as against a very different kind of cult
poet, Sylvia Plath.

Lowell and Berryman seem to be themselves in this sense,
but in fact they are not. An air of abandon is with these poets a
device which widens their poetic autobiographies into what
Berryman calls 'imperial sway', transporting a sprawl of
contingency as far as possible from the actuality of a 'case'.
The medium gives the message an authority and clarity which
leaves no room for further speculation, no room for 'chatter
about Harriet' in the old sense, or for its contemporary equivalent, the avid curiosity about the suicide of a Sylvia Plath, and
about her poems as part of its myth. Berryman's personal case
was as singular and desperate as hers, his suicide even more
spectacular, but this does not leak into his art, whose convention
succeeds in rejecting any appeal to such things. In spite of all
the seeming loose ends of talk, the name-dropping and the facts
thrown out, this poetry gives us neither need nor excuse to
establish details of when, why, where, with whom. 'I perfect
my metres', writes Berryman, 'until no mosquito can get
through'.

The specification for this is 'the construction of a world
rather than the reliance upon one existent', as Berryman wrote
in an article in *Shenandoah*. The originality of Lowell and
Berryman is to have taken the modern subject, the self, and
to have formalised it into the patterns and the themes of pre-
Romantic poetry, as if it were a subject like the Fall of Man or
the Progress of the Soul. So formal an emphasis on contingent
being contrives to dissipate any kind of Romantic or post-
Romantic naturalness, the chatty naturalness of Wordsworth
and Coleridge in their preface and poetry, as well as the more
conventional and more wearisome prose ego of our own century,
the Thomas Wolfe or Malcolm Lowry. Of course this originality
does not come out of nothing. The formalization of the Self is
an important aspect of what Pound called 'making it new' in
poetry; and well before that, and influencing it, are the various
stylizations of the ego represented by Browning's dramatic

method, Rimbaud's '*Je suis un autre*', and Whitman's claim to a
total vicarious experience in *Song of Myself*. Yeats's Masks and
Pound's and Eliot's personae—the Tiresias figures who are the
mouthpiece for what Eliot himself called the insignificant and
personal grumble of *The Waste Land*—are only the most sophisticated versions of the stylizing process.

But the breakthrough of Lowell and Berryman is in showing
that no such evident and artificial process is needed at all. They
have shown that there are other ways for the poet to avoid being
'exactly himself'. Lowell and Berryman are so present to us in
their poetry that the thought of their real live selves is not there
conceivable. This poetry thus creates the poet, but by an opposite
process to that in which character is usually created in a work
of imagination. We get to know Macbeth, say, or Leopold
Bloom, to the point where we enter into them and they become
part of us: like Eurydice in Rilke's poem they are bestowed *wie
hundertfacher Vorrat*, like the rain or the seasons, and their
individuality dissolves in our awareness. But these poets contrive to create themselves as entities so separate that we are—
as a condition of the formal device—not to share with them or
be any part of them. This simplest and most drastic form of
avoiding being 'exactly themselves' is also, and significantly, a
way of avoiding us, and our participation in their poetic being.

In this preface to the *Dream Songs* Berryman showed his
awareness of these matters, and exaggerated, perhaps deliberately, the convention of a formula.

> Many opinions and errors in the songs are to be referred
> not to the character Henry, still less to the author, but to the
> title of the work . . . The poem, then, whatever its wide cast
> of characters, is essentially about an imaginary character, (not
> the poet, not me) named Henry, a white American in early
> middle age . . . who has suffered irreversible loss and talks
> about himself sometimes in the first person, sometimes in the
> third, sometimes even in the second; he has a friend, never
> named, who addresses him as Mr Bones and variants thereof.

The tone of this may remind us of Eliot's own demure note on
the characters of *The Waste Land*. It is a kidding on the level
that both distracts the reader and reassures him: other writers,
back to Sterne and Pushkin, have sought to de-artificialize their
formal devices by a comparable candour or jocularity. Nor is it

wholly misleading. It is true that 'Henry' is not Berryman, in the sense for instance in which Norman Mailer in his books is Norman Mailer, but Berryman in verse. But this does not mean that he is changed or dramatized; the poem would be much more conventional if he were. All that the poem does is to confer total alienation on the actual being of Berryman, an alienation more aesthetically complete than any social alienation, and perfecting as a part of its formalism the partial and dolorous sense of that phenomenon that people suffer in actual living.

The kind of aesthetic cautery involved is even more marked in the shorter poems of Robert Lowell, from *Life Studies* onwards. But in both poets the break-through involved into the new freedom, and the new isolation, is exceedingly clear-cut. Their earlier poems, whatever their interest and promise, are at the same time muffled and over-emphatic; the matter and the manner of 'poetry' seems to impede and to falsify the utterance of the poet; and this is a sign of the originality of both Berryman and Lowell, for one cannot think of any other poets as good as they for whom the development of what seems a true voice is so important or so long postponed. Eliot as dandy in *Prufrock* is just as clear and authentic a voice as when he becomes the 'agéd eagle' or the sage; and Yeats as the dreamer of the Celtic Twilight is just as coherent as any of his later remarkings of himself, as the golden songbird of Byzantium or the 'foul old man' of the *Last Poems*. But the ambitiousness of Lowell's and Berryman's early poems, the determination to be 'great', and to write a great long poem, was for both an obstacle in the way of the form that would reveal and be the true subject, the Self.

The Quaker Graveyard in Nantucket and *Homage to Mistress Bradstreet* were big projects that would be at the same time American and traditional and impersonally objective, having both the glamour of the old and the significance of the new. Neither is truly a masterpiece, at least partly because both are so determined on that status, a pretension which awed or browbeat many readers into taking the fact for granted. Critics too: Hugh Staples has spoken of *The Quaker Graveyard* as 'a major poem of sustained brilliance which challenges comparison with the great elegies of the language'. To challenge such comparison seems indeed the purpose, and the rhetoric of both poems goes about it in an impressive and masterly way that is itself certainly an earnest of major poetic talent. But it is not poetry in the true and overwhelming sense in which mature Lowell and Berryman become, in which all suggestion of the poetical disappears into a clarity and force unknown to prose, and unhandicapped apparently by the techniques associated with verse.

This could be put in another way, not so favourable, or rather suggesting a loss as well as a gain. The willed arrest of alienation is also a form of verbal cancellation, which cuts off not only reader from poet but reader from poem. Many of Lowell's most impressive poems seem to destroy themselves in the act of creation, like a suicide caught in a camera flash the moment before hitting the ground; and this act of extinction parallels the way in which Berryman as 'Henry' removes any contact or intimacy between us while appearing to invite it so completely. Poem and subject with Lowell appear to die at the moment the words hit the paper, a word cut off by the moment of death. With Berryman the same word gives the impression of muttering itself perpetually, between an empty desk and chair.

It seems worth emphasizing again that this cutting of any bond of intimacy shows how much we have come today to take it for granted. The writer about meaninglessness, who deals in what is numb and mad, in the extreme situation, is a commonplace; but the greater the *dérèglement* he describes the closer he comes to the reader and depends on a personal relation with him. Like a drunk in a bar such an author needs his finger in our buttonhole; the further off he is from the habitual social and moral world, the more urgent is his need to share his alienation. Professor Fiedler, in *Partisan Review*, has associated Lowell with writers like Burroughs and Ginsberg, because, as he says, the young respond to the madness in him as they do towards the drugged or freaked-out mental states celebrated by their other favourites. But if this is so the young are missing the point. The world of madness they respond to has a camaraderie not essentially different from that of surfing or stock-car racing: it has the cosiness of a fashion in common. And such a togetherness is not really very far from the more conventional kinds of togetherness in American writing, for instance that of the 'poetry workshop', of the shoal poetry in which recent American schools have collectively excelled.

By contrast, *Life Studies* are not studies in living, or how to live. Exorcizing the bonds of intimacy and appeal, they achieve a manic and imperial authority, exhibiting a self which makes no distinction between the contraption of the poem and what Auden called 'the guy inside it'. When Lowell tells us in *Skunk Hour*

> I myself am hell
> Nobody's here—

we believe him not because he is telling us, but because the moment of reading seems indeed the last moment before there is nobody there; not even the poem.

> One dark night
> my Tudor Ford climbed the hill's skull,
> I watched for love-cars. Lights turned down,
> they lay together, hull to hull,
> where the graveyard shelves on the town . . .
> My mind's not right.

In this marvellously controlled and plotted poem the bald assertion—'My mind's not right'—seems neither less nor more than the fact. 'What use is my sense of humour?' asks Lowell in another of these poems. He may well ask, but he is not asking us. Every rift of these poems is loaded, but the kinds of craft or irony which form a comfortable bond between poet and reader and sustain the tone on its journey into the reader's mind, seem contrived here to fall flat on their faces. 'One dark night' echoes the first line of a famous poem by St John of the Cross, but we get no cosy usual pleasure from the recognition, because it seems to have given Lowell none to suggest it. He can make a statement which in another poet could not avoid coyness and collusion.

> My Grandfather found
> his grandchild's fogbound solitudes
> sweeter than human society.

No doubt it was so. The word 'human' ambushes us with a stare, seemingly unaware of its own charge of meaning. If it is pointed at us it manages to be unconscious of the fact as we too, for the moment, are; and this is what style means in Lowell.

It is not only a literary style. Its patrician unselfconsciousness has a solid social basis, reminding us how anxious most confiding poetry is to claim rootlessness or poverty of origins, to display a proper lack of class interest while being insistently and anxiously conscious of the impression it is making on us. Lowell has calmly founded his best poetry on an acceptance of the interest of his own social status.

Conventional self-consciousness today is not only social but linguistic. D. H. Lawrence spoke of the element of 'danger' in all new utterance, which makes us 'prick our ears like an animal in a wood at a strange sound'. It is a brilliant and economical point, and reading Lowell and Berryman instantly shows us how true it is, but unlike lesser poets they seem to be making no effort to make us 'prick our ears'. Such attempts lead to modern clichés about the 'daring' use of language. 'W. S. Merwin', writes Adrienne Rich, 'has been working more privately, profoundly and daringly than any other American poet of my generation'. Such an encomium does this good poet no service. It is the attempt to manufacture the 'element of danger' which leads to such inflationary terms. Failure to bring off a poem shows that all art is conceived in the lap of luck, but not that risks may be run by a 'daring' use of English, or that a successful poem lives dangerously on our behalf.

The language of *Life Studies* and *Dream Songs* does not seem in the least daring, only right; and it shows that a poem cannot succeed which strives to give the impression of taking risks with itself and with words. To some extent both Lowell and Berryman were compelled in their apprenticeship to be daring in this derogatory sense, since neither arrived with a style but had to search so hard for one. As Berryman wrote:

> I didn't want my next poem to be *exactly* like Yeats
> or exactly like Auden
> since in that case where the hell was *I*?
> but what instead *did* I want it to sound like?

The answer was in the labour that went into his long poem *Homage to Mistress Bradstreet*, which has an element of the conventionally 'daring' about it, but is none the less a hard intellectual exercise, embodying an idea which has clearly haunted Berryman, and which could be said to reach its final realization in the *Dream Songs*. That is, the idea of the gap between the poet as a living creature, 'a huddle of needs', sitting at a desk: and the poet as the author of his poems. Can the two ever become one? In the *Dream Songs* they could be said to do so, as near as can be accomplished. In the case of *Mistress Bradstreet* they fascinated Berryman by seeming about as far apart as they could possibly be.

> When by me in the dusk my child sits down
> I am myself. Simon, if it's that loose,
> let me wiggle it out.
> You'll get a bigger one there & bite.
> How they loft, how their sizes delight and grate.
> The proportioned spiritless poems accumulate.
> And they publish them
> Away in brutish London, for a hollow crown.

Berryman brings together his vision of the colonial mother and of the author of so much stilted and painstaking poetry, based on her reading of Quarles and Sylvester ('her favourite poets, unfortunately'). The significance of the vision is his continual awareness of the difference between the poet as a maker and as a person, a gap which the 'Henry' poems so triumphantly and remarkably ignore, making the two

> together lie at once, forever or
> so long as I happen.

There is an echo there from Dylan Thomas's most effective poem *Twenty-four Years*, which ends: 'I advance as long as forever is'. In *Mistress Bradstreet* Berryman sought to bring together the actual woman and her poems in and as a work of art: in the *Dream Songs* he seeks to unite his perishable and contingent self with the 'foreverness' of his poetry.

> . . . women, cigarettes, liquor, need need need
> until he went to pieces.
> The pieces sat up & wrote. They did not heed
> their piecedom but kept very quietly on
> among the chaos.

It is a part of the sophistication of this poetry to claim not to be dangerous but boring ('Life, friends, is boring. We must not say so . . .') and to involve us in itself not only through the presentation of life in utter disarray—divorces and neuroses and analyses, drunks and dryings-out—but through a certain implied conspiracy of worldliness with us—poet and reader are not taken in by life, they *know the score*. The word was a favourite of Robert Frost's, and Frost was himself in many ways a pioneer exponent of the complexities of the process. Frost in his verse affects to be a man of lucid and meditative homeliness: he was actually toughly, almost murderously devious; and much of the effect of his poetry is based on its subtle communication of his knowledge, flattering to the reader's worldly discernment and also inviting his appreciation of the 'score', and the performance.

Frost, like Yeats and even Eliot, was determined to be a poet in the most authoritative and worldly sense: so was Auden, so are Lowell and Berryman. For it is a paradox that the more inward poetry becomes, and the more specialized its audience, the more it seeks to make its mark by kinds of social power and sophisticated recognition. The indifference of the free democratic crowd—and where but in America would such good poetry have so small an audience?—produces a poetry of complex worldliness, determined to succeed in the only sphere in which success is possible. The public status and recognition of poets in Russia, in the smaller European countries or in Spanish America, puts them in a different class: to be a national poetic rhetorician, like Mayakovsky or Neruda, is to be in some sense naïve, to achieve power through naïveté. And not to be *taken in*, not to be thus socially and nationally innocent, is vital to the working of the poetry we are discussing.

Our last great naïve poet, Wilfred Owen, made the famous remark that his 'poetry was in the pity', and that all a poet could do in 1917 was 'to warn'. Personally Owen was something of a prig. But he found his poethood—and without the war he would not have been a real poet at all—in the hideous suffering which those at home were ignorant of, or preferred to ignore. This poetry is revolutionary, in that it directs our attention not to itself but to what it says. It may add to the stock of available reality, but the really important thing is that it 'expresses the matter in hand'. Whether or not the poetry is in the pity it is certainly not in Owen himself; there is no sense in which he is his own subject, as Rilke and Yeats and Valéry and Lowell and Berryman are. And socially he was inept as they were adroit: he could not organize the conditions under which he could become his own poet.

There is no great naïve poet with us today. Such a poet as Roethke has attempted to be one; he has not succeeded. And, going back a little, one could make the point by comparing the way war appears in Owen's poetry with the way religion appears in Eliot's. No one would question the sincerity of Eliot's religious beliefs, and yet the religion in his poetry is certainly an aspect of the worldly will: it has become himself and his poetry. A 'taken in' poet like Owen is not like this. Our relation to him is human; it resembles our relation to real people, and is for the same reason more potentially embarrassing. Lowell gives the game away when he writes that 'in the working-out of a poem I look for two things: a commanding deadly effectiveness in the arrangement, and something that breathes and pauses and grunts and is rough and unpredictable to show me the journey is honest'.

That is the voice of Frost, if he had spoken openly. We know, and the poet knows we know, how little honest the poetic art of the self can be. Which makes it all the more remarkable that Philip Larkin has contrived to make it so, or to seem so. He never spills the beans, as Lowell is doing in that statement, but he has other ways of dividing us from him by seeming to share the score with us. The example of Hardy has helped him enormously, for Hardy did not know or care about these matters, but produced private, public and occasional poems as the mood took him, a fact which makes him admirable to poets oppressed by the modern entail of the poet as self.

Larkin has emphasized his pleasure in and debt to every last and slightest piece among the great number of Hardy's poems. His own are few in number, and their tone has not changed since the publication of his second collection, *The Less Deceived* (Ophelia, we remember was 'the more deceived'). But though few, his poems enclose a large and usually featureless area of our inner and outer geography. The vocabulary of this place is in public rather limited, since it has only to convey such apprehensions as that we are not so young as we were; that life has made us and not we ourselves; that we seem to have missed our chances, if any; and that much more in life is to be endured than enjoyed. In this area, pleasure approximates to the moments when, like the nigger knocking his head against the wall, we leave off. The poems seem not so much epiphanies as intermissions, equivalents in art to such moments. If that does not sound much, it would also be true to say that they offer the most refined and ruefully accurate expression possible of a national as well as a universal area of this awareness. They are in fact very English, not sentimentally and exuberantly so, as John Betjeman's deliberately are (it is not in the least a pejorative word to use in praising *him*), and rejecting any kind of eagerness and enthusiasm in the reader. Enthusiasm is emphatically not Larkin's state of mind. His poems have the air of being very meticulously mounted and developed, as if they had spent months in the darkroom or years at the workbench in the garden shed. 'In every sense empirically true', like Larkin's young lady in the photograph album, they seem coaxed on to impassive celluloid as if to give the poetic equivalent of its dim candour; as if, too, they would accept with bleak relish the fate of its image:

> Unvariably lovely there,
> Smaller and clearer as the years go by.

This is not the image of Larkin himself but of his world. Our first impression may be that he is not included in the picture; and as we grow into his poetry it becomes clear that he is neither its centre and formal justification, as Lowell and Berryman are of theirs, nor has he the open and natural relation to it that Hardy has, or that Auden in his different way has. But though Larkin himself is not in the picture, the image of the photograph album gives an important clue to the process of arrest and suspension which determine, as it were, his identity for us.

He professes to be boring, as old photos are, and yet is absorbing, as they also are. Moreover, at one level, personality is dissolved in these poems into all our behaviours; while their verbal fastidiousness never seems to patronize the vaguely dolorous nature of humdrum self-awareness but to be its natural secretion. When Berryman tells us that life is boring he makes it a daring thing to say, as in America it indeed is, as well as the cry of a lost soul kidding on the level. For Larkin the fact is self-evident. He is too English to claim a lost soul or a peculiar wound; and his intimacy is that of the lounge bar, discreet, impersonal and occasional, as distinct from American confessional as from the convention of chat among the members of a coterie, which is Auden's elegant way of doing it.

Larkin's intimacy depends on its total suspension. When we next meet him in that lounge bar we are no further advanced in our acquaintance with him; the slate of our previous meeting has been wiped clean. However formalized our acquaintance with Lowell and Berryman may be, we do none the less receive from their poems the impression of its continuity. Larkin's poetry of arrest speaks to us in a low clear tone and is silent: the author never lets us know what happens between our meetings. He vanishes; and this in itself stimulates the imagination, as if we had met someone who intrigued us into making up things about him in default of finding out the reality. Carrying on the social metaphor we can say that a continuous poetry, however stylized our relations with its speaker, must sooner or later lead to boredom. Wordsworth and Coleridge we have with us always, like Carlos Williams or the late Berryman and Lowell. They are with us as one of the family, and very tedious their company can be.

The intensities of the poetry of arrest are all internalized; total contingency is focused by the intent gaze of the imagination. Like Lowell and Berryman, Larkin has for subject the nature of contingency itself, but unlike them he distils it into verbal essence. And for such a poetry the continuity of ordinary life, which the American poets contrive so effectively to stylize, is not a possible effect. As Larkin writes, 'Something, like nothing, happens anywhere.' But the moment of nullity must be enchanted. Keats and Tennyson are the great exponents, though involuntary ones, of such a poetry of arrest. 'He will not come', says Mariana, for the poem could not exist if he did. Perhaps he came later? Perhaps: but that is not what either a Tennyson or a Larkin poem can afford to be about. 'I choke on such nutritious images' says the poet who is turning the pages of the young lady's photograph album; and these master-images of bygone arrest, of random stillness, are the nourishment that the seeming slow growth of each poem requires.

This is worth emphasizing, because of the assumption that gives Larkin his credentials among students—and not only among them—that he is a poet of today's life styles, celebrating our common surroundings and customs. A poem such as *Here* led Betjeman to call Larkin 'the John Clare of the building estates'. This is as misleading as if, on the strength of *The Eve of St Agnes*, Keats were to be labelled the poet of social life in castles. In fact Larkin's use of his material is not for any purposes of description (though the magic life of *things* in his poems may remind us of many of Auden's) but to achieve those locked, half-concealed intensities of despair which are so much more obviously the formal basis of Berryman's art. Larkin's peculiar vision alienates his people and places precisely by gazing at them so hard when they aren't looking. By surrendering everything at the end of the poem to its own habitual and continuous existence, which the poem has interrupted, he endows that existence with a terrifying poignancy. Many of his poems take such a moment as that in which Keats's lovers on St Agnes Eve 'fled away into the storm'. They are starting their honeymoon, or being looked at in a snap of

> . . . a past that no one now can share
> No matter whose your future . . .

—but there can be no progress into what Wordsworth called 'the world which is the world of all of us'. It is by seeing that world in the mirror that the poet gives us such dazzling glimpses of it.

There is thus a droll sense in which his poems, like the poster girl of *Sunny Prestatyn*, whose image on a railway advertisement is rapidly defaced by the public, and who was therefore literally 'too good for this life', really are too good for it. They too are not 'earthed', cannot mingle with living as the poetry of progression can; they cannot unbend into verbosity or miscalculation, or extend into explanations. Larkin makes us perceive more clearly than the two American poets that poetry has survived and extended its range at the cost of masterly and absolute kinds of aesthetic alienation, which the lucidity and small scale of Larkin shows up. In many of his poems Larkin is concerned with compassion or love or the survival of what is human and traditional, but though these poems (*Church Going, An Arundel Tomb, To the Sea* and others) are as perfect as any, they do not 'come out' well when mounted like photos in a permanent collection, and when we turn back to pages in search of them.

They lack the inner drama, the unease of mirror intimacy, to which we become so addicted in Larkin, and which can no more be lived with on humdrum daily terms than our relation with the Americans can be. It is indeed possible to feel that the poet is doing it deliberately—giving a fine performance on the Larkin—while his real fans wait for the proper fix, the true flavour by which they know him and for which they have come out of themselves. It is rather significant that right and proper sentiments in Larkin are not in the least embarrassing because of the strength of the conspiracy between poet and reader, which appraises with secret equanimity. We might compare the evidently 'straight' sentiments of Berryman:

> Working & children & pals are the point of the thing,
> for the grand sea awaits us, which will then us toss
> & endlessly us undo.

or

> We will all die, & the evidence
> is: Nothing after that.
> Honey, we don't rejoin.
> The thing meanwhile, I suppose, is to be courageous & kind.

The poetry is not trying to impress us with its humanity: we know, and it knows we know, that it hasn't any. And the queer paradox is that for this very reason we can take these poets very seriously at bottom, because none of us—in this queer aesthetic relation—are *taken in*, even by what the poetry is saying. The deepest intimacy, far deeper than anything achievable in normal living, could be said to be involved in this relation, in which we can never seem to feel the discomfort of misunderstanding, inadvertence, or listening to the poet laying down the law. If he lays it down we understand why, and wait, even though the poem may end in the process, as does *To the Sea* in Larkin's latest collection (1974), *High Windows*.

> If the worst
> Of flawless weather is our falling short,
> It may be that through habit these do best,
> Coming to water clumsily undressed
> Yearly; teaching their children by a sort
> Of clowning; helping the old, too, as they ought.

Yes, there is that too: but what matters is our relation with the poet, not his comments on decent seaside pieties. The real truth of their decency is made possible by the aesthetic relation. The same thing happens in Larkin's novel, *A Girl in Winter*, one of the finest and best sustained prose poems in the language. One of the glimpses through its window is of a woman deprived of other human choice by having to look after a bedridden mother; while an extended genre piece, the funniest and most moving in the book, describes taking a sufferer to the dentist. It is the voyeur who sees these things, and the mirror-like confrontation, in the very act of keeping its back turned on life, shows us almost everything about how life is actually got through.

This conspiracy extends, I would feel, even to poems like *The Building* and *The Old Fools* which are deliberately massive performances—in the case of *The Building* verging on the allegorical—which are seemingly designed to inculcate the utmost gloom and despondency about the nature of living itself. If, like Leopardi, these poems were lucidly mellifluous musings on the horror and the hopelessness of our being here at all, their effect would be rather different—more monotonous —and though not necessarily more impersonal (Leopardi is certainly not that) much less intimately and dramatically absorbing.

In practice, however, our relation with Larkin is much too close, even cosy, for the poems to be in any sense horrifying or —as Clive James called *The Building*—'a real chiller'. Larkin would not tell us, as Berryman does, that these poems 'are meant to terrify and comfort', but as Clive James also percep-tively observed, they cannot help 'becoming part of life, not death'. More than that, our conspiracy with Larkin seems to imply that neither poet nor reader is taken in about the motives that underlie the fashioning of such poems and our reception of them. The clarity of observation, whether it is about what underpins our moral habit, as in *To the Sea*, or what speaks to us all, as we come to 'that vague age that claims the end of choice', is only made possible because we are not *there* but elsewhere, in fact in the lucid world of Larkinian art.

2. The Importance of Elsewhere

This central canon of the Larkinian aesthetic is explored in the wry poem *The Importance of Elsewhere*, in which the poet finds himself away from home, but in a place very like home. In that free world we and he are in a foreign country, ticket-of-leave men, licensed to see without taking part. The insistent and utter familiarity of what we are shown ('That this is a real girl in a real place,/In every sense empirically true!') becomes here a place not only of freedom but one where the familiar can be seen for the first time. In the poetry of progression we are, at least by convention, in our daily lives (and never more than when some big deployment of myth or symbolism is going on) but in the Larkinian suspension we are abroad, always knowing our proper place to be back home, where 'no elsewhere underwrites my existence'. The very practicality and intimacy of Larkin's verse, its almost uncannily reasonable and natural tone, as when he comments on our need for a job, 'the toad work'—

> Give me your arm, old toad;
> Help me down Cemetery Road

—this is achieved by our not being where work and seaside holidays really are. His tone puts us effortlessly in the favoured place in which an elsewhere underwrites us, the elsewhere of ordinariness he is apparently talking about.

A triptych poem in *High Windows* called *Livings* shows his skill at displaying ways of living as an elsewhere; and the last line of *To the Sea*—'helping the old, too, as they ought'— reveals the inwardness of the humour on which the tone is based. For to put it in an Irishism, in Larkin the characteristics of the poetry of arrest have moved a stage further: it is our mutual awareness of what such a poetry is that both makes the joke and makes the poem moving. Of course they ought to help the old, but the tone of the poem acknowledges that the process must take place 'elsewhere'. Larkin manages to get as much relish into good counsel as other poets have got into spiteful satire, and because the poet's humanity is in this humour one does not insult his poetry with clichés about 'compassion', any more than one would emphasize the pity in Owen's finest and most withdrawn poems, like *The Send-Off*.

> So, secretly, like wrongs hushed-up, they went:
> They were not ours:
> We never heard to which front these were sent . . .

Simple messages in Larkin strike home because they are withdrawn so far from what they speak of, not in any oracular sense, but by the sardonic bleakness of their admission that they have understood the needs of life by avoiding them. 'Self's the man', as another poem's title tells us, and it is self that gives the Larkin attitude to life its shrewd envy and its dispassionate humility. It is instructive to compare *For the Union Dead* with *Going, Going* and *Homage to a Government*, the two 'O tempora O mores' lament poems from *High Windows*; for though the English poet is far more subdued and oblique in tone, we may have the same feeling that things have not come out quite right, that none of these poems has the real thrust that its bitterness calls for and seems to vouchsafe. Both Lowell and Larkin are making a statement about society which does not involve their own self-preoccupations; in *For the Union Dead*, the gap between Lowell's sense of himself and his sense of America's past and present has to be resolved in the speciously violent exclamation of the last stanza—'A savage servility / slides by on grease'—and Larkin's vision of modern England lacks the authority of his own 'elsewhere', his own nuances of regrets and rejections.

His humour, too, in these two poems is merely deft, ornamenting without enriching, whereas in *The Whitsun Weddings* it triumphantly determines the whole complex movement of the poem.

> Just long enough to settle hats and say
> I *nearly died*,
> A dozen marriages got under way.

To find himself aboard a trainful of just-married brides would certainly have inspired Hardy, but to something more approaching the grim fun of folklore. Larkin's response is the more subtle for being more separated, in the modern manner, and for its discreetly humorous emphasis on the anomaly of his own position, for 'got under way' is a parody of what the Larkinian moment cannot do. The point is explored and emphasized in the marvellous close.

> . . . it was nearly done, this frail
> Travelling coincidence; and what it held
> Stood ready to be loosed with all the power
> That being changed can give. We slowed again,
> And as the tightened brakes took hold, there swelled
> A sense of falling, like an arrow-shower
> Sent out of sight, somewhere becoming rain.

'All the power that being changed can give . . .': the power of the poem—and the poet knows it—is in the function of *not* being changed. The tension between the standing ready to be loosed, and the not being, is poignantly and discreetly hilarious, a kind of humour that exactly goes with the old-fashioned aura of magic and sentiment, just as it does in those miniature masterpieces of Hardy like *The Parasol* and *The Self-Unseeing*. The difference is in the sad comedy exploited by the poetry of arrest: for what Keats called the 'swelling into reality' goes on out of sight, where the rain it raineth every day, and this poetry would be dissolved if it followed. The romantic beauty of those last images is also packed with a dense and down-to-earth suggestiveness of sex and longing, a Shakespearean inwardness printed in every detail.

Larkin proclaims how much he learnt from Hardy, his great love, but Hardy does not limn in the mirror, or does not seem to. His verse is more casually attached to the world than Larkin's can afford to be, and its banality is never so meticulous, so advertently adroit. It has the dilution and the garrulity of unselfconsciousness, that goes with the poetry of progression. And in this furthest sophistication of the poetry of arrest the poet must not only be a voyeur but must exploit the fact of being one. Keats, in *The Eve of St Agnes*, is far too devoutly intent to be aware of his voyeur status: Larkin quietly accepts it and the refinements he brings to it, which are as important as they are effaced. They appear at their lengthiest and most elaborate in that masterpiece, *A Girl in Winter*. We never discover what country Katherine, its foreign heroine, comes from; the few clues about her background are almost literally glimpses through a window. In a most ingenious sense we see the action doubly as a voyeur, regarding the foreigner Katherine, who lives 'elsewhere', while simultaneously seeing her English experiences with her, as a strange and amusing pattern that is not her 'real life'. This may sound tiresomely theoretical, and in a *nouveau roman* it would certainly be so; but in Larkinian fashion it is done with so much blandness and ease, and so much deadpan social comedy, that it seems as if nothing at all unusual were taking place. Almost everything comparable, like the poetic novels of Virginia Woolf and Stevie Smith, seems by contrast shrilly opaque and self-absorbed.

Profoundly original as it is, *A Girl in Winter* seems not only tranquilly unconcerned with experiment and technique but can also be devoured like a real novel, with total engrossment in what is going to happen. Many of the poems, too, have this 'nutritious' richness of the best fiction, and it is a singular thing that both in *A Girl in Winter*, and in such poems as *To the Sea* and *The Whitsun Weddings*, the author contrives to make humdrum habitual displays of niceness, pleasantness and goodness seem as completely fascinating and absorbing as the intrigue and wickedness which the normal novel concocts to entertain us, and to justify itself. This rare and remarkable ability of Larkin is partly made possible by the characteristics of the poetry of arrest—happiness is a still life, and *vice versa*, as the Old Fools have cause to know—

> The blown bush at the window, or the sun's
> Faint friendliness on the wall some lonely
> Rain-ceased midsummer evening. That is where they live:
> Not here and now, but where all happened once.
>   This is why they give
>
> An air of baffled absence, trying to be there
> Yet being here . . .

'Elsewhere' is all, certainly, that underwrites the existence of the old. And our elsewhere, in this context, may be the depth of being that shines in Larkin's Vermeer interiors, still life hallowing the normal, and increasing the terrible sense of unending disintegration.

> At death, you break up: the bits that were you
> Start speeding away from each other for ever
> With no one to see. It's only oblivion, true:
> We had it before . . .

And yet, all formalistic questions put by, it should simply be recognized that Larkin is good on goodness because his personality, which appears in his poetry as uncompromisingly as Hardy's in his, is totally sympathetic. That it is so may be owing to the secret humour of his own self-perception and to the peculiarities of his reticence, which, at moments as sudden as they are unemphatic, turns out to be not reticence at all.

> Parting, after about five
> Rehearsals, was an agreement
> That I was too selfish, withdrawn,
> And easily bored to love.
> Well, useful to get that learnt . . .

Thus the disclosure of *Wild Oats*; and a related point is made
less parenthetically in *Dockery and Son*.

> Dockery, now:
> Only nineteen, he must have taken stock
> Of what he wanted, and been capable
> Of . . . No, that's not the difference: rather, how
>
> Convinced he was he should be added to!
> Why did he think adding meant increase?
> To me it was dilution. Where do these
> Innate assumptions come from? Not from what
> We think truest, or most want to do:
> Those warp tight-shut, like doors. They're more a style
> Our lives bring with them: habit for a while,
> Suddenly they harden into all we've got
>
> And how we got it . . .

These are disclosures, not confidences, and what they disclose
is not an attempt at intimacy. Because his voice is usually so
low, Larkin is in a sense more elusive than either Lowell or
Berryman, although at such moments we seem far closer to him
than we ever are to either of them. And the next time we meet
him in the bar his personality may seem to have changed, which
theirs never do. The new Larkin is much less pondering:
suddenly delphic, even brutally facetious.

> Sexual intercourse began
> In nineteen sixty-three
> (Which was rather late for me)—
> Between the end of the *Chatterley* ban
> And the Beatles' first LP.

or

> When I see a couple of kids
> And guess he's fucking her and she's
> Taking pills or wearing a diaphragm,
> I know this is paradise . . .

Yet our sense of him is not shaken—we know it is the same man,
a plain and natural self in whatever guise he appears. So indeed
it is, and yet—as Larkin's early poems show—such a self has

been stabilized and clarified in and by poetry, just as Lowell's and Berryman's have been. In Larkin's first collection of poems, *The North Ship*, there is a high degree of competence and of effective Yeatsian usage, but no Larkin at all. The parallel with the more prolonged non-arrival in their work of Lowell and Berryman is obvious; and so is the difference between all three poets and their predecessors in this respect. Difficult not to conclude that the dynamic of today's best poetry is a setting up in it of the poet, which, when accomplished, constitutes an aesthetic goal. The poet has arrived in our midst, his newness defined by the personal reality of the self his art has brought to us.

Once *made* and not involuntarily *defined* (as a man too exactly himself), there can be no question today of any Yeatsian 'remaking'. Critics have remarked on the absence of development, in any traditional sense, in Larkin's poetry, and have usually concluded—surely rightly—that the notion is irrelevant to his achievement. Allowing for a more prolonged period of search and experiment, the same is true of Berryman and probably of Lowell too. 'Development' in their case would also be towards a particular sort of self-creation which holds off the immense and complex meaninglessness of the modern world by a self-creation outside it, adding to its reality but also separating itself from the rest of the sum. In this sense the work of all three poets could be seen as an admission of defeat by the world and a withdrawal from it, a withdrawal from the imperial confidence of Yeats who not only 'remade himself', but along the same lines and for the same reasons turned all about him into a legend, friends, religion, politics, even the cultural policies of the new Irish free state; while Auden, too, made a myth out of the climate of the thirties which had a real and potent poetic authority.

Yeats's famous epigram—'Out of the quarrel with others we make rhetoric: out of the quarrel with ourselves we make poetry' —is an accurate enough humanization of his formal method: the quarrel may be a convenience and a convention but it is certainly there in the rhetoric of his art. But this kind of artificial division would be unthinkable for Larkin and for the American poets; division with them is between the self they discover and the world they implicitly reject in so doing. Anything as theatrical as a quarrel with the self that the poetry has found would be unthinkable; and for Larkin, one feels, would constitute a kind of pretentiousness which by implication he dislikes in Yeats. 'I spent three years', he tells us in the preface to *The North Ship*, 'trying to write like Yeats, not because I liked his personality or understood his ideas but out of infatuation with his music'. In Yeats's poem *The Road at My Door*, the meeting with soldiers in the civil war sends him off into a quarrel with himself about what he could be or might have been.

> I count those feathered balls of soot
> The moor-hen guides upon the stream
> To silence the envy in my thought;
> And turn towards my chamber, caught
> In the cold snows of a dream.

Musical, and moving; though Larkin would probably have muttered 'come off it'. In our time we do not really think we could have been different from what we are, and Yeats's nostalgia for the notion of the complete man—'soldier, scholar, horseman'—seems not so much self-deception as a kind of play-acting to catch hold of a poem. But such play-acting implies a confidence in the part, in the audience, and the theatre, which does not exist today. Larkin's version of Yeats's mood has all the determinism, the bleak and behavioural acceptance of what has become of one, which in a curious way, and allowing for the difference in idiom, is equally marked in both Lowell and Berryman. Arrival at oneself for these poets is also—or is made to seem to be—a kind of Calvinistic predestination, a state that is part aesthetic grace and part human desperation, in which all other doors have indeed been 'warped tight-shut'.

> . . . though our element is time,
> We are not suited to the long perspectives
> Open at each instant of our lives.
> They link us to our losses . . .

Yeats's dream is of choice, a possible alternative heroism; Larkin is haunted by the possibilities that he knows—being himself now in the poetry—could never have materialized. Berryman and Lowell convey much more dramatically a similar sense of fate, the inescapable burden of being formed by parents and by early traumas: the suicide of Berryman's father, and his acquisition from a stepfather of a second name and identity. As with so much else, the American sense of destiny is far more spectacular than the British one, where 'Something, like nothing, happens anywhere', and yet it must impress us that the goal of all three poets should be formed by this awareness. The personal destiny makes a subject, a legend, which the outer world is no longer capable of affording. They talk about the outer world, but their poetic centre is the shape of their own lives. To make yourself in poetry is indeed a toy, a dream and a rest, both confirming your determined status and liberating you from it. Yet this kind of liberation is a far cry from the jaunty rationalization of Auden in *New Year Letter*, which belongs to a more sanguine epoch of Freudian optimism, creating its own kinds of will and power.

> Suppose we love, not friends or wives
> But certain patterns in our lives,
> Effects that take the cause's name,
> Love cannot part them all the same.

Larkin has no such faith. Love may be no less real to him for being a topic of doleful trench humour (we may remember the ambiguity in *Wild Oats*—'That I was too selfish, withdrawn, / And easily bored to love'—the verb subduedly enclosing both loving and being loved) but Larkinian truth can only be arrived at through the medium of self-mockery. The ways of doing this are subtle, so much so that we cannot doubt the genuineness of the process—genuine, that is, in terms of art—whereas most poets who try this difficult feat, like Housman, give an impression only of showing off. What makes Larkin seem so genuine is the impeccable quality and deadpan timing of his performance —his feint of shying away from the spectre of sexual inadequacy in *Dockery and Son* (...'He must have taken stock / Of what he wanted, and been capable / Of ... No, that's not the difference: rather', etc.) is a good example, and better still is the comic business of a superlative poem in *High Windows* called *Sympathy in White Major*. The poet speaks of making for himself a Lucullan gin and tonic, and then

> I lift the lot in private pledge:
> *He devoted his life to others.*

He creates a cliché of himself as 'a brick, a trump, a proper sport', feigning that the poems he writes for others put him in the same class as those worthies whose labours on behalf of cricket club or Oddfellows' Union are celebrated in fulsome speeches—and concludes:

> *Here's to the whitest man I know—*
> Though white is not my favourite colour.

The equation of poet with do-gooder has the usual Larkinian absurdity, but is not all absurd: the image of such a man is one of the losses which the 'long perspectives' reveal and Larkin's love of English life makes the fantasy of belonging to it through the exercise of his art not only absurd but poignant. But the real thrust of the poem is in the second of its three stanzas.

> While other people wore like clothes
> The human beings in their days
> I set myself to bring to those
> Who thought I could the lost displays;
> It didn't work for them or me,
> But all concerned were nearer thus
> (Or so we thought) to all the fuss
> Than if we'd missed it separately.

Others use or 'wear' their fellows through being a part of them, members of one body. Larkin, the benefactor, brings art to those not so wholly involved in this process ('the lost displays' suggests not only a recreation of something gone or going but of something more fundamentally adrift—the lost and abandoned). Art fails both its audience and dispenser, but—the crucial point—makes both feel closer to life. It is assumed that the reader too 'misses' life—'all the fuss'—but to feel the writer has missed it, and turned the process into art, produces a species of solidarity and consolation.

This is a lame rendering of one of Larkin's most concentrated and pellucid poetic sentences, but the business of the poem is so complex, so terse and so funny that it seems worth while to labour the point in the interest of our understanding of how the technique works. Several of the most successful *Dream Songs* have the same power of pulling us instantly into the quick world of the poem while not being poetic at us, leaving us breathless with the speech and sureness of the performance. Like Berryman's, Larkin's vocabulary can use words that are almost overwhelmingly poetic and *bien trouvé* (*'rain-ceased'*, *'sun-*

comprehending', *'immensements'*) while giving no impression of gusto or satisfaction in them—the kind we too often feel in Yeats's choice of what he called 'the right word that is also the surprising word'. Larkinian eloquence does not seem craftily combined with direct or slangy speech but a natural part of it, and such a rich ease is only found in the greatest performers—is in fact Shakespearean. Larkin's English shows how much life there still is in the old thing: it is both less self-conscious and more three-dimensional than the American language, more capable, above all, of kinds of intensely satisfying accuracy, low-key phrases that exactly define an indeterminate state. Interestingly, one of the comparative failures in performance is a burlesque about 'Jake Balokowsky,' a young academic at an American university, the imaginary future biographer of Larkin, in which the American idiom does not sound quite right by Larkinian standards, and the self-mockery is too much on parade to be revealing.

It is, finally, an index of what we get out of this poetry that if some kind of quick or unexpected peep into the interior is lacking, the poem can remain too much a performance. 'Now you see me, now you don't', with its suggestion of pier sideshows and baggy holiday trousers, would be a not inappropriate epigraph. A comparison with the straightforwardness of Hardy is again apposite; for his confrontation in a poem with unborn pauper child, or journeying boy at midnight on the Great Western, is absolute: nothing is needed from inside the poet to complete the picture. A poem from Larkin's *The Less Deceived* takes an account from Mayhew's study of Victorian London of a child prostitute who was drugged and raped to fit her for the profession. *Deceptions* contrasts her experience with that of her seducer.

> Slums, years, have buried you. I would not dare
> Console you if I could. What can be said . . .
>
> . . . .
> For you would hardly care
> That you were less deceived, out on the bed,
> Than he was, stumbling up the breathless stair
> To burst into fulfilment's desolate attic.

The metaphysical point is bound to usurp the actuality, as the poetry knows and needs: it is its way of making 'all disagreeables evaporate' while retaining a steady image of the fact. And for the lurking self the message is that emptiness is always less deceived than fulfilment, for all fulfilment cannot help being implied in this hideous form: the breathless stair that led here to the desolate attic leads everywhere in life to the cold hillside. But Larkin moves us most here by shutting off that lurking conviction, as he shuts off the trench humour that goes with it, and imposes a calm gravity ('For you would hardly care . . .') in the necessary gap between poet and victim.

Larkin does two things which are so uncommon today as to be almost unattainable in poetry and in art generally. First, like Keats, he makes 'the disagreeables evaporate': he creates supreme beauty out of ugliness, emptiness and contingency, the trapped and the doomed. Secondly he keeps us continuously interested in himself, always wanting to hear more about him. Both gifts he shares, *mutatis mutandis*, with the American poets, and the second, especially, in our time, is little less than miraculous. For the art market would appear to be utterly sated with the self: on every side the personalities of those who write importune us, shoving into ours—as Auden says of Lust and Shame—'their inflamed faces'. In modern writing intrusiveness is all and privacy mocked and decried; Larkin's poetry is unintrusive, private, and yet totally forthcoming.

But even more important is his updating of the fundamental aesthetic that Keats took as much for granted as Spenser, and T. S. Eliot as Matthew Arnold: that the business of poetry is to delight and console, to calm and to satisfy; above all, to entrance into completeness the inadequacies of living. It is to the interest of many writers now to assume the opposite: that what is boring and squalid—or, worse, merely grossly familiar—should be faithfully reproduced and underlined in any art that is honestly and fearlessly 'with it'. They do so because they are incapable of producing that paradox of transmutation which these three poets have achieved, by finding in poetry the forms and the voices of themselves, and dividing these in words from the rest of our existence.

Uses in Shakespeare

CHAPTER I

1. Living in the Present

Every reader of Shakespeare feels at some time that he is creating what he reads, and is participating in the actual process of art. No doubt this process has its dangers. W. H. Auden warns against the critic who treats a work of art as if it were his own discovered document. Yet Shakespeare freely allows us the illusion.

> Heaven does with us as we with torches do,
> Not light them for themselves: for if our virtues
> Did not go forth of us, 'twere all alike
> As if we had them not. Spirits are not finely touched
> But to fine issues . . .

It is this generosity in the debate of 'fine issues' which ultimately distinguishes what Shakespeare offers us from what we get from other writers.

> No man is the lord of anything
> Though in and of him there be much consisting
> Till he communicate his parts to others . . .

This is the whole atmosphere and aroma of the plays, that what they reveal is a common possession. We never feel, as we do with Goethe or Proust or Henry James, that Shakespeare is soliciting our awareness of some acute perception or felicitous phrase, while at the same time retaining it, so to speak, just out of our reach. It is in this respect, above all, that he transcends all the literary genres. He is a playwright and theatrical craftsman who can bestow upon us all, in some degree, the status of novelists and sages.

He bestows it on us: it is only in our view, from the end of a long perspective of familiarity, that there lies behind each of his plays the shadow of a gigantic and seemingly limitless novel. The apothecary's shop in *Romeo and Juliet* lends us all for the

185

moment the appetite and curiosity of a Balzac; the financial losses which that solid citizen, Dogberry, so characteristically shows off about, set us thinking along the lines of *Middlemarch* or *Little Dorrit*. Caliban might have been developed imaginatively by Dickens or analytically by Musil. Behind the swift passage of the plays there is time for whole lifetimes of events, formed by centuries of shaping speculation.

The weight and density of time is an impression generated by the nature of Shakespearean dramatic action. It is of course illusory, because a play consists of a number of words, which take a given period of time to recite in the theatre, or to read in the study. But the Shakespearean character appears to bring to the action in which the play involves him the invisible lifetime which, as a represented human being, he theoretically possesses, but which the artist who has to deal with the exigencies of form and convention usually keeps out of sight, unless a specific dramatic need requires it. The apparent freedom of the Shakespearean character implies the presence of all the hours and years his consciousness has accumulated.

The consequence produces the whole paradox of Shakespearean drama, and the division in it between enactment of a play and experience of a whole world of art. It is a division much more remarkable, and more far-reaching in its consequences, than Shakespeareans who have grown accustomed to the plays, as to a second nature, are usually given to assume. In fact it is the most singular thing, it would not be too much to say, about the whole nature of Shakespeare's achievement, and one that cannot be ignored or explained away by those who—like Wilson Knight—seek to demonstrate a coherent and harmonious metaphysic within the world of each play.

It would be truer to say that there is always a gap between our image of the play—what Maurice Morgann in the eighteenth century would have called our sustained *impression* of it—and the actual experience we receive when we hear the words on the stage or pick up the book and read them. Everyone must have experienced the feeling of surprise, perhaps disconcertment, involved, which may quickly wear off as our minds refocus and bring the two images of the play together, the immediate impact with the whole sum of our previous conception. None the less the momentary gap makes for something important to our aesthetic freedom. We may have briefly seen Hamlet as a clever show-off, Macbeth as a go-getter who inspires nothing but repulsion and tedium, Coriolanus as an *âme damnée* for whom excess alone has any flavour. Such impressions are too involuntary to be very subtle, and we are probably glad to subsume them in our more considered awareness of the play as a whole. But they have done their work; they have prevented our continuing to think about the play in the same way. In certain cases—*Othello* is the most striking—the contrast between the immediate emotion and the backlog of our considered view can be very marked indeed, so that we might almost think it an intention of the design. For what has become known, since Bradley took the hint from a student, as the 'double time scheme' in Othello is not just a question of comments in the dialogue which imply a much longer duration than the apparent brief and continuous dramatic action. It must represent our sense of the massive scope and ambiguity of the situation—the provenance and status of Othello, the culture of Venice, the history and fortunes of Iago. And, over against this, the brutal immediacy of the emotional explosion, and the manipulation of coincidence into fatality.

In other plays—*Hamlet* and *Troilus* are the most striking examples—we may feel that behind the brilliance of the action, and its power to absorb us, there is nothing really there at all. 'The play's the thing', in every way, and Hamlet distracts us from his total extemporaneousness, his lack of any prolongation into the personal, with his 'had I but time . . .' Here the process might be said to work in reverse. Our *considered* impression is of the complete impermanence of the dramatic action: but our immediate feeling when seeing or reading—perhaps at some such words as those of Hamlet to Gertrude: 'I must to England. You know that?'—may suggest a sudden, solid, and uncovenanted actuality, a free space for appraisal of one in whom we are still interested, about whom the ways into knowledge still might exist. In this way characters grow in our minds, and diminish again into the mere necessity of dramatic appearance or *vice versa*. And by this constant cycle they remain alive, with the potential of all living things. Shakespeare's masterpieces wax and wane between what could be termed novel and play, between what Henry James called the 'relations that stop nowhere' and the circle of performance in which they must be arbitrarily resolved. But there is one play in which this creation seems to have no part. *Troilus and Cressida* has no novel in it to fill our minds between performances, and, conversely, no coherent seconds from fiction time to startle us in performance when we have already formed our judgment on it as a play. It remains purely and simply a play, confined to the time it takes to act. The other plays possess the dimension it lacks, but it has an atmosphere and spirit unique to itself and lacking in them. An enquiry into its two-dimensional unity reveals a great deal about the ways in which division works in the being of the other plays, and in our response to them.

Troilus exhibits a time element that produces persons and situations not elsewhere found in the plays. It has often been pointed out how frequently it invokes time and its powers. Time is, of course, one of the most frequent topics of the commonplace not only in Shakespeare but in all Elizabethan literature; the most notorious and by its very familiarity the most reassuring. It is merciless, devouring, all-conquering . . . Or it can conquer everything except love, everything except art. Or it is both judge and redeemer, serving 'to unmask falsehood and bring truth to life'. We are lulled by these commonplaces, which seem not only familiar to us but doubly familiar from their frequent and regular recurrence in the miniatures of lyric and in the discursive poetry of high sentence. Moreover, as Kenneth Muir for one has observed, there are actually even more references to time in *Macbeth* than there are in *Troilus*. It is evidently not the emphasis on time that counts here but the dramatic use made of it. In all Shakespeare's other plays we feel that the present time, as enacted on the stage, not only depends upon the past but is in the service of the future. Lear has made his plans; the action will reveal their consequence; the unseen future will underwrite a return to normality of a kind, be guarantor, as Edgar says, of 'we that are young'. But in the formal impact of *Troilus* there is neither past nor future: everything takes place in, and ends in, the present.

We need not look far for the formal justification for the device. We all know (even today) how the Matter of Troy began, and how it ended. Our action, as the Prologue informs us, will take place in 'the middle'. What follows from this? That the playwright can abolish past and future if he wants to, and see what the consequences are if he does. Novelist's time—and in general Shakespearean time—accumulates character and

perspective, and almost any playwright borrows enough of the
novelist's time to produce the appearance of these two things.
His actors are in the midst of their lives, and his action will
admit—if only tacitly—that it cannot tell the whole of their
tale, and that other things are in progress outside it. But what
if the playwright turns the other way and instead of borrowing
time from the novelist deliberately renounces it, and all the
space and coherence it assumes? Suppose he implies that if
novelist's time does not exist for him he is left with the headless
and senseless trunk of an action, devoid of the reality which can
only come from knowledge of what went before and must come
after? This is where such a playwright as Beckett begins, starting
from the metaphysical premise that life can have no sequential
sense or meaning, that all is an ever-repeated mumble of the
present. Shakespeare could begin from a more formalised
hypothesis: you know the beginning and end of this business,
so they need have no meaning in terms of what I am about to
show you of the middle. The only surprise here must be a
perpetual present.

A characteristic paradox is made of this. It is *because* we know
how the siege began and ended that Agamemnon can say

> What's past and what's to come is strewn with husks
> And formless ruin of oblivion.

Agamemnon, like all the other figures in the play, cares nothing
for the logic of past and future, and if neither exists the present
itself can have no coherent meaning—he himself no coherent
personality. That is the logic in the dramatic world of *Troilus
and Cressida*, the more terrible for being implicit and uninsistent.
And it is a world that makes us, by contrast, sharply aware of
how the sense of character in a Shakespeare play normally comes
into being, between an accumulation of impressions that depend
on novel time, and a quick, often contradictory, response to the
dramatic moment.

2. *The* Troilus *Atmosphere*

Let us consider the first scene of Act III, in which Pandarus,
Paris and Helen chatter together and sing a song about love.
It is like a glimpse in a nightclub, but whereas in real life the

spectator might be sufficiently intrigued—enough of a novelist as it were—to wonder about their relationship and about the rest of their lives, Shakespeare inhibits even so small an attempt at coherence, by depriving the characters of historical and personal significance. The scene makes us feel as confused and unresponsive as if we ourselves were in the same state as the other guests in that nightclub, immersed in the same experience of the contingent and the banal. No novelist can do this, because in drawing our attention to the contingent and the banal he puts us on the outside of it, and manipulates it so that it is fully under our control. This difference is crucial. In novel time the absurdity of the contingent becomes a positive pleasure to be entertained by; but in *Troilus* we are too be-nightmared by the world of the moment to contemplate it with such enjoyment. Like the actors themselves, we are borne passively on the moment by moment tide of the action, and we find when it is over that we still cannot get it into shape.

The sense in which Shakespeare here denies and dissolves history might be compared with the drinking scene on board Pompey's galley in *Antony and Cleopatra*, where he deftly and dynamically confirms it. In *Troilus* he appears to deny that the famous and the legendary ever existed as time has reported them, or that we would ever find anything at any moment in history beyond scraps of idiotic dialogue and meaningless event.

And this is because the convention of play time is reduced virtually *ad absurdum*. The realization makes clear the play's unique status in the Shakespearean canon and explains things about it which on any other interpretation seem wilful and puzzling at the best, and at the worst downright unsatisfactory. The point to recognize is that we are puzzled because there is nothing to be puzzled about, because behind the glitter and coruscation of the language and the rapid charade of the action there is nothing that adds up. We do not know what the characters are like because there is neither time nor occasion to find out, and for the same reason they have no idea of themselves. Neither we, nor they, can be aware here of the other world, of the novelist's world, in which time stretches into past and future, supplying the reality of persons, creating space and leisure, value and meaning.

Ulysses is concerned to impress upon Achilles that such a world can only be maintained by constant action and endeavour.

The irony of his advice is that it is intended merely for the moment, and that Achilles is in fact spurred to action by the random eruption of another moment—the death of Patroclus. Ulysses is a charade of policy as Nestor is one of age, Troilus of fidelity, Cressida of faithlessness. 'He must, he is, he cannot but be wise' is the ironic comment on Nestor. But all of them must, are, and cannot but be voices imprisoned in role and argument, figures condemned to tread the mill of time without ever being made free of it. Compared to their undifferentiated and claustrophobic world the predicament of Macbeth seems like freedom itself —'as broad and general as the casing air'. For it is in Macbeth's own consciousness that coherency and purpose have become extinguished, have become a tale told by an idiot. In the world outside him the logic of time proceeds with its serene, restorative, but for him terrible assurance. He cannot but contemplate the shape and consequence of his action stretching before and after, and thus he becomes himself, the real Macbeth, situated in the real and unforgiving dimension of history.

Everywhere in his work, not just in the history plays, Shakespeare's sense of the past is of 'time's jewel', giving meaning to human destiny. It is so assured, so comprehensive and so inevitable that we take it for granted. He is our supreme creator of history, as he is also in one sense our supreme *religious* writer, in whose providence all things have their place, as for Yeats's crazy Jane 'all things remain in God'. It takes a Scott or a Pushkin to revive this authority; and it is no accident that in *Boris Godunov*, the best of the many plays that have tried to re-create a specifically Shakespearean sense of history, the old scribe Pimen is made to soliloquize about the past. 'Is it long since it swept by, teeming with event and turbulent like the ocean? Now it is silent and tranquil.'

The fate of Macbeth, as of Godunov, is 'silent and tranquil'. With Timon they have their everlasting mansion, and their reality is assured. 'What's done can't be undone.' Whatever the contrast between them, Lady Macbeth is united at last with her husband—an ironic second marriage—when she admits the law of responsibility and causality. Very different is Cressida's comment on her relation with Troilus: 'Well, well, 'tis done, 'tis past, and yet it is not'. She has no sense of, does not want to know, what has taken place: pleasure, boredom and infidelity are alike unsorted phenomena of the moment for her, and she is denied past and future awareness to the point where she is no more than a voice speaking lines in the theatre. Someone said of Marilyn Monroe that she was 'discontinuous with any idea of personality'. It is the same with Cressida. She becomes her words; our 'present eye praises the present object', as Ulysses says, and looks no further.

Shakespeare's technique here deliberately abandons his usual sure mode of creating a complete human being, complete not only in terms of history but in relation to a family and a social situation. Such creation may be only in a hint or a touch—as in the personality of a Paulina in *The Winter's Tale*, or an Aumerle in *Richard II*—but the sense of character as logically and soundly related to environment is something of the greatest importance to his art that we can usually take for granted. In the Troilus legend all is arbitrary, and again we may feel that the playwright sardonically emphasizes this aspect of legend into a corner-stone of theatrical technique. We know nothing about these people, but this is the story of how they behaved: it is thus as accurate as it is paradoxical to see the legend as a moment in life, left hanging on a note of mockery that is very far from being the 'monumental mockery' which Ulysses sees as the fate of bygone reputation, and action left behind in the past.

Handled in this way the Shakespeare tale becomes virtually a parody of representation and action, the Aristotelian concept of the play. Parodied, too, is the concept of time that goes with this. The critics who a few generations later were to misunderstand Aristotle and make a fetish of the Unity of Time, held that the duration of a dramatic fiction should ideally be the time taken to act it. Dryden praised Ben Jonson's *The Silent Woman* for this reason, and when he decided to rewrite Shakespeare's *Troilus* he must have approved of it on the same grounds. It may also be significant that he subtitled his adaptation 'Truth found too late', thus suggesting that all the *appearances* of the Troilus situation are misleading, and that his play discovers and presents its reality. That reality turns out to be that Cressida was faithful after all; that she only flirted with Diomedes to please her father; and that the only way she can prove this is by self-immolation on the battlefield where Troilus, after slaying Diomedes, himself meets death. Dryden's version may be preposterous, but its mockery is indeed 'monumental'; its artifice creates dramatic certainty and—to a limited extent—dramatic satisfaction.

Dryden's Cressida reveals herself in her actions and in the time of the play, and that is good enough, however devoid of interest or plausibility that self might be if we could consider it in novel time. In one sense at least, therefore, she is a kind of degraded sister of the great heroines of classical tragedy, like Antigone herself. The role of Antigone is completely identified with the action—there is no time for the two to be separated—and there is no room for different kinds of, or conceptions, of Antigone. Equally there should be none for Shakespeare's Cressida. She was false, and in play time there is an end of it. She does what she does because there is no syllable of time

> no orifex for a point as subtle
> As Ariachne's broken woof to enter

in which she could do otherwise. And yet we may have the uneasy but challenging impression that this is because she is a parody of the heroine whose time is only in the play; that her nature is divided, not 'in itself' but in terms of the usual Shakespearean form; that she is a dweller potentially in the land of the novel who is here compelled to exist solely in the swift time of the play.

Before looking in more detail at Cressida herself let us see what effect this may have on her relation to the play. The parody of Aristotelian action would be, can only be, *acting*. The word is often used in a derogatory sense, which implies a discrepancy between the character represented and the person acting the part. 'An affected Desdemona' is a criticism of the actress, not of Desdemona's character: there is a gap between the way we imagine the real girl and the way in which she is being represented on the stage. But action for Cressida is purely a question of doing the part; we have no image of her other than what we find her to be on the stage. Neither she nor the other actors are concerned with the fundamental and fascinating problem of representing Shakespeare on the stage: how to embody a character who has his being, not only in play time, but in duration and space of a very different order, and in the most complex and comprehensive literary form the world has ever seen.

In practice there are two ways of getting round this division, which cannot—and indeed probably should not—be smoothed over. One, the more nearly impossible, is for the actor to become in real life what he conceives the character to be, as Stanislavsky taught his cast to attempt, and as the great actor Salvini temporarily 'became' Othello. The other and more frequently successful way is for the character to be interpreted so that we neither forget nor are even intended to forget that this is an actor giving an interesting version of a part.

But in Shakespeare's only play to take place totally in play time the problem does not even arise. Here are actors who have labelled and incontrovertible parts. Reading *Troilus* we may find ourselves thinking how well this would act, whereas when we read the rest of Shakespeare we enter a natural world as well as one which is to be acted. And if the reader of *Troilus* is always rather like a producer leafing through a brilliant manuscript of a play, the spectator is not unlike that same producer glad he has backed his hunch; who notes that the audience might laugh even louder if Thersites got his timing a shade better; and is gratified by the reception Cressida gets for her sallies.

> Pandarus: You are such a woman! One knows not at what
>   ward you lie.
> Cressida: Upon my back, to defend my belly; upon my wit,
>   to defend my wiles; upon my secrecy, to defend
>   mine honesty; my mask to defend my beauty; and
>   you, to defend all these. . .

Though it does not get its cue for a guffaw until the line 'things won are done; joy's soul lies in the doing', whose significance, in this play where the present moment is all, is not merely bawdy, the audience receives Cressida's next speech in the same spirit as the one above.

> Words, vows, gifts, tears, and love's full sacrifice,
> He offers in another's enterprise:
> But more in Troilus thousand fold I see
> Than in the glass of Pandar's praise may be. . .

No need to ask whether this is 'true', whether she has really fallen in love with Troilus for his own sake. Cressida is like

Chloe, the *ingénue* in *The Poetaster*, asking if Mars has anything
to do with Venus. She and the audience alike merely know that
she has got a good line. 'I played Julius Caesar. I was killed in
the Capitol. Brutus killed me.' These are the facts of the theatre,
and these are the accents of its standardized professionalism. In
this sense *Troilus* is at one with the accents of the restoration
stage, and beyond it that of Sheridan and Shaw. When Charles
Surface advises Lady Teazle to take a lover, he knows, we know,
and Lady Teazle knows, that the reasons he gives for doing so
have no connection with the motives and moves of those who
take lovers in real life. The play's moment is the thing. We
are drawn into the same conspiracy when Synge's Playboy ends
his act with 'Now wasn't I the foolish fellow not to be killing
me father in the days gone by?'—or when Shaw's Candida turns
to her husband and to her lover and says: 'I give myself to the
weaker of the two.'

The final stage of the act is reached when Brecht makes his
actor proclaim that he *is* an actor, and that nothing he says or
does is to be imagined as taking place in real life. This sophistication is already half-established in *Troilus*. It could rightly be
argued that *Troilus* is not by any means unique—all of the
comedies and many of the other plays flash out at times with
the same sophistication. In the last act of *The Tempest* ('Our
revels now are ended') Prospero speaks almost with the voice
of Brecht. But these admissions and jests about the nature of
the play and play time are counterweighted by the great open
world of its imagination. The bright young things of *Love's
Labour's Lost*, the comedy which—as Dryden perceived—most
resembles *Troilus* in its convention, are performing their parts
as it were in conjunction with the other young men of the
audience. And opposite them both, as in *Midsummer Night's
Dream*, are the genuine comic characters—Nathaniel, Holo-
fernes and Armado—whose sense of themselves appears
absolute, and not of the stage. Playing Hector in the pageant
of the Nine Worthies, Armado rounds on his courtly persecutors
and reminds them—and us—of the real world offstage, a world
that accepts the past and links it with the present.

The sweet war-man is dead and rotten . . . beat not the bones
of the buried: when he breathed, he was a man.

Absurd as he is, Armado instinctively reveres the idea of

greatness, and the image of Hector conjured up in his words has all the majesty that for him belongs to the past.

It is in general true of the tragedies that when the play is over the novel begins, but in the comedies the two often appear to coincide. Armado's outburst makes us want to hear more about him than we do, but what we hear is enough to set the surrounding action in a corrected comic perspective. Armado intrigues us not as an actor in comedy but as a man. So does Antonio in *The Merchant of Venice*, and Feeble, the woman's tailor called up for service in the army of Henry IV. These nuances of Shakespearean individualization are immensely hard for an actor to register in the few seconds that are all that play time allows him, but even in play time they exist, an earnest of the other sort of time that lies in the background of Shakespearean creation.

Compare them and what they imply with such a speech in *Troilus* as that of Diomedes to Paris, about Helen, which in its sudden bitter forcefulness has apparently the same power to arrest our attention and focus it on the speaker.

> She's bitter to her country. Hear me, Paris:
> For every false drop in her bawdy veins
> A Grecian's life hath sunk; for every scruple
> Of her contaminated carrion weight
> A Trojan hath been slain. Since she could speak
> She hath not given so many good words breath
> As for her Greeks and Trojans suffered death.

In practice, surely, we feel here no corresponding interest in Diomedes, only a slight surprise at the outburst of pacifism delivered by means of him. There is no hint of a novel time correlation between the speaker and what is spoken: Diomedes is an actor with a strong speech, nothing more. And we may wonder in the circumstances, *is* the speech really so strong? It has the robustness of a speech in Jonson, and it also has the unsubtle force of a speech in the modern post-Brechtian theatre, a speech allotted to an actor in play time: what it does not have is the Shakespearean resonance of words that could only be uttered by one character, giving us a glimpse of his whole and involuntary being. Such self-revelation is the true way in which drama creates character; and it cannot exist in *Troilus* because it depends on the existence of an inescapable self that lives beyond the moment and the word. The actors of *Troilus* have no such self, and so the indignation of Diomedes is no more meaningful than the bewilderment Achilles affects to feel after Ulysses has plied him with 'reasons' for taking the field.

> My mind is troubled, like a fountain stirred,
> And I myself see not the bottom of it.

Such a semblance of introspection is without meaning—perhaps deliberately so—because there is nothing there to look in at.

It is the same when Cressida jokes with Pandarus, and subsequently avows in stilted soliloquy that she 'loves' Troilus. Compare this with Desdemona's encouragement of Iago's witticisms when Othello's fate at sea is still unknown. The actress who plays Desdemona must at this moment be longing with every fibre of her actual being for Othello to come, and must convey that longing in the restraint of one rapid phrase— 'There's one gone to the harbour?'—while at the same time she smiles and jokes with the two officers. Her social face saves them the embarrassment of seeing her distraught, while gently intimating that the cause of her hidden distraction is none of their business. Perhaps a Mrs Siddons could do it, as a Salvini could electrify the whole audience with his '*Keep up your bright swords, for the dew will rust them*', without meaning to do so, without apparently realizing that what he has said reveals so potently the manner of man he is.

But *Othello* is perhaps the furthest Shakespeare ever went in the direction of total dramatic illusion; it is hardly surprising that there are historical records of spectators leaping up to revile Othello for his stupidity. And, it is remarkable that *Othello* and *Macbeth*, which of all Shakespeare's plays leave the strongest illusion of novel time unbounded by play time, should have followed *Hamlet* and *Troilus*. There may be reasons for this, or there may be none. An epoch and a reign was over; the war of the theatres had gone cold; and the clever young melancholic, in the presentation of whom Shakespeare in his quiet way had been content to follow in the wake of Marston, was no longer the glass of fashion. A greater degree of illusion came into vogue; the artifices of the play as a play receded, and with it actors who are virtually acting the part of actors, like Sartre's waiters. The young men who saw themselves in the figures of Hamlet and Troilus could certainly not identify with Othello, with Iago and Macbeth. The stylizations of *Hamlet* and *Troilus* lead up to what might be called Shakespeare's most sustained burst of naturalism.

Hamlet, who could be bounded by a nutshell and count himself a king of infinite space, would have listened with appreciation to Troilus on love.

> This is the monstruosity in love, lady, that the will is infinite and the execution confined, that the desire is boundless and the act a slave to limit.

So would Jack Donne and a hundred other clever young frequenters of plays. The most seductive aspect of the two young heroes lies in the apparently irrelevant extremes within their natures. They are full of thoughts and dreams, which they explore as they explore their sensations, but they can also be resolute and sudden, ruthless and hard. Such divisions in the hero are an old device of Shakespeare's—we find them as far back as *Titus Andronicus*—and they have an obvious dramatic effectiveness. In *Troilus* they are different however: in keeping with the nature of the play, its abstraction, they remain at the level of *idea*. When we hear from Ulysses that, unlike Hector, Troilus is pitiless in battle, we have no context, other than the old proverbial one of love and war, in which to digest this information, even though we hear Troilus himself asserting the fact towards the end of the play. His appearance of personality is not enough to feed on such a fact and increase into a person. But, as I suggested earlier, Hamlet's conscientious prowess at fence, or his priggish disdain at the drunkenness of the Danish court, augment without emphasis all his other symptoms of, and occasions for, reality—the reality indicated by his family, by the court, and by the drama and dilemma in which he is placed. Without that dilemma, his relations with Ophelia would be the purely metaphysical, Donne-like, ones of Troilus with Cressida.

Like the cast of *Troilus*, Hamlet starts as actor and amateur, a gentleman who could engage in disputation or improvise a dramatic burlesque, as Patroclus imitates the Greek leaders for Achilles

> Like a strutting player—whose conceit
> Lies in his hamstring, and doth think it rich
> To hear the wooden dialogue and sound
> Twixt his stretched footing and the scaffoldage.

Hamlet too is one of these who

> On the cause and question now in hand
> Have glosed, but superficially; not much
> Unlike young men, whom Aristotle thought
> Unfit to hear moral philosophy.

But then he finds himself both ranting and speculating in deadly earnest. It is clearly a short journey from the half-involved, half-selfconscious rhetoric of Hamlet to the atmosphere of *Troilus*; but in *Hamlet* the contrast between actor and sufferer is cunningly subsumed under the other dramatic conflicts of the play, and becomes an aspect of his desire and revulsion, gentleness and ferocity, madness and sanity and madness. After he has declaimed of piling Pelion on Mount Ossa the Queen comments:

> This is mere madness:
> And thus awhile the fit will work on him;
> Anon, as patient as the female dove
> When that her golden couplets are disclosed,
> His silence will sit drooping.

Hamlet's state is a way of enabling the playwright to let himself go in terms which in Troilus become glittering and ironic tropes, egregiously filled

> with terms unsquared
> Which, from the tongue of roaring Typhon dropped,
> Would seem hyperboles . . .

and which an audience of Hamlet's peers would laugh at in a 'straight' context. In both *Hamlet* and *Troilus* attention is drawn to the difference between dramatic poetry presented as conscious fustian, and as living involuntary utterance. The actor who plays the king in *Hamlet* might have availed himself parenthetically of the kind of phrase—'And duller should'st thou be than the fat weed / Which roots itself at ease on Lethe wharf'—which his father's ghost employs on Hamlet. And it might be Patroclus mocking Agamemnon by imitation when Ulysses speaks of making Achilles 'fall'

> His crest that prouder than blue Iris bends.

Such virtuoso enjoyment of extravagance seems to mark Shakespeare's lack of any need to distinguish in these plays, in the interest of dramatic illusion, between fine rhetoric for its own sake and the real and individual voices of drama. Both Troilus and Hamlet use language indifferently, and this is in keeping with the arbitrary extremes in their natures, extremes intended to appeal to the curiosity and vanity of young intellectuals. By contrast the language in *Macbeth* and *Othello* strikes us as possessing a true dramatic idiom, as involuntary as personality itself; and this is emphasized in *Othello* by Iago's specific mockery of Othello by parodying his natural mode of expression. The knowing game of stage parody, played against Marlowe through Pistol in *Henry IV*, and through the apprentice Ralph in *The Knight of the Burning Pestle*, is thus transformed by Shakespeare's naturalism into a way not only of establishing personality but of suggesting the hidden deeps of mockery, of envy, of resentment at distinctions that lie between one human being and another.

If Hamlet does not always speak like a man of this world it is because he lives in different worlds, as both playgoer and victim of its plot: his drama is that of a young man acting who becomes a young man acted upon. Troilus's self-absorption is not so unlike Hamlet's, but it is concerned entirely with the sensations of the moment. The attitude to time is again the key.

> You that look pale and tremble at this chance,
> That are but mutes or audience to this act,
> Had I but time . . .

Hamlet invokes novel time, the spacious dimension which the play will not let him have. For him it is a matter of infinite concern that his wounded name shall be restored, to live behind him in the love and knowledge of his friend Horatio, who will speak

> to the yet unknowing world
> How these things came about.

But absence of novel time, and what goes with it, seems the very point of *Troilus*. 'Hector is dead, there is no more to say.' To live in reputation and in friendship can have no place in *Troilus*, where all such things are dissolved in the expediency of the moment. We must contrast with this not only *Hamlet* but the powerful ties and dignities of friendship which triumph over politics in *Julius Caesar*. But these things are nothing in *Troilus*, as the tone even of the Prologue makes quite clear.

> our play
> Leaps o'er the vaunt and firstlings of these broils,
> Beginning in the middle; starting thence away
> To what may be digested in a play.

3. The Divisions of Rhetoric

The absence of value is contained and revealed in the absence of time, its most effective correlative in terms of art, for it is most unlikely that Shakespeare is simply giving direct expression here to a mood of disgust with society. Time is here the formal instrument for his habitual artifice and self-exclusion; and the instrument also, it may well be, to set the tone for a play specially commissioned by the young intellectuals at the Inns of Court. For this of course there is no direct evidence. Although a tradition exists that *Troilus* was never acted in the public theatre, Coghill and others have plausibly argued that it takes a conventional place among the tragedies of the time; and against this one can only urge a more or less personal sense of its peculiarities as a play. If *Troilus* was not aimed at an Inns of Court audience, whom was it aimed at?

A logical result of the play's time techniques is the domination of Thersites, who seems at times virtually to 'speak for' the play in a Brechtian sense, a sense unique in Shakespeare. And yet play time consumes him too. His rebuttal is not to triumph outside the play, not to increase and live on in our minds as 'the hatch and brood' of novel time. But he is unique in receiving no real setback or corrective at the hands of his fellows, as do all Shakespeare's other cynics and railers. Parolles, Apemantus, Jaques, Enobarbus, Falstaff, Iago above all—they are in their various ways placed and diminished by the positive mass and movement of the plays they are in. But Thersites is disconcertingly on top in his. Most obviously and smartly he scores off Patroclus, the false railer and tame cynic of Achilles, who likes to hear him pageant the Greek generals and provide what Ulysses calls 'the stuff for these two to make paradoxes'. Patroclus attempts to claim Thersites as a fellow clear-sighted man, who like himself sees through the farce of greatness and of life in general, but Thersites treats him with all the disdain of the independent shop steward for the chief of the bosses' union. No one can stand up against Thersites because all unknowingly share the same conviction with him, the conviction that everything is meaningless except the present moment. Thersites is top dog because he alone draws the logical conclusion that there is nothing to life but disputation and conquest, war and lechery—'nothing else holds fashion'. The others who follow the fashion without being aware of it, are men of action in the most damning sense.

Thersites concludes that there is nothing but wars and lechery because he cannot see that the legend and the beauty, the art and the meaning of the past and the future proceed precisely from the war and the lechery of the moment. The present moment reveals the legendary Helen sprawled untidily in the arms of a Paris who calls her 'Nell', and the death of Hector the Great as a few seconds of sordid butchery brought about by chance. At any given moment Thersites is right. The play pushes his logic to an extreme which becomes almost an implicit parody of those who despise art, and time as its matrix. So far from being in opposition to his fellows Thersites here is their representative and spokesman.

Another kind of satire may underlie the glitter of the play. The point about metaphysical argument of the kind the young intellectuals of the Inns delighted in was its expedience, its pointscoring, its omission by the rules of the game of imponderable values and permanencies. Shakespeare might perhaps be quietly amusing himself at the expense of his clients, the young men who would not only be applauding but (like Donne) learning from his ingenious arguments and what Milton in *Comus* makes his Lady scornfully call

> gay rhetoric
> That hath so well been taught her dazzling fence.

For Agamemnon and Nestor have dazzling arguments to prove that the failure of a communal design is really a good thing, because it will show who is trying hardest. Ulysses outdoes them both in ingenuity and animation to prove that things would go better if they all pulled together; but what unites them with their opposite numbers in Troy, and subordinates them to

Thersites's view of things, is the blind immediacy of their intentions.

Every Elizabethan used rhetoric in this way, and for effects as graphic and artistic as possible, but Shakespeare is alone in drawing a particular sort of dramatic conclusion from the logic of its use. Translate the intentionalism of rhetoric into terms of action and you have mere appetite, careless of everything but its object.

> Then everything includes itself in power,
> Power into will, will into appetite;
> And appetite, an universal wolf,
> So doubly seconded with will and power,
> Must make perforce an universal prey,
> And last eat up himself.

Action, like lechery, eats itself in terms of this drama and leaves nothing over. The irony of these grim words is that they describe *raison d'état*, 'the specialty of rule' and 'the mystery in the soul of state' which Ulysses relishes; and though his 'need to take the instant way' and 'let not virtue seek renumeration for the thing it was' blinds him to the implication of what he says, there is a kind of dawning horror of his own words as he speaks them. Eating is the very image of absorption in the present, and both Helen and Cressida are compared by Troilus to the leftovers of appetite; there is a meaningful irony in the argument offered by Troilus for keeping Helen.

> the remainder viands
> We do not throw in unrespective sieve
> Because we now are full.

The play's logic presents the girls in this light, as it presents even Hector. He too is the victim of the moment and its impulses, even though he alone in the play can see time as the end rather than as the moment.

> The end crowns all
> And that old common arbitrator, time,
> Will one day end it . . .

But even he is a dire example of the truth in this play of his brother Troilus's exclamation—'what's ought but as 'tis valued?'

—for he is valued as a status symbol of invincibility, to be eliminated by the Greeks and preserved by the Trojans. He dies without words, with no blaze of self-illumination like Hotspur, who affirms with his last breath his survival in the idea of eternity.

> For thought's the slave of life, and life's time's fool,
> And time, that takes survey of all the world
> Must have a stop.

Hector's sudden reversal of his wise decision to return Helen to the Greeks shows him as much the victim of immediacy as the others in the play. And though he assures himself that 'never did young man fancy with so eternal and so fixed a soul', the truth of Troilus's love is that it consists only in moments: the moment when he is giddy with desire and 'expectation whirls him round'; the moment when he sees Cressida together with Diomedes. 'This is, and is not, Cressida.' 'I cannot conjure, Trojan', says Ulysses, sardonically disclaiming any power upon the appearance of things. His brother's death becomes for Troilus another such moment. 'Hector is dead, there is no more to say'. He cannot say like Brutus:

> I owe more tears
> To this dead man than you shall see me pay.
> I shall find time, Cassius, I shall find time.

But the most conscious contemners of permanency and value are Agamemnon and Ulysses.

> What's past and what's to come is strewn with husks
> And formless ruin of oblivion;
> But in this extant moment, faith and troth,
> Strained purely from all hollow bias-drawing,
> Bids thee, with most divine integrity,
> From heart of very heart, great Hector, welcome.

The 'divine integrity' of the extant moment determines the exercise of Agamemnon's nobility. Faith and truth are alone there. The irony of the phrase consummates the spirit of the play, as does Ulysses' dismissal of the scraps of good deeds past as 'alms for oblivion'.

4. Cressida as a Character

There is an odd sense, none the less, in which Cressida herself *does* strike us as a real person, in spite of her role as a commonplace in the play's externalized and intellectual scheme. It is partly a negative impression, based on our intuitive response to the attitudes the characters take towards her. When Ulysses calls her a daughter of the game we may feel obscurely that he is wrong, and, if we feel so, it is at this moment that she gives some sort of impression of personality. Ulysses' view of her is determined by his own role—indeed we might say that he himself acquires a measure of extension as a character by his refusal to interest himself in that of Cressida. The other actors are partly realized by the same indirect method. If we wonder how far Thersites is justified in claiming that Diomedes is totally unreliable ('The sun borrows of the moon when Diomed keeps his word') or that Patroclus is a womaniser as well as the boy-friend of Achilles ('the parrot will not do more for an almond than he for a commodious drab') then we are beginning to take some interest in the psychology of both Thersites and his victims, though the play will not of course satisfy it.

For the senilely chivalric old Nestor, Cressida is 'a woman of quick spirit', which for Ulysses means being a 'sluttish spoil of opportunity'. So she may be, or become, but Ulysses is not interested in why it should be so. Chaucer, on the other hand, was deeply interested in her motivation. I used to suppose, which I take to be the fairly general reaction, that Chaucer's and Shakespeare's Cressidas had very little in common; but now I wonder whether they are not in fact based on the same kind of interest and understanding on the part of the two writers, and even whether Shakespeare—with that sleep-walker's sureness of instinct which makes it irrelevant to ask whether or not he was 'interested' in such a character—may not have formed his Cressida from Chaucer's.

The thing they chiefly have in common is that neither of them knows what she wants, and so they become the victims of what other people want. Social exigencies compel them to act in ways which society then condemns. This fate, which with some women might be sacrificial, is with them merely distracted.

Both Cressidas distrust men and yet depend on them, and both are in a continual state of inadvertency and division.

> Troilus: What offends you, lady?
> Cressida: Sir, my own company.
> Troilus: You cannot shun yourself.
> Cressida: Let me go and try.
>   I have a kind of self resides with you,
>   But an unkind self that itself will leave
>   To be another's fool.

These are the most revealing words Cressida utters. They show, for one thing, that her existence is indeed a matter of what other people think of her, that she is as she is valued; but they also show an exasperated consciousness of the fact. She is a mess and she knows it; she would rather, as Chaucer's Criseyde thinks she would, be 'my owene woman, wel at ease', but where is the hope of that? She has not a moment to try: forces inside her and out will prevent it. It is of course in keeping with the spirit of the play that Shakespeare does not make the great parade of sympathy for his heroine that Chaucer does: her predicament is not focused on as a debated tale ('men seyn, I not, that she yaf hym hir herte') and a matter for excuse. None the less Cressida, like Criseyde, is in a predicament, which the play's action exhibits but does not explain. Neither's doings are acts of the will.

Certainly Cressida is very different from all Shakespeare's other women. Even his loose or his evil women are, as it were, robustly and wholeheartedly so—they have confidence and single-minded assurance. They have in abundance that quality which Tolstoy so unerringly detects and so sympathetically displays in Natasha Rostov of *War and Peace*—the entire rightness of being themselves. And in his most admired women Shakespeare presents the most sublime qualities of love—faith, confidence, serene self-assurance, unalterable even when it 'alteration finds'. In their faith 'Time is the nurse and breeder of all good'. Desdemona serenely rejoins to Othello's exclamation that his happiness is too great for anything except death to succeed it:

> The heavens forbid
> But that our loves and comforts should increase
> Even as our days do grow!

Juliet, Rosalind, Portia (both of them), Hermione in *The Winter's Tale* ('the Emperor of Russia was my father') above all Isabella in *Measure for Measure*, and Lady Macbeth, in whom confidence and self-satisfaction assume respectively their most ambiguous and their most terrible form. There is such striking unanimity that one can hardly doubt that their author himself profoundly admired—revered even—the qualities he portrayed. Nor is he alone here. I suppose it is a traditional ideal of Western culture, found at its greatest in the beauty and assurance of the great portraits of the Mother of God. Troilus's cry,

> Let it not be believed for womanhood!
> Think, we had mothers . . .

shows that it has its deep root in interior psychology.

No wonder then that the play in which this attitude is absent should be so drastically and jarringly different. Instead of creating and organizing the assurances of selfhood Shakespeare divides and dissolves them. Sexual infidelity and military experience are the cracks which gape open to ruin all distinction. Troilus's stunned horror at the division in Cressida

> Of this strange nature, that a thing inseparate
> Divides more wider than the earth and sky

is a recognition not so much of falsity as of the fact that she is not a single coherent person, in herself or in time. The modern spirit may learn to accept and even to exploit this incoherence —the dissolution of what Lawrence called 'the old stable ego of character'—and to relish the flavour of modernity it finds in *Troilus*. And it is certainly true that the confidence and assurance of Shakespeare's women, however timeless its mastery in terms of the individual, seems to belong to the past rather than to the present. The chorus of masculine praise in the nineteenth century for what Brandes called Shakespeare's 'noble and adorable womanly figures' now strikes us as suspiciously nostalgic. Sheltered men are trying to get behind Shakespeare in their admiration for dream figures who project the reassurance but none of the tiresomeness of wife or mother. Cressida is certainly no help here: division has gone so far indeed that she is not even in their sense a woman; she shares with Troilus and the play's other characters the male emptiness of experience, indecision, helplessness—divisions of the kind the play touches on again and again in unexpected contexts.

> This Ajax is half made of Hector's blood;
> In love whereof, half Hector stays at home.

All the characters in the play are both victims and intriguers, betrayers and betrayed, but it is in the heroine that this loss of stability appears most emphatically. The 'truth' of Troilus goes by default in such a play; it is on the division of Cressida that Shakespeare concentrates. Where Chaucer traced Criseyde's hesitations with meticulous leisure, and placed them in the context of all human uncertainty about life and love—over which the fidelity of God presides—Shakespeare shows division through a formalization of time. It seems just possible that the germ of such a treatment came to him from literature, and not from Chaucer but from Henryson's poem *The Testament of Cresseid*, which we know he had read. Towards its ending Cressida, who has become a leper, happens to come face to face with Troilus, who is still defending Troy. Each fails to recognize the other, though Troilus cannot help thinking he has seen that face before somewhere. Shakespeare presents something oddly similar with greater subtlety, and with none of the poet's rather unctuous relish in the transformation. Instead of the poem's elaborately postponed tableau, he shows how the same kind of impression can be made only hours after the lovers have parted. 'Was Cressid here?' The moment is indeed a nightmare one. For the last lesion in the mind is not to recognize the person we have just seen, and may see again. And the play images for us the madness of such a moment.

Wilson Knight has remarked that in this play 'the mind of Shakespeare is engaged with purely philosophic issues'. It is quite true that the analytic processes of the play, however ambivalent their course and purpose, are so unlike anything else in Shakespeare that they do appear almost as a deliberate metaphysical query. But we should beware of supposing that Shakespeare himself is thus 'engaged': the impression may come from the method he has used, the form and style that he has given to the play. One would suppose that once that form and atmosphere have been established, all else may flow naturally and logically from it. The exchanges of Ulysses and Achilles, as of Hector and Troilus, give a brilliant if brittle *impression* of philosophic discussion, the sort of effect that such a piece can give of it, to titillate an intelligent audience, and create an air of intellectual immediacy which will make them sit up. But in a sense the method brings its own nemesis, and 'eats up itself' by its own success. The play is 'intellectual' in a potentially self-damaging way, dealing so much in arresting and stimulating moments that we can find no differentiation of values inside the world it offers. It contains none of the characters who do not represent but *are*—in some wholly pragmatic sense—good and evil, nor those opposed worlds of order and of unregeneracy which we find even in the comedies. So that when Wilson Knight goes on to suggest—and he is by no means the only critic to do so—that the decisive element in the play is a contrast between Greek rationalism and Trojan chivalry, a deliberate demonstration of the triumph of ruthless Greek methods over a Trojan culture which retains in however unexamined a form some decency and honour, he seems to me to mislead us. And, incidentally, to embarrass the play. For if Shakespeare did indeed intend some such confrontation, the method on which he constructed the play has backfired on him. In *Antony and Cleopatra* there can be no question of the gulf between Rome and Egypt, and of its significance in terms of the play's dimension and imagination. But the gap between Greek and Trojan is merely notional, and is deflected by the impact of 'philosophic issues' arising out of the urgency, the tyranny in fact, of the moment, which affects both sides equally. In English, and especially in the Tudor literary tradition, Trojans were the good guys and Greeks the bad ones, a fugitive Trojan prince, Brytto, being supposedly the eponymous founder of the British kingdom. This tradition Shakespeare goes along with, but surely no more than that. It is an irrelevance, and hence perhaps a weakness, in a play that is full of oddity. But it is wholly logical, for in working inside the medium of the moment the dramatist forgoes any vantage-point outside it. He cannot tell us what he thinks, or what to think, in terms of the values that lie outside immediacy.

What he can do is, like Pandarus, in the play's parting line, to 'bequeath you my diseases'. We recoil from such a world without being invited to do so, because it makes us reflect on the way we act and live. If the play really seemed strongly 'pacifist', or were some such theme as that 'evil arises from the betrayal of loyalties' to be offered to us, we should have no trouble in getting on terms with it, and putting ourselves outside the nightmare unease of its presentness, as our feelings traditionally lead us to do with tragedy. Love and faith are betrayed in *Othello*, but by external action: they are not found to be things of no significance in themselves. Not only its form but probably its audience inhibits these in *Troilus*, and if it is 'a young man's play', perhaps even a parody of a young man's play, it explains much about Cressida's negated role. Shakespearean obligingness, amusement and satire, would be focused at and on the young 'whom Aristotle thought / Unfit to hear moral philosophy'. Troilus's remarks on love, like all the metaphysics in the play, are brilliantly self-curious and self-defining. Some of Cressida's ('You shall not have it, Diomed, faith you shall not') are, for want of a better word, from the heart, but the predicament of the heart has no place in this man's world. Cressida's negation in this world is like Ophelia's in hers—in a world given up to explaining and declaiming they have the misfortune to seem to feel. This in itself queries the concept of infidelity, a young man's idea in the play like every other; for these young men are certainly not fit to hear a moral philosophy of love which gives it real meaning. Cressida's status and problem in such a society constitute an, as it were, aborted novel, a novel that no one in that society has the time or the inclination to read.

CHAPTER II

1. The Meaning of Impression

'I have never understood the difference', wrote Ionesco in *Expérience du Théâtre*, 'that some people make between the comic and the tragic.' The comic, he goes on, seems more hopeless than the tragic, because 'the comic offers no escape'. A perfectly sound point, though it has become something of a cliché, and a facile one, in today's theatre. There is in fact a very important difference, which reveals itself not in relation to contemporary ideas about drama, but in the light of the great drama of the past, Shakespeare's included. Tragedy is always straight: that is to say, whatever is revealed in it is revealed in the privacy of our own response, not in the publicity of the actors' performance. Everyone concerned with the theatre today, including Ionesco no doubt, thinks that the interest in a play is how it can be made 'to offer no escape' for an audience, how the acting and direction can manipulate their feelings in certain directions. Incongruity is the indispensable but nowadays decidedly shoddy, mechanical and flyblown method which is adopted for the purpose: nothing keeps the audience so firmly in hand, not in the hand of the author—though a living author is of course in the fellowship of the process—but that of the actors and director.

When I say that tragedy is revealed in the privacy of our response, I do not mean that we have a private one that is like no other, but that on the contrary we all respond in the same way, though in the solitude of our separate listening, to the words in which the nature of the tragedy is there for us. That is why the interference of actors and of directors distracts us, often repels us, those of us, that is, who have come—as many have not—to listen to the words. And it is in the nature of those words to remain with us, adumbrating the larger and more shadowy work, what I have called the novel, which lies behind a Shakespearean tragedy. This does not include Hamlet

211

electrifying the audience at the climax by stabbing Claudius and then pouring the poison into his ears, a spirited touch by David Warner in the 1965 Stratford production, which was warmly praised by Jan Kott, author of *Shakespeare Our Contemporary*. This is indeed the tyranny of the moment, for the audience are being deliberately distracted from the timeless phenomenon of *Hamlet* by an actor who is drawing attention to a bright idea he has had about a few seconds of it, seconds which he is going to impose on the audience as a deliberate and arbitrary sensation. Now the significant thing is that this would not in the least matter in the case of *Troilus*. So much of a play is it that the cast really are in control, and they and the director can do what they like without interfering with the form and being of the play, and the novel behind it.

This would again be in keeping with the possibility that the piece was bespoke by those young intellectuals, to whom Shakespeare was sardonically surrendering the subject as valueless because literally timeless, lacking the power 'to unmask falsehood and bring truth to light'. We must also bear in mind —on evidence from *Cymbeline* and elsewhere—Shakespeare's probable familiarity with the dialogues of Lucian, in which gods and heroes are treated with determined flippancy. Whatever Shakespeare himself thought, he knew such a treatment would appeal to the cynical and irreverent young. Besides, the treatment was common in antiquity itself. In the *Alcestis* of Euripides, for example, the story is as touching as it is full of cynicism and buffoonery, as if not only to show the muse of comedy and tragedy the same, as Socrates claimed in the *Symposium*, but an act of heroism as itself ambiguous and anticlimactic.

*　　　*　　　*

There exists a further possibility, which connects with all these but brings us to the margin of a much wider question. Do other Shakespeare plays offer us in some measure both the detachment of tragi-comedy and the exactness of a dramatic spectacle which does not divide into a play and novel? Might *Antony and Cleopatra*, for example, affect us in something of the same way that *Troilus and Cressida* does? Of course its scope is far grander, as are its tone and theme of love, and Rome and Egypt are not confounded together in the bewildering moment; yet the movement of the play does seem to tend persistently away from any tragic climax or interior revelation, and towards some such banal acceptance as is expressed in the phrase: 'that's the way things are'. The impression was registered by A. C. Bradley in his comment that the play leaves us 'saddened by the very fact that the catastrophe saddens us so little'; and H. A. Mason, in a recent study to which I shall presently be referring in more detail, makes the point that 'Antony and Cleopatra do not quite know where they stand'. This certainly raises an echo from *Troilus*, perhaps of Achilles' perfunctory comment that he does not see into the bottom of his mind; and the implication of 'quite know' well suggests a state of rather ordinary muddle, of not being able to catch up mentally with events, which is in the greatest contrast with their sense of themselves and their dilemma variously conveyed by Othello, King Lear or Macbeth.

To perceive the nature of this contrast we must first take an excursion into the theoretical territory of Shakespearean characterization, that concept developed by critics out of their response to the acting. The first great characterizer is of course Maurice Morgann, whose essay on the nature of Falstaff, and whether or not he is a coward, is historically by far the most important landmark in the field. Before Morgann this aspect of Shakespeare was not seen as presenting any particular problem, and the growing admiration—become unbounded well before the end of the eighteenth century—saw no special paradox in Shakespearean portrayal. It is true that Dr Johnson rejected the neo-classic insistence on propriety of type, which had made Rymer exclaim that soldiers are men of honour who just don't behave like Iago. 'Denis and Rymer', said Johnson, 'think his Romans not sufficiently Roman, and Voltaire censures his kings as not completely royal', but he emphasizes that a character in Shakespeare is commonly not an individual but of a species, 'a just representation of general nature', an example of what Warton called 'consistency' and knowledge of the 'passions, humours and sentiments of mankind'. To a surprising extent Hazlitt and even Coleridge echo these sentiments: neither is so subtle or so surprising as Morgann.

Morgann's most revolutionary pronouncement is that 'the *Impression* is the *Fact*' in our awareness of Shakespeare. Some of his most pregnant comments occur in a lengthy footnote:

The reader must be sensible of something in the composition of Shakespeare's characters, which renders them essentially different from those drawn by other writers. The characters of every drama must indeed be grouped; but in groups of other poets the parts which are not seen do not in fact exist. But there is a certain roundness and integrity in the forms of Shakespeare, which give them an independence as well as a relation, insomuch that we often meet with passages which, tho' perfectly felt, cannot be sufficiently explained in words, without unfolding the whole character of the speaker . . . every part being in fact relative, and inferring all the rest . . . A felt propriety and truth from causes unseen, I take to be the highest point of poetic composition . . . it may be fit to consider them rather as historic than dramatic beings; and, when occasion requires, to account for their conduct from the *whole* of character, from general principles, from latent motives, and from policies not avowed.

The parts which are not seen, the passages 'perfectly felt', the 'felt propriety and truth from causes unseen'—all this is the right tribute, however ambiguous the currency.

Like Johnson himself ('There is something in the nature of acting which levels all distinctions' was the Doctor's jibe at his friend Garrick) Morgann took a poor view of players, calling them 'the worst judges of Shakespeare'. Yet he plays into the hands of the interpretative acting of our time: indeed he is virtually its patron saint. He does not, however, tell us as they do: *'What the play's really about is . . .'* By contrasting our 'mental impressions' with the more conventional literary response of 'the understanding', he not only anticipates the romantic philosophy of subjectivism but suggests the plays do not see human nature in terms of principles, species and fixed laws, but of vagaries, contradictions, enigmas and uncertainties. He is not, like his successors, concerned to see himself in these mirrors; he does not suggest, as Coleridge disarmingly does, that such characters must be fascinating because they resemble himself. Even his part-flippant argument that Falstaff is no coward is really a stalking-horse, under cover of which he makes his real point in the pregnant footnote I have quoted. His point is that no placing of such a character is possible, according to the ordinary needs of convention, narrative logic, and dramatic convenience. The plot of *Henry IV* seems to call for a coward and a braggart, as a foil to the noble prince, but what we get is a man at once adroit and perceptive, shrewd, humorous and tough-minded, a man in short who is not a foil to Hal at all but a kind of *alter ego*. They are two of a kind: hence their mutual attraction and understanding, and hence the Prince's need for separation. Morgann's point implies that Hal cannot be 'placed' any more than Falstaff can be, and for the same reasons.

Morgann was neglected. The nineteenth-century attitude became as stereotyped as that of the previous century: the rule of nature or dramatic propriety was replaced by the rule of the dramatically *characteristic*. Local colour is used for its own sake, because by surrounding a character with an appropriate atmosphere and environment it makes him what he is. The failure of blank verse drama, in its attempted revival, was caused as much by this misunderstanding as by the killing precedent of Shakespearean dramatic verse. Byron for example, in *The Two Foscari*, imitates a Shakespeare history and does it pretty well. His love of historical accuracy is typical of period and genre, but even more so is his characterization of social or historical role. Nearly fifty years later Tennyson's play *Queen Mary* repeats exactly the same kind of errors, a fact unintentionally underlined by a reviewer, who wrote when it came out in 1865:

> We should be surprised to hear that any true critic would rate *Queen Mary*, whether in dramatic force or general power, below Shakespeare's *Henry VIII*, and our own impression is that it is a decidedly finer work of dramatic art. The morbid passions of Mary, the brief intervals of her lucid and energetic action, the gloom of her physical decay and the despair of her moral desolation, together make up a picture which it would be impossible for anyone who entered into it ever to forget.

Exactly. The *study* of Mary, intended to be so Shakespearean, is just the opposite. Imagine these phrases applied to Lady Macbeth. The Victorians did these things more thoroughly than Byron, and bloody Mary is pursued to the bitter end by Tennyson in what is, none the less, by no means a bad play. The paradox of nineteenth-century appreciation of Shakespeare is that it is at once so just and so misguided, just in its appreciation and misguided in its reading of Shakespearean omniscience. If Shakespeare had known what Hamlet was like we should not ask questions about him. And it is at this point that the novel comes in. In its context Scott could really environmentalize his characters. Flaubert knew what Madame Bovary was like. The nineteenth-century mistake was to suppose that the Shakespearean dramatic form could work like the novel and be interchangeable with it.

It is remarkable that Pushkin, a shrewd experimenter and connoisseur of literary forms, should have perceived this from outside England, at the time when Hugo in Paris and in England Wilson and Barry Cornwall (from both of whom he adapted work) were endeavouring to vie with and outdo the Elizabethans. He writes to a friend about the tendency of modern dramatists to *compromise* their characters as he puts it (the letter is in French). He explains his meaning with an example from *The Two Foscari*. 'The conspirator,' he says 'even asks for a drink conspiratorially, and that's ridiculous'. To compromise a character is to forbid him human variety and unexpectedness, to confine him to a dramatic role; and this is just the point that Morgann had made. Falstaff, the braggart, the jester, the *miles gloriosus* and Lord of Misrule, is not compromised by these roles—he escapes them. Pushkin makes the same sort of point about Shylock, who should be above all a miser (like Molière's *Avare*, whom Pushkin censures) but who turns out to be a man of complex animosities and vulnerable human passions.

Pushkin instantly grasped the fragility, as well as the strength of Shakespeare's method, the fact that the unexpectedness which produced the illusion of a whole dossier behind the character, was in fact only sustained from moment to moment by a dramatic skill. 'He always finds the right thing for a character to say at a given moment'. And the right thing is not the properly 'characteristic' thing. From that paradox much depends, including the main nineteenth-century misunderstanding. Novalis's famous phrase 'character is destiny', quoted in the course of their novels by both Hardy and George Eliot, also forms the chief instrument of character appraisal in Bradley's work on Shakespeare. The nineteenth-century novelists who had Shakespeare in their blood, or were inspired by him, interpreted it in the sense that environment is destiny, or at least the interlocking action of personal passions with an environmental situation. This is as true of Scott as of Mérimée, Balzac and George Eliot, the intention to create a characteristic 'case' becoming increasingly prominent as the Shakespearean inspiration thins out. There can be no doubt of it in Scott's story *The Two Drovers*, though it is unlikely that Scott deliberated the potential for a tragic personal clash between English and Highland backgrounds, as Hardy was to deliberate such factors in *The Mayor of Casterbridge*.

Morgann and Pushkin are aware in their different ways of the volatility of the impression that strikes them: the nineteenth century assumed it could be documented, almost that it rested on documentary evidence. German critics like Rötscher and Ludwig take it for granted that Shylock is formed by his background, the clannish sect dwelling in the middle of a hostile society whose members hold all the advantages, who can afford such luxuries as carelessness and generosity, and who are as bitterly resented by the Jewish alien for their virtues as for their vices. We find Heine insisting that Jewishness was what really mattered in Shylock. The same sort of build-up was made in Othello's case. What matters is not the obvious point that Shakespeare had no experience of negroes and Jews—although he would have known of the Lopez case in which the Queen's Portuguese-Jewish physician was framed and executed by Essex for being a suspect foreigner. What matters is that Shakespeare not only acquired information by means of chance scraps from books, and lightning instinct acting on hearsay, but that he created his characters with no more solidity than such rapid inspiration required, and that the exigence of his work dictated. He did not have a nineteenth-century novelist's reflexes, the reflexes which involuntarily determined what Tennyson and Browning were to make of their Straffords and Queen Marys.

2. *Send for Macbeth*

All this today is obvious enough. And yet the legacy persists. We are still apt to confuse our sense—dramatically so absorbing to us—of the involuntary self-revelation of a character, with an assumption of the hidden background that seems ever on the verge of being revealed. And we still prize the characters with whom we slip into the intimacy of a situation, a total case background, unacknowledged by them but perceived by us. Some years ago L. C. Knights wrote a celebrated essay called 'How Many Children Had Lady Macbeth?', in which he strove to counter the heresy that there was a whole domestic history of the Macbeths in the play's background. In vain; that heresy still remains something like holy writ; and held, like so many articles of belief, without full consciousness or examination. A recent book by H. A. Mason, *Shakespeare's Tragedies of Love*, makes this abundantly clear. Again and again Mason invokes Macbeth as a model to reveal what he feels to be the shortcomings, the shifts of policy and evasions of meaning, in the other tragedies. We are at home with Macbeth: we know him through and through, because Shakespeare also seems to know him through and through. 'I really think I could stand a stiff examination on that lady', protested Henry James in reply to objections that he had not fully perceived every aspect of Mrs Brookenham in his novel *The Awkward Age*, and Mason quotes him with approval. Could Shakespeare have said the same about Othello or Antony, Cleopatra or Lear? No, but about Macbeth he could. 'Send for Macbeth' is therefore Mason's watchword when he feels that Shakespeare has failed, as it were, to reach the high standard set by that character.

Mason's book is not only an extreme case, though by no means an isolated one, of our expectations of the novel still being wished upon Shakespeare: it also shows both how misleading and how illuminating such an approach can be. For Mason, Shakespeare succeeds when he works like a novelist and fails when he does not. Nor can it be disputed that Macbeth *is* a novelist's character. In two contexts Mason makes it known to us, by negative definition, what he considers the criterion of such a character. Othello is emphatically not one. This is interesting, because Dr Leavis, in his essay on 'The Sentimentalist's Othello', had remarked that here was a play suited to the psychological novel approach favoured by Bradley 'if it had been made with moderate intelligence'. Leavis proceeded to exercise such intelligence, pointing out that 'for those who take what Shakespeare has to offer' the character of Othello is a case study in self-deceiving egotism. But however brilliant and successful, such a study must come below Shakespeare's 'very greatest work', his great syntheses of insight in the dramatic poetry of the other tragedies and tragi-comedies. Mason depreciates *Othello* still further, but on different grounds. Where

Leavis sees a George Eliot Shakespeare, developing a masterly analysis of egotism, Mason sees one falling well below the novelist's standard, a Shakespeare who did not know what he was about, extemporizing as he went along in a play so full of internal contradictions that he probably never read it through again, let alone revised it. Therefore Othello is 'not a serious character'. Similarly, though the situation of *Antony and Cleopatra* seemed a promising *donnée* (Mason uses the Jamesian term) Shakespeare found after he had begun that there was no way of developing it satisfactorily. He pressed on none the less; but hence the two great lovers are not 'serious characters' either.

In his second context Mason observes: 'Lear is not continuously present to us and is never present as a whole. A novelist would have made everything clear.' A good novelist's character is thus serious, and continuously, present. One would not quarrel with that, nor with the view that Macbeth measures up to it. To suggest the general agreement and implication that we are here in the novelist's world, I cannot do better than quote Emrys Jones's book *Scenic Form in Shakespeare*.

We are probably on more intimate terms with Macbeth than we are with any other of Shakespeare's characters (not excluding Hamlet) and from the presentation of the hero the whole play takes its mood, one of profound inwardness. From the start Shakespeare locates the action in a region deep in our minds.

Jones also suggests the cardinal virtues of the novelist's art by the use of a striking and unexpected compliment, one often used to praise Jamesian structures but rarely Shakespearean ones. He speaks of 'the formal coherence of the play as a whole, its elegance we might be tempted to say . . .' And Mason adds yet a further point: the total and tormented fluency of Macbeth, which indeed makes Hamlet seem a mere contrivance, a straw man allotted striking remarks and arbitrary soliloquies.

What makes the damnation and degradation of Macbeth bearable is that he has the words that enable us to be inward with his state. What makes Othello an intolerable spectacle is the collapse of his power to tell us or himself what is going on. We have to stand outside him when he is beside himself.

The final need: we must identify. Othello attitudinizes and spouts poetry where Macbeth thinks, suffers, and feels as we do. The 'serious' character in Shakespeare turns out, not unnaturally, to be one of us.

It may seem odd on the face of it that we should identify so readily with the predicament of a murderer, and not with the situations of Othello, Antony, and Lear, not (that is) with the presentation of sexual jealousy, a stormy seesaw love affair, or with a typically solutionless family deadlock in which father wants the impossible—three situations which most human beings have actually had to live through. Yet something like this is certainly the case. It is precisely the distance from us of Macbeth's problem that lets us identify with it, that makes it readily soluble, so to say, in our own kinds of mental pre-occupation. Macbeth's murder, and the solitude to which it reduces him, is strangely like so many other and less extreme human dilemmas which the novelist deals in: for example Tolstoy's portrayal of Anna's and Vronsky's adultery, and the realization of themselves and their relation to society which it brings. And as in the novel we can both identify and feel detached. Our communion with Macbeth is complete; that with Othello, Antony or Lear is in various ways partial and defective.

By the same token, that Macbeth is 'elegant', in Emrys Jones's well-chosen word, indicates something important about the way our minds go past its brute actuality. Blood everywhere, yes, in vision and in the fact; but that blood is less grossly, less disturbingly present than Othello's fantasies, or than the actual handkerchief which he asks of Desdemona to wipe his nose, the same that Iago tells him he has seen Cassio wipe his beard with. Less disturbing, even, than Lear's wiping his hand before he proffers it, because it smells of mortality. And it is at this point that we must surely part company with Mason, and with his desire to read *Macbeth* as an absorbing novel, by whose standard of intellectual coherence the other plays are to be judged and found wanting. For the fact is that his Macbeth, however true to our imaginative impression, is not the Macbeth in Shakespeare who says, 'I have done the deed'. Both Mason and Leavis, who condemned the 'sentimentalist's Othello', have gone the whole way in creating not a sentimentalist's but an intellectual's Macbeth, a man with whom they are so familiar and so much at ease that they disregard the dramatic action that in fact makes him do what he does.

As a devotee myself of the approach to Shakespeare which depends on our sense of the novel in him, the unique division and co-existence between novel and play, I feel an anxiety to protect my mystery by pointing out the perversions to which Mason's attitude can lead. For his view is that Shakespeare at his best has the *intentions* as well as the instincts of a novelist; and that when, through accident or indifference, he betrays or compounds them, his subject risks a loss of 'seriousness', and his achievement is at best imperfect. This cannot be true. It is because Shakespeare's intentions are so definitively hidden from us that we are entitled to assume, in our own time, the presence in its world of something like the novel's. On good and sufficient evidence we are entitled to say that he set out with the intention of transforming the old play of Hamlet or of Lear, or the figure of Othello that he found in Cinthio's Italian *novella*. But we cannot say, or even imply, that Shakespeare *intended* in Macbeth a study in the anguish of existential choice, or in Othello of what Froude called 'the sincere hypocrite'. Mason will not admit this. His method insists on the hypothesis of a Shakespeare seeing the possibilities in a subject as a novelist might; and succeeding, or failing, in their realization.

In so doing he—and Leavis too—disregard the necessary division between novel and play, a division which does not destroy the coherency of the Macbeth world though it certainly makes nonsense of any conception of its unity. But since when have any such conceptions made sense in relation to Shakespeare, though of course nothing is easier than to fabricate and impose them in the interest of a particular line of interpretative appreciation? The fact is that Macbeth is two people, though their roles are perfectly in harmony with each other. He is the man of conscience and consciousness, with whom we are completely inward; but he is also the usurper of Scotland, the man 'not without ambition but without / The illness should attend it', who goes to murder—as Bradley says—as if to 'a terrible duty'. The point of this Macbeth is that he *does* commit murder, and not one but many. He becomes a monster. It is a point that some identifiers, like Mason, for whom Macbeth is that supremely serious character, the suffering intellectual, tend to disregard.

But in his excellent book *Shakespeare and the Students* D. J. Enright gives us a salutary reminder of what it entails.

> Robert Bridges was not alone in thinking that the Macbeth who felt the horror of the deed as clearly as Shakespeare's hero would not be able to commit it. One can sympathise with this point of view: Bridges was nearly right. The terror of the play lies in the fact that, when all is thought and felt, Macbeth is still just able to commit the deed. No offence against psychological truth is involved; for one thing, the actual commission of the deed is quickly carried out, and the very ease of the physical operation commends it to one who is involved in an arduous nightmare of horrible imaginings and agonising calculations. If we pause to admit the complexity of any human psychology worthy the name, perhaps we shall find that Shakespeare was simply being 'realistic' once again.

That is certainly true; and we do well to remember that, however close to us he may be in thought, Macbeth is cut off from us by action. We are fully in the novel but we cannot wholly partake in the play. For murder we substitute in our own minds some more familiar manner in which consciousness itself has turned sour, the ripening possibilities of living seeming blasted by an overwhelming sense of misjudgment, weakness, or self-betrayal. We are lucky if we can find nothing of the sort within us, though we are more than humanly unfortunate if it is as irrevocable as Macbeth's experience.

This is obvious enough, for the point would be that not only is Macbeth singularly unfitted for the role of intriguer, murderer and usurper—as all Shakespeare's great tragic heroes are unfitted for their roles—but that he wants just the same things from life as we do. There is nothing peculiar about him. He wants to bask in a deserved reputation, to be respected by 'troops of friends'; to be liked at parties; to be happy with his wife, even if childless now, and to accept the open promise of the years.

The secret that links action firmly to character, play to novel, is the irony of Macbeth's situation. Although he is so ordinary, *because* he is so ordinary, no one understands him but us, the audience, his inward intimates. His wife thinks she understands him, but it turns out she does not, and the discovery helps to destroy her. It is a most important formal aspect of the play, which the novel in it depends on, that understanding of one's fellows in the complex world of power and politics is not easily come by. Duncan is deceived in Cawdor—'there is no art / To find the mind's construction in the face: / He was a gentleman on whom I built / An absolute trust'—and the Fourth Act at the English Court underlines the point with the length and ceremony of a history play. The play announces a problem, on which indeed the plot depends: the novel secretly and comprehensively solves it. Each thus enhances the other. For nothing could be more 'elegant' than the impression that we, and we alone, are inside Macbeth in the novel, while all the dramatis personae are outside him—the living and the dead butcher—in the play.

Mason's error, it seems to me, is to suppose that the coherency of Macbeth is so unique in Shakespeare; if there is coherency in this confrontation and interrelation of novel and play we shall find it everywhere in his art. But Mason is unwilling to extend his intellectual appreciation to other plays. And certainly there are good reasons for his difficulty. He shows us, and it clears the air, that he cannot tolerate a Shakespeare who seems too gripped by the immediate exigence of his matter, its dramatic requirements, to appear as a unifying and perspicuous artist. Two things especially bother him, and determine his refusal to bow the knee before what is usually taken for granted as 'great' in the context of Shakespearean tragedy. Macbeth is 'continuously present' to us because in the art to which the critic responds his consciousness is more important than his acts; but Lear, Antony, Othello, are all in their various ways too involved in the impulse and assault of the moment to appear outside its action, so that at their edges and those of their plays (to quote Mason) 'some quite serious questions are left obscure'. Secondly, Mason seems to find it difficult to tolerate the effects of human incongruity which contribute to this blur, and which may be produced either by Shakespearean carelessness and inadvertence, *or* by his consummate skill in conveying the nearness of human weakness and nobility, muddle and fantasy, moments of clarity and of self-deception.

3. The 'Serious Character'

Mason's dismissal of Othello as 'not a serious character' cannot itself be lightly dismissed. In a sense we have no right to expect, even from Shakespeare, a character 'deeply studied and elaborately justified' in James's or George Eliot's manner, a character whose predicament is so fully exhibited that we cannot but feel full community and sympathy—and yet in Macbeth we have one. The reason may be that in *Macbeth* what I would persist in calling the novel and the play work in so well together; but the opposite natures of the two modes make it unlikely that the same miracle could occur again. In *Othello*, clearly, play and novel appear staringly, almost painfully, separate and in contrast. Perhaps this is the reason for Mason's refusal to consider the character of Othello as 'serious' in his own terms of the novel. The consistency of Macbeth as a character comes from Shakespeare's ability, in that context, to keep an unwavering eye upon him, and to stay on the inside of him. In *Othello* he cannot, at least does not, do this.

Yet the plays are close together, both in chronology and in spirit: both are masterpieces of dramatic excitement and absorption; also, compared with *Hamlet* and *Troilus*, of dramatic naturalism. I have already touched on the point during this essay, and some years ago, in *The Characters of Love*, I attempted an extended critique and appreciation of *Othello*. Every time I have looked at *Othello* since then I have been struck by the lack of freedom in the play, by the sense of a theatrical challenge consummately dealt with in detail, but too great for any liberation of thought and feeling, except outside it. Our sense of freedom in Shakespearean tragedy is paradoxical, but essential. Both Macbeth and Coriolanus (a personality we must look at later) are obsessed and fixated, and yet our sense of them, and our sharing in their experience, does not seem claustrophobic. The obsession of Othello does appear to imprison us, not an as idea but as a dramatic situation. We can identify more with Iago's envy—the concealed dynamic of the play—than with Othello's jealousy.

It may be that what I would call our sense of freedom in Shakespeare might mean the same, at least at times, as what

Mason calls 'seriousness'. And it may be that the predicament of Othello did not engage Shakespeare's imagination as totally as Macbeth's; in which case the audience's state of mind might echo the dramatist's. We cannot live in *Othello* as a complete experience, and the irony of this is all the greater because the stuff from which its drama is made is so familiar: sexual jealousy, suspicion and incredulity, envy and malice as a vocation, the busy solitude of incomprehension. We might suspect that it is just because of these familiarities that Shakespeare's instinct impelled him to divide so drastically the world of the play from the world of the novel where these things have their being. Where *Othello* is concerned it makes literal sense to speak of novel and play, because the play's source is a *novella*, a cautionary tale by the Italian moralist Cinthio. Shakespeare's alterations of his source are usually revealing, as both *Hamlet* and *King Lear* can witness, but nowhere else does he seem to strain so consciously and so deliberately to alter the tone and tenor of the original. Novel and play are—literally again—at odds; and the sense of the metaphorical novel in a Shakespeare play, which for me gives its sense of what I call freedom, is bound to lose out in the struggle.

We can see it doing so precisely in the impression that Shakespeare is so keen to suggest a kind of freedom. What should be effortless, and appear unconscious, can here look factitious and contrived. Othello is deliberately invested with freedom of being ('Keep up your bright swords, for the dew will rust them'): in his speech as he advances to murder ('It is the cause, it is the cause, my soul') and in his great concluding speech, it is invoked almost operatically on his behalf. In this artifice, this careful production of what should be natural, we may detect the causes of any unease we feel. I still believe there is no need whatever to be censorious, with Dr Leavis, about Othello, and to maintain that Shakespeare is exposing him. The trouble seems to be the opposite: that he is not allowed to expose himself, to share himself with us as Macbeth does, and that his creator is concerned, not to expose, but to remove him and protect him. Whatever happens he cannot be allowed to appear like his original in the *novella*, a husband of long standing, conspiring in the brutal and furtive murder of a loyal and faithful wife.

Cinthio, as philosopher, is concerned to point morals. One

such is that the appetites of women can be destructive, and the attraction of opposites perverse. Burton moralized in similar vein. Middleton and Ford, in their plays, make impressive drama out of perversion and perverse attractions. Shakespeare seems to go out of his way to discountenance this theme, and to put the theory of it in the mouths of those who, like Iago and Brabantio, have a direct interest in or need to hold it. But everyone has theories about sex. If Shakespeare did not, he was remarkable, but he may at least have gone along with a general and Platonic *sententia* of his time about passion: that it partakes of the lowest and the highest in us, the angel and the brute. Mason makes a shrewd point here, suggesting, in so far as he is prepared to let Shakespeare off about Othello, that it may have been his intention not to make his hero very 'real'. 'I take it to be part of his design to detach us from his hero by making him repellent as well as attractive, and at the same time inviting us to see a general problem just where the particular case becomes too appalling to dwell on'.

Although Mason imputes a nineteenth-century novelist's sophisticated motivation to Shakespeare, what he says is at least plausible in terms of the dramatic problem. Even Macbeth is a kind of object lesson: suppose Othello to be a more evident one, where the nature of the case made it both easier and more 'dramatic' to dwell on what was both bestial and noble in the human exemplar? We do not need to reflect on the fact that we are seeing God and the Devil in Macbeth, we do not even need to be conscious of it. But sex can be so painful an area that we may prefer to moralize it in this way, turning *Othello*— with Shakespeare—into a spectacle in which complex actuality has been overlaid with an exemplary display of the hell into which a noble nature may fall, of the tragedy 'of one that loved not wisely but too well'. If so, we are all together with Shakespeare in a 'sentimentalist's' conspiracy, and the author intended we should be? An intent of such a kind must seem unnatural for Shakespeare: certainly we can feel Macbeth developing without any suggestion of one.

And yet it does seem possible that his genius for improvisation and involuntary realization of an individual was hampered by the task he took on in *Othello*. We can see how he changed the general *theory* of his hero, even as he changed him to a man just married (a point Mason again ignores). That was a brilliant stroke, brilliant in terms of dramatic plausibility, but though it makes Othello's gullibility more excusable it cannot make it more aesthetically acceptable. The crucial point here would be the decision, no doubt taken before the writing began, to remove the story to a high tragic plane. Leontes and Angelo, in emotional circumstances not unlike Othello's, emerge naturally as individuals, but they are figures in tragi-comedy. It is natural they should be ridiculous as well as painful, pompous as well as touching, and that Angelo's spasms of self-knowledge should not redeem him from a situation in which neither his real distinction nor his false dignity can avail him. He is an extraordinary creation, emerging out of the play almost before the author seems to know what is happening, and nearly changing its whole tenor in the process. He develops without effort from the 'unjust Judge' of Shakespeare's source, as Macbeth develops from the powerful usurper of Holinshed. But Othello seems to be propelled on the stage ready made, as it were; the decision to alter him radically having been taken beforehand and every dramatic muscle tensed in readiness for the transformation.

This beginning might well account for the impression Mason gets, that developing the play in the way he chose 'blocked' the full power of 'Shakespeare's intelligence'. What disturbs me is rather different: it is the inevitable nullification of naturalism by the pressure of the plot. For like *Macbeth* and *Lear*, and unlike *Troilus*, *Othello* runs over with the natural overplus and bounty of Shakespearean creation. Its 'novel' is packed with matter, packed with scenes from the photograph album, images of the past and possibilities of the future. But the needs of the play denature the novel: the plot's merciless rigidity turns what should be free and spacious (the castle and marriage of the Macbeths, the geography of Lear's kingdom) into facts that are all pointed at us. We are oppressed by significance; nowhere else does Shakespeare spend his riches to get such obvious value.

Like many before him, Mason blames Shakespeare for ineptitude and carelessness, in making Emilia give the handkerchief to her husband and say nothing to her mistress, etc. The trouble seems to me again just the opposite. Shakespeare's powers make it all too dreadfully plausible. And they are the powers of what Enright rightly calls his 'realism', directed here towards the prosecution of a brilliantly precarious plot. It is entirely in character for Emilia to be so feather-headed as to forget all about the handkerchief; she cannot connect one thing with another; her intelligence is as rudimentary as her instincts and courage are sound. Earthy as she is, she can recognize something is wrong, Othello troubled and suspicious. Isn't he jealous? she asks, and Desdemona replies:

> Who, he? I think the sun where he was born
> Drew all such humours from him.

The famous words promise freedom only to withdraw it instantly. Like Emilia, Desdemona is so aptly, so fatally in character. The words show us her glowing dream of her new husband, as much outside the actuality of their situation, and its dangers, as she herself was outside Othello's dream. Such accuracy, such 'realism', can give one at times a leaden sensation, the symptom of all that is most effective, and depressing, in the art of *Othello*. We are so aware of the inexorable effectiveness of the words in her mouth, the thumb of her creator upon her. It is not, to put it mildly, a sensation that Shakespeare gives us very often. The 'realization' of Shakespearean character usually frees it from the demands of the play: here it works to imprison it in them more closely.

Shakespeare seems himself the victim of his plot, his powers taken by it into custody at an early stage. Such service would have been perfect freedom to Racine, but freedom for Shakespeare is another matter. He has followed his instinct of making his hero incongruous with the situation. As Macbeth is not the man for murder, so Othello is not the man for suspicion and intrigue. He has an instinctive generosity of spirit; if we do not believe that, and do not believe that all the genius of dramatic poetry is directed to making it true, then we might as well also believe that Macbeth, like Dr Johnson's patriotic butcher, really feels 'no uneasy sensation' at the thought of doing in Duncan, that he has decided to do it from the beginning, and only hesitates in order to give the appearance of conscience. Of course such speculation would occur to no one in Macbeth's case, but the critics question Othello's nature and motives just *because* it is so important for the play for him to be the man he is. Desdemona, too, is condemned to be herself, in all the unawareness of love, out of equal necessity. We realize this when Auden observes in his essay on the play that she may have been technically innocent on this occasion, but given a

few more years of marriage to Othello she might well not
have been. The free characters of Shakespeare could shrug this
off—it would merely enhance their freedom, but apply it to
Desdemona and it shakes the whole brilliant and precarious
tragic structure. Oh well, if *that's* it, and Iago was right about
Venetian girls, what's all the fuss about . . .?

No wonder, as Mason points out, that we cannot identify
with and enter into two people condemned to be so exactly
their dramatic selves. They are not soluble in our consciousness
like Macbeth; we have to stand outside them. To see how the
process works in detail it is worth comparing two speeches:
Macbeth's before the murder; and Othello's outcry at his loathed
situation, and at Desdemona's isolation from him in her
apparently shameless refusal to admit guilt.

> If it were done, when 'tis done, then 'twere well
> It were done quickly. If the assassination
> Could trammel up the consequence, and catch,
> With his surcease, success; that but this blow
> Might be the be-all and the end-all here,
> But here, upon this bank and shoal of time,—
> We'd jump the life to come. But in these cases
> We still have judgment here; that we but teach
> Bloody instructions, which being taught, return
> To plague the inventor: this even-handed justice
> Commends the ingredients of our poison'd chalice
> To our own lips. He's here in double trust:
> First, as I am his kinsman and his subject,
> Strong both against the deed: then, as his host,
> Who should against his murderer shut the door,
> Not bear the knife myself. Besides, this Duncan
> Hath borne his faculties so meek, hath been
> So clear in his great office, that his virtues
> Will plead like angels, trumpet-tongued, against
> The deep damnation of his taking-off:
> And pity, like a naked new-born babe,
> Striding the blast, or heaven's cherubin, hors'd
> Upon the sightless couriers of the air,
> Shall blow the horrid deed in every eye,
> That tears shall drown the wind.—I have no spur
> To prick the sides of my intent, but only

> Vaulting ambition, which o'er-leaps itself,
> And falls on the other.

>   Had it pleas'd heaven
> To try me with affliction; had they rain'd
> All kinds of sores and shames on my bare head;
> Steep'd me in poverty to the very lips;
> Given to captivity me and my utmost hopes;
> I should have found in some place of my soul
> A drop of patience: but, alas, to make me
> The fixed figure of the time, for scorn
> To point his slow and moving finger at!—
> Yet could I bear that too; well, very well:
> But there, where I have garner'd up my heart;
> Where either I must live, or bear no life,—
> The fountain from the which my current runs,
> Or else dries up: to be discarded thence!
> Or keep it as a cistern for foul toads
> To knot and gender in!

In Macbeth's soliloquy a feverish internal concentration not only contrasts with, but takes off into, images of space and depth and air. The calculation is precise and preoccupied ('If . . . If . . . But . . . First . . . Besides . . .') and it is worth noticing that Macbeth himself does not claim to feel the emotion he imagines in the response of others. He is much too concerned with the anguish of the moment to notice the meaning of words like 'pity', so that their appearance seems unconnected with himself, almost absent-minded. For in the background of his muttering, great chords seem to sound and build up of themselves, culminating in the great blast of the image, *That tears shall drown the wind . . .* The paradox is that out of his chess-like concentration, and ours with him, the great general considerations and proofs of humanity move inexorably in from the outside.

Othello's speech has the opposite effect. It shows, not a self-deceiver, but a man trapped in his own attempts at self-liberation. Nothing from the outside avails him. If only *any* other disaster had struck . . . Any and every external burden could be borne, but *not* the sense that the self's most hidden and personal part has been taken over for these alien indifferent couplings. Every word of Othello leads us unendurably to the ego's vulnerable centre. Every word of the equally self-centred Macbeth calls up forces that are free and terrible outside.

It is a technical question, relating to the emotions involved. In one sense, in such poetry, both Othello and Macbeth are only recorders, immensely sensitive, of these different but equally universal emotions. One kind rushes outwards, the other coils ever more tightly inwards; and how this happens is graphically realized. To censure Othello for his emotion is to disown it: we exult in our minds' sailing from the particular to the general with those of a man about to do murder; we detest them being trapped in the hell of an obsessed and self-bewailing cuckold. But, to reduce the technical point *ad absurdum*, a Macbeth in the other's position could only be an Othello. We are the victims of Shakespeare's experimentation in tragic technique, and to be in the hands of such a master cannot always be a comfortable experience. We go through it with Macbeth gladly, but we exclude ourselves from Othello by isolating him with the patronage of our observation.

In one sense, then, the tragic experiment has been too daring in the case of Othello: it risks failure, by reason of the emotions involved. And Shakespeare too no doubt sensed this. For he connives in our protection, and in protecting us. Since Othello cannot be liberated in and through our emotions he must achieve an artificial freedom on a grand scale, through his own act and deed. This is the point of his last speeches; and in his farewell— 'Soft you, a word or two before you go'—we are aware of how superbly Shakespeare, rather than Othello, is handling the situation. It is not Othello who is 'cheering himself up', in Eliot's phrase; such an idea supposes that the tragic progression is running itself, through its own momentum and intensity, as it does in *Macbeth*. It is Shakespeare who must cheer the audience up, an audience who have found the drawn-out conspiracy of the plot exasperatingly painful. To use jealousy as the tragic fuel is a daring operation that calls for careful control, and a kind of wary coolness not like Shakespeare's natural port of creation. I have spoken of the creator's thumb on Desdemona, and in the Willow scene there is a deftness and exploitation which really does verge on the sentimental—that quality being defined precisely by the effect of sad-sweet contrivance, for all Emilia's salt in the sweetness. The innocence of Desdemona and the earthiness of Emilia are both too evidently contrasted with Othello's obsession. Both are confined, like the hero, in the isolation of their unawareness; and both are as evidently confined—or in Pushkin's term 'compromised'—by their roles. Where they are concerned the tragedy has most obviously no freedom left to work with. Shakespeare's sense of Desdemona's sexuality, and of her being sexually besotted by Othello ('She was too fond of her most filthy bargain') is implied in the novel but has nothing to work on in the play, for, dramatically speaking, such a theme cannot be kept away from Iago's, and Emilia's, world of appetites that diminish by nature, and passions soon compromised by calculation.

Hidden somewhere in this background is Shakespeare's enormous, instinctual knowledge of what really goes on: in this instance of how Othello is disturbed, without knowing it, by the physical warmth of Desdemona's passion for himself, and his apprehension of how such a passion seems directed in its very nature towards the whole world of men. He is betrayed by his unpreparedness for the incarnation of feelings which he has himself aroused, just as he must be dismayed—again hardly knowing it or knowing why—by the social manners and unthinking social confidence of Desdemona. Her behaviour with the two officers at the harbour is as revealing as her demeanour before the Venetian senate, as her replies to Othello's words of joy as he steps ashore in Cyprus. On these occasions we have no sense of her creator and his requirements at her elbow, but only of the natural map of love, presented with the full intensity and Venetian colour of Shakespeare's maturity.

There is another and more disconcerting side to Shakespeare's knowledge of what really goes on. For the play, and for the tragic beauty it enacts, he put Othello and Iago at opposite poles. In Cinthio's story they are not only comrades but fellows of the same moral order. And, for all that Shakespeare can do and has done, there is a sense in which they still are. Both are men concerned above all to make their way in the world and to impose their will upon others. Both have acquired the personality that will best fit their different natures for the process. By nature they are indeed unalike, as Cassio is from both, but all three share in the common acceptances and assumptions of the life of power. This, again, is part of the underworld of the novel which the play must exclude.

But it is this buried freedom which determines the play's

nature, for when freedom is undone by the plot we remain intensely aware of it, and of what has replaced it. It is this sense of division methodically set up by the works of the tragedy which gives it unique and powerful selfhood. Novel and play are deliberately separated and set against each other: and our participation in the first makes our exclusion from the second particularly poignant and painful, but ultimately revealing. Isolation is thus not only the theme of the tragedy but its method, for as the two lovers are cut off from each other, so are we from them, and from the 'novel' in their background which gives them freedom, and us with them. Mason's complaint about our having to stand outside Othello is exactly the point of the process: and the process is realistic. We do have to stand outside other people's pain, the more so if it seems grotesque in resembling nothing we could feel ourselves, for we never believe that we could be taken in as Othello is. Othello has the words (I have quoted them) to make us 'inward with his state', but that state is by definition self-confining. It is perverse, however understandable, to depreciate it by comparison with Macbeth's. The more solitary Macbeth's predicament makes him, the closer he comes to us. The emotions that drive Othello work the opposite way. We should be able to understand and participate in both experiences.

We should be, but it seems not all of us can. The reason must be that the process in *Othello* involves, at some level, a powerful and primitive intoxicant, and this intoxication is the only *immediate* source of freedom in the working of the play. When young, at our first experience of it, we feel the impact of it most, an impact that Shakespeare must certainly have intended; and what we feel is a dramatic poetry akin to opera, to music, to a shattering display of natural forces. If we cannot feel this intoxication, or reject it, we are losing out on the play. Its function is, of course, to distract us from that terrible and static tableau in which hero and heroine are locked, the tableau of uncomprehending love, in which his public confidence and personal insecurity is matched with and isolated from her fatally complete confidence in him. It is a situation which cannot be broken by any of the more or less patronizing interpretations put forward by those whose real aim is to deflect the reader from any direct participation in the play, who need—by one means or another—to feel superior to the *Othello* situation.

Shakespeare's realism gives us the natural history of Othello's jealousy and Iago's envy, but in themselves these are, and must remain, 'permanent, obscure and dark'. All our knowing post-Freudian attempts at illumination are sealed off by the removal of Iago's motive. But they remain the curse of stage Othellos. It is an impossible play to act because there is only one possible way to act it—straight—as Salvini and Valk used to do; and they were both foreigners with effortless voice domination. An actor with ideas, like Olivier, with his West Indian Othello, is more disastrous in this play than in any other, because he compromises the poetry which is the antidote to the play's painfulness. The realism with which Shakespeare backs up Othello's rhetoric enables us both to see through it and to enjoy it, but we can do neither if the actor is himself inviting us to do so. We can apprehend, ourselves, the nature of the passions involved—the sexual violence generalized in the hero, and the sexual submission in the heroine—provided that actor and actress are not offering these as pathological phenomena for our critical scrutiny.

In both plays naturalism is at its height: that is to say the emotions involved seem almost overpoweringly real and present. In terms of my suggested method of understanding what happens in Shakespeare's world, this is because the 'play' and the 'novel' of *Othello* and *Macbeth* are both firm and massive entities, in the one case working harmoniously together, and in the other violently and deliberately opposed. Lacking the relation of these entities the worlds involved would not be so complete, so absorbing and exciting, so tense with felt experience. The characters, in particular, would not have the immense importance they do. This comparative absence of 'a novel in the play' I have commented on in the case of *Hamlet*, discussed at length in *Troilus and Cressida*. And the idea of the distinction between novel and play may help us in the appraisal of how other plays work, most notably *Antony and Cleopatra* and *Measure for Measure*.

4. 'Antony and Cleopatra' and 'Coriolanus'

On the face of it *Antony and Cleopatra* has all the space and the density we associate with naturalism. But it is too unitary an organism to avail itself of these apparent riches; it lacks the characteristic perspective and emphasis given by the novel/play differentiation. One reason for this is very simple: Shakespeare is following, in a relaxed and easy manner, a single source which seems to have presented him with no real challenge to divagation. But this is far from being conclusive. In *Julius Caesar* the shadow novel is, by contrast, very much taking shape in the background. Brutus and Cassius, their natures and their friendship, offer in it the same field of query as the presentation of Caesar himself. Above all, the significance and status of *friends*, in a moral and political crisis, challenges both the source material and the limits of the immediate drama. It is a word that constantly recurs, suggesting the most crucial human contexts and responses: the reaction of Caesar to his friends the conspirators, of Brutus to his feeling for Caesar, of Antony at Caesar's death. The friendship that is void in Octavius ruins Cassius's plans, and achieves its most moving significance in the quarrel scene and in the aftermath of the battle.

We have seen how *Othello* is divided, and in how graphic a way, between what might be called a novel about love and the envy of love, and a play about jealousy. Shestov demonstrates the same kind of division in Macbeth when he attacked a famous Danish Shakespearean of the time for calling Macbeth the greatest exemplar in literature of the power of conscience and retribution. Rubbish! exclaims Shestov in an essay I mentioned earlier, *Shakespeare and His Critic Brandes*. Tragedy in Macbeth is the challenge of freedom which confronts him in consequence of his thought and deed, the horrifying freedom of Dostoevsky's 'Underground Man'. Shestov, with typical Russian intransigence, refused to admit that his and Brandes's view of the matters were perfectly compatible, as compatible as is the novel of friendship in *Julius Caesar* with its dramatic theme of political power.

A similar compatibility gives the same extra dimension to *Coriolanus*. The political system of republican Rome swarms with an immediacy of dramatic life and incident, and against this background appears what may be Shakespeare's closest approach to a personal case history, done in a spirit of perceptive curiosity. Shakespeare approaches Coriolanus through Plutarch, his informant and mentor, though Plutarch was able to give the

Roman rebel less sympathy and understanding than to his own fellow-Greek Alcibiades, with whom he linked him in the parallel lives. Shakespeare does not 'compromise' Coriolanus, but he certainly appears to define and to 'place' him, in a study of almost Freudian determinism. Indeed it seems an open-and-shut case. His frenetic impatience and violence, his insanely courageous exploit at the capture of Corioli and his equally suicidal contempt for prudence and reason in his dealings with the Roman people, are clearly marked as symptoms of his effort to escape the implacable domination of his mother.

It is paradoxical that what makes Coriolanus an exceptionally well-defined character, even by Shakespeare's standards, is the fact that in his mother's eyes he is a mere aspect of her being. She it was who 'clucked him to the wars and brought him home, laden with honours', and his greatest achievements belong to her for he is the instrument of her personality. He cannot cut the umbilical cord, and it is his tragedy, whose only 'clearness' (to use Macbeth's significant word) comes when he realizes his servitude to the full, and hence is for a moment free of it. There is no 'world elsewhere', as he boasts, no chance for him to 'stand as if a man were author of himself and knew no other kin'. The still centre of his realization is marked with the most explicit stage direction in the folio: *Coriolanus, holds her by the hand, silent*. He sees now that all the force he has exerted against foes, plebeians, his own country, was really hers. And from her, too, will be the death that he forecasts for himself at the hands of the enemies he has led on Rome.

> But, for your son, believe it, O, believe it,
> Most dangerously you have with him prevailed,
> If not most mortal to him. But let it come.

And it comes. Aufidius, the Volscian commander, has read Coriolanus in the light of this relationship and perceived how to exploit it. At the psychologically correct moment he mocks the 'boy of tears' to his face, and provokes the explosion that leads to the hero's death at the hands of the outraged Volscians.

> 'Boy'! False hound!
> If you have writ your annals true, 'tis there
> That, like an eagle in a dovecote, I
> Fluttered your Volscians in Corioli.
> Alone I did it. 'Boy'!

'Alone I did it'. Coriolanus has had, outside Rome, his moment of truth; he returns now to the blind affirmation of self, to the thrusting down into the dark of the knowledge that he is not his own self but his mother's. In his last frenzy he is back in his old world, and the last outburst with which he claims it has a kind of maniacal dignity.

A novelist today—a playwright still more—would present this Coriolanus in a consistent Freudian perspective. His dramatic function, and downfall, would reveal to reader and audience its hidden source. Shakespeare's hero is almost so determined—indeed that he *is* so determined makes the monstrous progression so effective—but for one wholly unexpected and liberating circumstance. True, it may be accidental or inadvertent; it certainly does not appear to point a deliberate meaning at us, as does Shakespeare's alteration in Plutarch's account of the capture of Corioli. Plutarch's Coriolanus has not only a great man's disdain for the spoils of victory; he also asks for and obtains the freedom of an old Volscian friend and benefactor. Shakespeare's modification of this incident is as meaningful as it is 'realistic'. He asks for the man to be freed, but has forgotten his name. Nothing is done, for the reaction from his exploit overcomes Coriolanus, and he calls out, with his usual exasperated impatience, for wine. The moment of liberation is mute; the old acquaintance unsaved; the headlong progress continued. But if this alteration seems to underline a determined conception of Coriolanus, it is contradicted in one wholly unexpected direction. Shakespeare's instinct seems to have been to provide his hero, inconspicuously, with one unlikely seat of calm and repose—his wife. 'My gracious silence', as he calls Virgilia, provides a refuge from the pattern in his life that cannot be altered, and what other writer would suggest that so mother-dominated a figure as Coriolanus might be happily married to a wife with whom he has a wholly different and blessedly tranquil relationship? And perhaps not with his wife only but with all women other than his mother: with Valeria too, who Plutarch tells us was much revered in Rome.

> The noble sister of Publicola,
> The moon of Rome, chaste as the icicle
> That's curdied by the frost from purest snow
> And hangs on Dian's temple. Dear Valeria!

As fervent in tone as it is cold in artifice, the image transforms the text, emphasizing again the 'world elsewhere' which both defines Coriolanus and yet frees our conception of him from too exact a definition, just as their final meeting emphasizes the nobility of his mother as well as her intolerableness. For him the moment of self-realization is also—and very poignantly—a realization of how much he loves both her and Rome. It is this that enables him to take a decision that one might think impossible to his maniacally conditioned nature, a decision made in stillness and silence.

*   *   *

The personality of Coriolanus himself, apparently the cause of all the turmoil and intrigue in swarming Rome, and yet having a hidden coherency which is detached from them, means that this play has not one but two novels in its background. One of them is afforded by the political implications that go beyond the dramatic action: the other by the nature of the hero—what 'makes him tick'—which raises queries outside his own tragedy. Each gives point and perspective to the other, and makes us realize how lacking *Antony and Cleopatra* is in any of these divisions. However different its atmosphere and background, *Antony and Cleopatra* does seem, like *Troilus and Cressida*, wholly a play; its protagonists actors who are at the same time too *acted on* to produce a coherent part. We have seen how much Shakespeare's great and sustained burst of naturalism depends on an exploitation of the formal device that in drama men may not be what they seem. 'Certainly men should be what they seem', says Othello to Iago, his exasperation naturalizing a tradition of stage villainy that goes back beyond Richard III's 'I am not what I am'. Variations on the discrepancy are vital to the techniques of naturalism, but in *Antony and Cleopatra*, bursting as it is with natural life, they are strikingly absent.

Mason comes to the conclusion that Shakespeare intended to write a great tragedy of love, but that through some loss of inspiration or will, nothing much occurred; for him Antony's conduct throughout remains 'essentially unreal', and the attempts at giving expression to a 'great love' factitious. I feel there is a good deal of point in Mason's reaction to the play, but that he goes wrong in suggesting that Shakespeare's imagination must have been fired by some ambitious purpose which he then disappoints us by not bringing to fruition; that Shakespeare *tried* to make Antony the paragon of heroic love, and that we become conscious—quite painfully so in Mason's view—of his inability to convince us.

Suppose Shakespeare never intended anything of the sort, but just went along with the source material to see what would happen? Antony was no Othello needing to be transformed at the outset, and no Macbeth to be revealed inwardly to us rather than to his fellows in the drama. There was no clue to be insensibly guided by, as Shakespeare may have been guided into a dramatic perception by the violence of Coriolanus, adding his own corroborative touches. The only interest of Antony may be that he shows how Shakespeare needed some 'line'—the obsessions of Macbeth and Othello, the singular situations of Hamlet, and King Lear, and Angelo—to set his most characteristic powers at work, to divide his hero from the drama and set him in the ambiguous perspective of the novel. Antony has nothing to offer. Everything is open and above board; it is all there in Plutarch. We are to have none of the uncovenanted rewards of naturalism, but nature herself; rather boring, rather touching, wholly explicable.

We might put the matter by saying that Antony and Cleopatra have nothing to do but be actors; nothing but to utter the golden speeches, make the heroic assertions, touch us at times and leave us sceptical at others. The ironic paradox is that for this very reason actors find the two great parts almost impossible to play —as they understand playing parts. For what 'interpretation' can be made? If there was no 'line' for Shakespeare to get on the pair, the actors are in worse case still. There is nothing to be got out of a speech like Cleopatra's exordium of Antony— 'His legs bestrid the ocean, his rear'd arm / Crested the world . . .'—except the commonplace knowledge that such women magnify their dead husbands or lovers with a passionate display of loyalty that has its ridiculous side. Naturalism has here no arts left to excite us, though it has a wonderful range of episode to amuse and to distract. Mason feels that every speech shows the inadequacy of Shakespeare's embodiment of the lovers. Of 'the wonderful epitaph' which Cleopatra speaks over Antony—

O withered is the garland of the war,
The soldier's pole is fall'n . . .

he says 'I am unable to feel it as generated out of her own mind or to relate it to the Antony of the play'; and of her next speech, when she rhetorically exclaims

> Then is it sin
> To rush into the secret house of death
> Ere death dare come to us?

he remarks that it is 'theatrical in the best sense . . . at the lips' ends, but not going deep'.

'Going deep' would mean revealing and embodying the manner of woman she is, which for Mason presupposes that there should be something striking and remarkable to embody, as there is with Lady Macbeth. But why should there be? In this play there isn't: its nature has turned out different. I agree with Mason that flatness is the risk Shakespeare finds himself running in *Antony and Cleopatra*, compound it with marvellous language as he may, but this is the reverse of meaning that a great subject or conception has fallen flat. It just *is* flat, in itself, and Shakespeare, ruminatively following Plutarch, has a genius that does not need to disguise the fact. It is a very different and in a sense more interesting discovery than the decision to treat the Troilus story as the formal parody of a moment from the Trojan War, for the benefit of clever young men who would appreciate it; but the consequences in art are not so very different. For the trouble about ordinary behaviour, in crises and out of them, is that it does not go 'very deep'. Ordinary people easily become worked up and histrionic, and when they are they repeat much the same sort of thing again and again. They justify themselves; they make excuses and endless resolutions; they try, half-confusedly, to achieve pathetic or dignified utterance. And in all this succession of speech some notes strike false or iterative and unmeaningful, some piercingly true, which does not mean true to anything 'deep' in a dramatically realized individual, but to the eternal human response to things, and that, when overwhelmed by them, we indeed do not—as Mason disapprovingly puts it—quite know where we stand. Mason himself defines the human response to unmanageable crisis when he comments that 'Antony both talks himself out of and is talked by others out of reality'. That process is going on with us day by day in hundreds of sitting-rooms and hospitals and crematoria services.

So it is clear that Shakespeare's reality has the last word here, and in a final sense, the sense that cannot include the formal divisional hypotheses of play and novel—those hypotheses that make both for extreme individuality, and the unbounded speculation that feeds on such individuality. In *Antony and Cleopatra* Shakespeare rightly found himself content with a situation which his intelligence, in the imaginative working out, sensed to be all on the surface, in a way that could none the less be rendered with a felicitous bravura. Such an unerring superficiality at every point of the action involved a more than just understanding at every point of Plutarch's confused and multiplied scene. Those great events *were* impressive, in the most straightforward way, and they seem to have impressed Shakespeare as much, and in the same ways, as they impressed Plutarch and his translators, Jacques Amyot and North. It was a world in which the opulence seemed extraordinary, the stakes more than human. Antony's legs really did bestride the ocean; at his voice, 'like boys unto a muss, kings would start forth, and cry: "Your will?"'. Such grandeur seems an aspect more of the world they live in than of the characters themselves, and the schoolmaster's words about Antony offer the poetry that seems commensurate with such a world.

> I was of late as petty to his ends
> As is the morn-dew on the myrtle leaf
> To his grand sea.

The poetry of the play, full of humour and agility, Tiepoloesque gorgeousness and nervous strength, has all the qualities needed for the depiction of such a world, and it belongs to that world rather than to the individuals (we have the impression in the play of an exotic milieu with its own characteristics, rather than individual characters themselves, just as we may do in life if we penetrate briefly the professional precincts of actors, politicians, or the very rich). Shakespeare has of course—his one innovation on Plutarch—brought out the figure of Enobarbus to act as it were as guide and intermediary into this sumptuous place, a man who both derides and depends on it, is both participant and spectator. A normal Elizabethan audience—not the kind who may be presumed to have enjoyed the belittling of state and legend in *Troilus*—would have responded to this portrayal of greatness, and would have appreciated just as much the demonstration, as psychologically appealing as it is 'true to life', that in moments of emotional and business crisis the fabulously great turn out to behave in much the same ways as you and me.

Taken in this way the play is superb: the faults Mason finds are in fact its particular virtues. In *Julius Caesar* Antony was still hidden from us, and full of possibility, his strength still unmeasured and his nature to be guessed at. And by the usual novel/play paradox we feel closer to him in this uncertainty than we do when, in *Antony and Cleopatra*, all is declared and on the surface. His questionable quality intrigued us, but now all is commonplace. As is Cleopatra, and her maids. This does not mean they do not move us. T. S. Eliot remarked on the genius which added two words to Plutarch's record of Charmian's dying speech to the guardsman.

> It is well done and fitting for a princess
> Descended of so many royal kings.
> Ah, soldier.

Plutarch's 'noble' becomes 'royal'—a subtle change—but, more than this, Charmian's last exclamation is faithful to the whole nature of the play's poetry. She makes her 'speech', and then death wrings from her a last appeal to the comfort and support of a living man. It is the same with Antony's speeches. When Mason complains that Antony is 'a stage figure' when he declaims:

> The shirt of Nessus is upon me, teach me
> Alcides, thou mine ancestor, thy rage—

and so forth, the reply is 'of course'. Shakespeare has naturalized dramatic rhetoric to the confused needs of a man going under in a crisis, grasping at straws, propping up his persona, appealing frenetically to friends and mistress. Such flexibility in the poetic utterance brings its own reward, and its own penalty: the monotony of repetition. It makes no sense to speak of 'getting to know' this pair, for what they say is immediately comprehensible, surrendering the seeker's interest that is as implicit in dramatic as in fictional art. But when Antony says, 'I am dying, Egypt, dying . . .' or when he gasps out to the Queen (mistakenly of course)—'None about Caesar trust but Proculeius'—showing his real solicitude and making nonsense of any ideas of their *Liebestod* together, we are as moved as when Cleopatra turns to her maids after Caesar has left and says: 'He words me, girls, he words me.'

Bradley wrote that Antony is 'more than love's pilgrim; he is love's martyr'. This is absurd, except in the humdrum sense (which Bradley may have obscurely intended) that we are all pilgrims and martyrs of whatever situation controls us in life, and by controlling us is too much for us. Behind the relation of the pair there is no depth, no tragic passion, nothing undisclosed. One could say that because they know each other so well they are not worth our while to know—to know, that is, in the sense in which we wish to know the men and women we meet in great art. And there is a final point, unacknowledged by Antony and by the play's pretension, although it haunts its actuality. Had Cleopatra never existed Antony would still have been defeated and brought down by Caesar. Plutarch's soothsayer, echoed by Shakespeare, knew this; and we feel that Antony knows it too and so does Cleopatra herself, though its admission would dissolve the conspiracy of passion which, like other conventions of love, even between those who know each other so well, must exist between them. Shakespeare saw from Plutarch that Cleopatra's survival was ultimately as independent of Antony as his downfall was of her. It is the figure of Caesar, with all it implies of humiliation and the end of her 'lifestyle' that brings her to suicide.

Mason feels that Shakespeare again compounds and conceals the failure of the heroic theme by making even Caesar join in the lamentations at the hero's fall. 'We cannot mistake the author's intention', he says, in taking a 'self-indulgent delight' in hyperbole, and incongruously giving the speech to Caesar. Whatever Shakespeare's intention, the effect is obviously of a final realism: the greater Caesar makes out to be the fellow emperor he has so totally worsted, and referred to in private as 'the old ruffian', the greater the cause for official congratulation. Propriety, of the kind which the Caesars of the world are never remiss in, requires this murmur of magnanimous regret over the defunct business rival; and reminds us that the *mise-en scène* of the play is indeed the great business of the world. There can be no two views of what constitutes failure or success in that business; and Antony has failed, not through love and certainly not redeemed by it, not even through a loss of will that might make him more endearing than his competitor. His lack of single-mindedness lends itself neither to the tensions of the drama nor the queries of the novel. There is none of the necessary and technical problem in treating him which Shakespeare found in the case of Othello, and which makes Othello so interesting a case. He and Cleopatra owe their greatness to their position and to the world they move in; and it is that world which is the real dynamic of the play, basking in Nilotic riches or shining with civil swords. It makes them a great pair: in a smaller world they would have been a small one.

5. *Measure for Measure*

By way of an epilogue to our case let us finish with a brief look at *Measure for Measure*. For if *Coriolanus* has two novels in it, and *Antony and Cleopatra* neither a play nor a novel, *Measure for Measure* is a unique hybridization in form: a play whose accompanying novel, one of the most promising in the canon, is deliberately aborted. From the third act the play conforms to the rigorous pattern of a tragi-comedy, exemplifying the kind of moral point which the Italian intellectual and moralist Guarini had laid down in his own play, *Il Pastor Fido*, as proper to the form. We hear no more of the potentialities that would have made up the perspective of novel and the tension of drama, and the two characters who promised them, Isabella and Angelo, are kept firmly in hand for the rest of the action.

We need not regret anything; the play as it stands is rich and rewarding; but the kinds of possibility in it illustrate with a singular clarity the sorts of division in form and intent which are so enlarging in Shakespeare. In it a pattern of meaning is clearly intended, but it is one not wholly compatible with the material deployed and the characters as revealed. The fascinating thing is that those two characters have obvious tragic potential, which the play is forced to keep down, and yet they could also have been characters in another sort of comedy. Indeed they came from one. Had Shakespeare followed his main source— George Whetstone's clumsy two-part comedy of 1578, *Promos and Cassandra*—Isabella would have yielded to Angelo's demands on her virtue in order to save her brother Claudio's life, as Cassandra yields to the judge Promos. And Claudio—his life preserved in spite of Angelo's intent, as is Andrugio's in the earlier play—would have forgiven Angelo in the finale for the sake of the sister who had sought to save his life: for this sister is now happily married to the judge who had seduced her and then ordered her brother's death.

The point of potential significance in the farrago of the earlier play is the strange relation between the unjust judge and the girl with whom he breaks his bargain; and it is to this relation that Shakespeare was clearly attracted. But it may be significant that Whetstone's play was never acted, and that Shakespeare saw that the growth of the relation between the judge and his female victim, then mistress, was one that the stage could not successfully display. If comedy it would turn flat; in tragedy the brother would have had to die, and the guilty pair—judge and victim sister—would have enjoyed a damned relationship that would isolate them and must end in disaster. Promising in a way; and yet it would court the too explicit, becoming, with whatever greater degree of subtlety and humanity, a situation such as Ford treated, notably in *'Tis Pity She's a Whore*. Shakespeare's instinct was no doubt sound; and yet what follows from it is equally revealing, and perhaps the most striking instance of my 'novel and play' thesis, for he could not help suggesting two fictional characters wide open to speculation, about whom speculation—in terms of the play's denouement— is doomed to disappointment.

Yet the suspended 'story in it' is in a sense the ideal artistic compromise. We are greatly intrigued by Angelo and Isabella: but we do not have to feel our interest dissipated in the necessities of action. When he turned the play into a drama in verse, called *Angelo*, Pushkin clearly sensed this potential of interest, and with his usual skill and instinct in matters of form was able to make an ideally economical use of it. No mock seduction with Mariana takes place. Isabella renounces Angelo—for that is the impression that Pushkin, without explicit comment, contrives to give; and she returns to the convent. Angelo is reconciled with Mariana and forgiven by the Duke, who has no designs on Isabella. Isabella knows that her brother is safe when she urges forgiveness for Angelo, so that her emotion in that scene becomes one of renunciation rather than a heavenly forgiveness over and above what is demanded by 'measure for measure'.

It is plain that Pushkin was not impressed by that act of

forgiveness, and indeed it is dramatically one of the weakest things in the play, however needful to the harmony of plot and moral. It is overshadowed by our sense of the relation between those two strong and strange characters, who do indeed seem made for each other, and who in confrontation have been compelled to realize the truth about their natures, a realization which hovers on the dangerous edge of intimacy. For Angelo and Isabella would not be the interesting, indeed fascinating, characters they are, if it were not for the incongruity of their formal position: they are tragic characters, on the side of death, who are compelled not only to have their relation dissolved by comedy, but themselves cajoled by comedy to the point of a kind of salutary humiliation.

It is true that in other and earlier comedy Shakespeare developed the technique—so brilliantly exemplified a century or so later by Molière in *Le Misanthrope*—of putting into it characters who were not at all at home in the comedy world. The point of Malvolio, as of Antonio in *The Merchant of Venice*, is that they don't fit in; and the different uses that the comedy world can make of that fact. But the case of Angelo and Isabella is altogether different. For one thing they have each other, a formidable, if undeclared, bond of intimacy. But more important, they have qualities of inherent distinction; they have blood and breeding: such a metaphor from the racing world seems suited to our impression of them. In their rejection of the uses of the world, its brothels and jesting and cakes and ale, there is nothing of the self-excluding pathos of Antonio or Malvolio's puritanical conceit. It is true that they give themselves away, but the ways in which this is done have a kind of delicacy or 'elegance' which would not be out of place in Macbeth (Leavis compares Macbeth's and Angelo's soliloquies). We have it in Isabella's reply to the nun's account of convent privileges.

> I speak not as desiring more;
> But rather wishing a more strict restraint
> Upon the sisterhood, the votarists of St Clare

—and, notoriously, in the vehement language of martyrdom— 'the impression of keen whips I'd wear as rubies'—which she uses to her brother. Angelo's torment is genuine, the kind of which only a fine conscience is capable, but he has also, and knows he has, the *pour soi* front ('my gravity, wherein—let no man hear me—I take pride') which may be worn alike by the hypocrite and the man of distinction. As Pushkin observed, Angelo is an odd sort of hypocrite: one might almost say that he conceals his finer self when he discovers his baser one. Isabella, we may feel, intuits both; and it is, or at least it might have been, her downfall, the thing she could lose her heart to, and see herself in the process. Angelo's despairing discovery of the absurdity of desire within himself ('Blood, thou art blood') can only be redeemed by the genius of comic understanding. He must undergo the humilation of the obsessed man in comedy, humiliation conveyed with wonderfully unobtrusive economy in Isabella's account of his instructions for their rendezvous.

> With whispering and most guilty diligence,
> In action all of precept, he did show me
> The way twice o'er.

It is no wonder that the moment of forgiveness is so muted, an anticlimax, when we consider that Angelo would rather die than be involved in the comedy reconciliation; and that Isabella's apprehension of him, together with her own desire for some martyr's extremity, have been turned aside into these pat uses and all too human reconcilements. Shakespeare has certainly failed—and it is no wonder that he has—in ending the play on an unequivocal note of quasi-divine reconciliation and forgiveness: to that extent the Guarini model was too intractable for his genius to be crammed into. But what has obliquely happened is much more Shakespearean, and in a formal sense even perhaps more satisfying. We could try to define it by saying that the demands of death have had to come to terms with life—life at its most undignified and unregenerate, but where good nature and accommodation are the necessary virtues for anyone who must say, with Pompey, that he is 'one that would live'. Nowhere, perhaps, does Shakespeare give more effective and imaginative endorsement to what becomes in the process a proper philosophy of comedy; the philosophy that declines to be 'absolute for death' and says with Parolles of *All's Well*: 'Simply the thing I am shall make me live.'

But it is the presence in *Measure for Measure* of these two who in their own way are 'absolute for death', who in a different order of play might indeed have had something like a real *Liebestod*, which gives this philosophy its dramatic point and its spreading fictional overtones. The Duke, too, is touched with the brush of comedy, and is equally fastidious that its pitch should not cling; but the Duke's role in the play is too formalized, too necessarily artificial, for him to have the same kind of freedom that Shakespeare was able to retain in his project on behalf of Isabella and Angelo. The hypothetical spousals of the Duke and Isabella—the union of divinity and regenerate humanity on the moral-symbolic level—are but faintly suggested; and rightly, for Shakespeare is in no position here to give his ending that naturally 'paradisal' quality of a romance, the quality achieved at the end of *The Winter's Tale*, whose play/novel relationships have a good deal in common with those of *Measure for Measure*.

One can sympathize with the director of a recent production who had Isabella left alone on the stage at the play's end, twisting a glove in her hands as she contemplates the uncertain and disturbing aspects of this new development, the Duke's proposal, that—for the 'Guarini model' *Measure for Measure*—means a formal and harmonious completion. That, with a vengeance, is to emphasize—and over-emphasize—the intractable vitality of the novel that broods within the play. It is wiser to leave such things to our imagination, for Isabella and Angelo *are* successfully subdued to the comedy ethos, and it is right and proper that they should be. The humanity of the play depends on it, and nowhere in it are the two excused from the absurdities of living. Yet something in them stands outside, strong in the protest of its own integrity and its own difference, asserting the division that Shakespeare lives by, challenging the unity that he can always do without.

*Of course the creative process always be-
gins in division, in ideas and inklings tumbling over each other in the darkness, in
Dryden's phrase; but this necessary commencement is not the point. We take for
granted that the work of art represents a
solution, a confluence and a harmony—
getting the statue clean away from the
marble, as D. H. Lawrence called it—and
again the obvious truth in such metaphor
is not what is here in question: what matters, rather, is the extent to which disunity
and division may themselves become
aspects—indispensable and irremovable
ones—of the artistic whole. . . . The point
would be how such a literature works on
us, and how we work upon it, finding
what accident rather than intention put
there, and perceiving ourselves how contradictions enlarge and emancipate the
world of experience it offers.*

Here is one of those rare books which at
once sets forth the grand overview of a first-
rate critical mind and provides the general
reader with a fresh and revealing look at the
very roots of literary creation. It is John
Bayley's belief that critics in their search for
cohesive schemes have tended to impose too
unified and tidy a notion on the motivation
and achievement of major creators of poetry
and fiction. He strongly feels that contradictions—disunity and divisiveness—are what
give many masterpieces their lasting vitality,
and that these conflicting pressures on the
writer from within and without are indis-